The Art of Storytelling:
From Parents to Professionals

Hannah B. Harvey, Ph.D.

THE
GREAT
COURSES

PUBLISHED BY:

THE GREAT COURSES
Corporate Headquarters
4840 Westfields Boulevard, Suite 500
Chantilly, Virginia 20151-2299
Phone: 1-800-832-2412
Fax: 703-378-3819
www.thegreatcourses.com

Hannah B. Harvey, Ph.D.

Professor, Storytelling Program
East Tennessee State University

Professor Hannah B. Harvey is a Professor in the Storytelling program at East Tennessee State University and an internationally recognized professional storyteller. She earned her Ph.D. in Performance Studies/Communication Studies at The University of North Carolina at Chapel Hill, where she was also a teaching fellow, and her B.A. from Furman University. She is the managing editor of the journal *Storytelling, Self, Society* and a past president of Storytelling in Higher Education, the professional organization for scholars of storytelling within the National Storytelling Network. As a scholar-artist, she studies storytelling as a pervasive cultural force and an everyday artistic practice.

Professor Harvey's research and teaching specialty is performance ethnography, which unites theater with anthropology: Scholars investigate everyday storytelling as an embodied cultural practice. As a performance ethnographer, she develops oral histories into theatrical and solo storytelling works that highlight the true stories of contemporary Appalachian people. Her ongoing fieldwork with disabled coal miners in southwest Virginia culminated in a live ethnographic performance of their oral histories, *Out of the Dark: The Oral Histories of Appalachian Coal Miners*, earning her a directing award from adjudicators at the Kennedy Center American College Theater Festival in 2007 and three year-end awards from professional critics in 2005. Her written research has been honored by the American Folklore Society and featured in *Storytelling, Self, Society*, among other publications. Her research has been presented at the National Communication Association, the Oral History Association, the International Festival of University Theatre, and the Canadian Association on Gerontology.

Professor Harvey has delivered award-winning performances and workshops at festivals and universities in the United States, the United Kingdom, and Morocco. Her energetic style brings to life humorous and compelling stories from the worlds of personal experience, oral history, folklore, and myth. Critics have called her work "very funny" (*Theatre Guide London*) and "deeply moving" (*Classical Voice of North Carolina*). As a solo storyteller, she has been featured at the National Storytelling Festival and in the International Storytelling Center's Teller-in-Residence program. Her international performances as a member of the North Carolina–based Wordshed Productions earned a five-star review in the *British Theatre Guide*. Professor Harvey has led workshops in storytelling at the National Storytelling Festival in Tennessee; in the adaptation and performance of literature at the Edinburgh Festival Fringe in Scotland; and in cross-cultural storytelling at University Hassan II, Ben M'Sik, in Casablanca, Morocco.

Professor Harvey's students at Kennesaw State University selected her as an Honors Program Distinguished Teacher and for the Alumni Association Commendation for Teaching Impact. She is proud of her Storytelling students' achievements, from garnering professional credits (including a four-star review from the *British Theatre Guide* for her students' group-storytelling adaptation of *Beowulf*) to simply enjoying and becoming more critically aware of storytelling in their everyday lives. ■

Table of Contents

Table of Contents

Table of Contents

Disclaimer

This course includes stretching and breathing exercises for storytellers; you should take into account your own level of physical fitness before performing these exercises. Neither The Teaching Company nor Hannah Harvey is responsible for your use of this educational material or its consequences.

The Art of Storytelling:
From Parents to Professionals

Scope:

The gift of storytelling may be one of life's most powerful—and envied—skills. A story well told can make us laugh, weep, swell with pride, or rise with indignation. A story poorly told can be not only boring or uncomfortable but positively painful to experience. We all want to tell good stories, but we don't often realize how fundamental storytelling is to the human experience. Storytelling isn't just entertainment; your story is what grounds you. It gives you a sense of purpose, identity, and continuity between the past and the present. This course takes both a practical and an intellectual approach to understanding how storytelling works and how to use artistic storytelling techniques to enhance your stories, big and small. Each lecture will help you build your repertoire of stories, often inviting you to get up on your feet through guided workshops on specific aspects of your stories.

Our introductory lecture looks at the nature and prevalence of "orality" in society today and helps us see how much of our lives are spent telling stories. We'll consider how your experience of telling and listening to an oral story is different than your experience of writing or reading a story. Telling does many things that writing simply can't do, and it does those things quite powerfully for your audiences. The next three lectures help us see storytelling as a relationship among the teller, the audience, and the story. We look in-depth at these interconnected parts, beginning with your relationship with your story and the different ways we're drawn to stories. You'll discover some resources for finding different kinds of stories and why it's important to choose stories that matter to you personally. Perhaps most important, we'll look at the effect your relationship with your audience has on how, why, and even whether or not you tell your stories. This relationship with your audience is what sets storytelling apart from all other forms of communication or entertainment. In all these interconnected relationships, there are a variety of contexts you must consider and establish: physical, emotional, intellectual, and social.

We then move from "what is storytelling?" to "how and why are some stories so powerful with audiences?" Having looked at what storytelling involves from a broad view, we now look underneath the surface to question what oral stories do for us in our families (culturally), in our minds (psychologically), and in our human spirit.

For some answers, we turn to three major genres of traditional stories. One of the first places we encounter stories is in our families, and these seemingly small stories are often the ones that stick with us, shape our sense of who we are, and get passed down to our children. When you lose a family member, that person exists primarily through stories. Family stories are as complex as family relationships are; often, we want to tell family stories to our friends, but how do you bridge from inside the complex world of the family to the outside world? We'll look at many examples of how to contextualize your family stories to connect them, playfully and powerfully, with the outside world. Family stories are an example of oral traditions, as are fairy tales. We often think of fairy tales as simple children's stories, but these lasting stories contain complex themes (many of them sexual!) that help children and adults integrate and deal with the conflicting facets of human psychology. We look at how some of these contradictory desires play out in the fantasy world of "Little Red Riding Hood" and how fairy tales can entertain both children and adults. Fairy tales and myths often follow a trajectory of events that Joseph Campbell called the "hero's journey." The hero's descent into the abyss and the battles that take place there with "the dragon" mirror the psychological battles we encounter in our own personal lives. The final lecture on traditional stories helps you identify your own personal hero's journey. We take a guided walk through one of your stories, mapping your journey and identifying archetypal figures that can connect powerfully with your audiences.

With this foundation in what, how, and why, we turn to storytelling craft and technique.

The workshop-based lectures begin by seeing the process of story development as a cycle of telling, writing, imaging, playing, and rehearsing. "Rehearsing" can be as simple or as involved as you wish for any given story; it involves stretching yourself, just as you would stretch any muscle before you prepare to perform in a game. You may be surprised to find that you need to give yourself permission to stretch. You begin this process by visualizing the world of your story, which is a particular way of remembering a story that does not involve word-by-word memorization. We then consider multiple points of view in telling stories and the role of the narrator as a guide who connects the audience with the other world of the story. We investigate character development and kinesthetics, helping you find humor, dimension, and playfulness with the people in your stories. The structure of your story is the container that holds these different elements—narrator, visualized events, and characters—and many different structural forms are possible for stories. The emotional arc of your story—where your story goes emotionally—is a different thing than this structural trajectory of events; we'll discuss how the two intertwine and influence your audiences. Your voice, along with your body, is a crucial instrument in your telling; you'll practice warming up this instrument and building layers of intonation with your stories. Because we all have some degree of nervous energy when we speak in public, we'll also look at the mechanics of performance anxiety and how to channel nervous energy into an energized performance.

We then turn to some specific issues you may face as a storyteller, with practical advice for how to approach them. Through many examples, we'll learn the best ways to address specific audiences, including children and organizational audiences.

Our final workshop lectures tie together the whole storytelling experience by looking practically at introductions, conclusions, and everything in between—how to keep your audience's attention through repetition, audience participation, and other elements of the craft of storytelling.

We'll conclude with a return to our initial observations, with new insights into the nature of orality and its continuing role, side by side, with the written word. Storytelling makes up the bulk of our daily lives. If every story has a narrator, whose perspectives influence the stories we hear and the stories that influence our material decisions? What are the implications of our choices as storytellers in creating meaning for our audiences and in the world? Storytelling is who we are and how we live our lives. This course aims to help you find even more humor, enjoyment, and fulfillment in the stories you tell as you discover your own voice as a storyteller. ■

Telling a Good Story
Lecture 1

Most of our lives are spent telling stories. Storytelling is at the core of the human experience. Personal stories are what ground us—what give us a sense of purpose, identity, and continuity between the past and the present. Oral storytelling is the primary way that people remember and record the peak moments of life in their families. In this course, we will examine how you can tell stories better—that is, tell stories in a way that brings them to life for other people, both within and outside of your family or your community.

The Study of Storytelling

- In academia, storytelling studies are found across a wide variety of programs—communications, theater, performance studies, education—because storytelling directly taps into many different fields.

- Our approach to storytelling in this course will take the perspective of a scholar-artist. We will not only learn practical guidelines for storytelling, but we will also come to understand the nature of "story" and storytelling.

- By analyzing how storytelling works—how we use stories in everyday life and why we tell stories—we can become better practitioners of storytelling as an art form.

The Functions of Stories

- Written narratives are stories that we find in print, while oral narratives—stories—live in conversation or in our memories. They are often not written down, but they come alive through our voices and our bodies as we tell those stories.

- Stories serve multiple functions for us. For example, orally told stories can delineate relationships and set parameters.

- In my family, whenever we gather for a holiday, someone has to make the "pink salad." This salad is special to the cooks in my family because the recipe is a story that we share only inside the family.

- In other words, the recipe delineates borders between our family and the outside world: the people who know the recipe and the people who don't!

- It's a small thing—a "story" about a salad—but it separates our family and defines us as a cohesive unit.

- Stories also make life coherent; they give us a sense of who we are and where we've come from, and they give us a picture of the future that we can either work toward or avoid.
  - A story about my grandfather's hands gives a sense of history and the trajectory of his life. And it makes death bearable because in the story, death is not the end of my grandfather— he is still holding my hand. You may have people in your life who still hold your hand, too, whether or not they have passed away.

  - When you're telling someone a story, you're doing more than just relaying a message; the story is a container for our deepest longings, hopes, and fears.

- Stories also question life. Storytelling forces self-reflection: It puts up a mirror to yourself and to culture.
  - Your story gives you access to yourself; in other words, it's how you get a handle on yourself—if you don't recognize your story, you can't change it.

  - In some sense, that's what therapy does: It helps you shape a narrative for a listener, and in hearing yourself tell your own story and having someone question it for missing or forgotten parts, you can listen to and change your story.

- Stories reveal human truths, which are different from facts. Facts are what happened; truths are about what those events meant to people.
  - Many stories aren't factual. A story about a gingerbread man who runs away from home and gets eaten by a fox is completely fictional, but it gives us a way to see a truth: how foolish it is to run away from the wisdom of people who love you for the sake of having your own way.

  - Such stories act on us, often invisibly. Many of the ideas we have about what is truly important in life—ideas and values that motivate decisions—come from stories.

The Focus of Storytelling
- Stories don't live on the printed page but in spoken words and in images that we carry in our minds. The primary work of oral storytelling is to convey the images in the mind of the teller to the listeners. Storytelling is focused on image and storyline, not the memorization of written lines.

- Memorizing is the challenge of live theater. But storytelling is about knowing a series of images so well that they live in you so that you can call them back up, although not with the same words every time. You don't need to write down stories about your childhood; you know them by heart and can call them up at any time.

- Maybe you're thinking, "But I don't have any stories! My life is very ordinary; nothing ever happens to me." But as you hear stories being told in this course, it's likely that you will come up with many ideas for stories of your own. In future lectures, we'll talk about the kind of journal keeping that storytellers use to develop their ideas into stories.

Outline of the Course
- We'll start this course by looking at the basics of the storytelling process. It's important to understand that storytelling is a living collaboration that involves the teller, the audience, and the story.

The stories you tell are constantly adapted to each different audience you encounter; they aren't delivered in one fixed, intact form.

- We'll examine stories that have staying power. We'll look at classic stories—from family stories to traditional fairy tales and myths—and explore why certain stories have lasted for so long, even across cultures.

- Throughout the course, we'll also practice, using how-to workshops that will help you develop your stories, make them more engaging to your audiences, and even make them more enjoyable for you to tell.

"Hands"
- The story of my grandfather's hands illustrates some of the qualities of oral storytelling.

- As we've said, storytelling is ephemeral. It's also economical—nothing is wasted. "Hands" could have included many more details, but it was trimmed to focus on a few specific things.

- Stories are also "additive"; that is, they build on themselves.

- "Hands," like other stories, contains certain oral memory aids, for example, the repeated images of hands. These images unify the story, but they also serve as a memory aid for the teller.
  - When we look at some of the earliest stories on record—those that come out of an oral culture—we see this same kind of redundancy. For example, we find repeated modifiers for "Beowulf, son of Ecgtheow" in *Beowulf* or "Enkidu, the faithful companion" in the Epic of Gilgamesh.

  - These repeated phrases highlight the fact that someone had to remember these stories.

- Also like an epic, "Hands" is action-centered. The story moves from planing wood, to working on engines, to building houses. Storytelling is focused on action and on *agon* ("struggle").

Hands

One of the things I remember most about my grandfather was his hands. You see, my grandfather learned carpentry from his father. And by the time I knew him, his hands were tough, and those knuckles were just like big marbles set into his fingers, they were so large. He used to come home from work when I'd come to visit, and take that big hand, and pat me on the head with it—and when I was young, I didn't think about where those hands had been to make them so leathery and big.

When he was a little boy, my grandfather [Tom Jr.] would follow his father, ... Tom Sr., out to his workshop, and he would sit there and study his father while he worked. And Junior, my grandfather, he'd go tagging along behind his father as his father went up toward his shop. He said, "I was taggin' along behind, wonderin' what he was a' gonna do." ...On this

© Design Pics/Thinkstock

particular day, Junior sat as his father took down this big old poplar board—real dry wood. He always said, "Poplar works good, you know; it's good lumber." And he got this board down and looked at it, and laid it up on his workbench, and he started planing it, you know. Junior just stared, that old wood of the shop, and freshly cut boards, and outside, the apple tree Tom Sr. had grafted. ...

And as he watched, he learned. And he used those young, strong hands to plane the boards himself. And when the war broke out, he took those hands to Guam, and he used them to reach inside the big engines of bomber planes that flew out over the Pacific. Those strong hands that held his bride so tightly when he came home, alive—alive!—from the war. And when he came home, those hands picked up a hammer and wood, and they shook his father's hand and the hands of young couples and preachers, because he and his father built houses, and they built churches. He always said, "We don't build homes; we build houses. You can't build a home—you have to make a home. It takes a heap a' living in a house to make it home."

Those hands, he washed and washed so that he could hold his baby girl, so small, her head fit right into the cup of his palm. And then his second baby girl—right there, nestled against his fingers. Hands that held the rod and reel, the fish, the fork, and the belly. Hands that planed, like his daddy. Hands that held a walking stick for hours as he continued to exercise after triple-bypass surgery. Held the walker, held the bedframe—held the tiny foot of his great-grandson; that foot was dwarfed by those big bones and marbled knuckles, covered in smooth skin. A hand that held mine—like he'd done all my life. Like he still does, even though those hands are far away.

You can tell a lot about a person, just by looking at their hands.

- Note, too, that those actions happened in a specific context. I didn't say that my grandfather went to war (an abstraction) but that he worked on a plane in Guam.

- Storytelling is central to the survival of the family and of specific people. Important people in our lives pass away, and what we have left of them are the stories we share.

Suggested Reading

Langellier and Peterson, *Storytelling in Daily Life*.

The National Storytelling Network, www.storynet.org.

Ong, *Orality and Literacy*.

Rydell, ed., *A Beginner's Guide to Storytelling*.

Questions to Consider

1. How is your experience of telling and listening to an oral story different than your experience of writing or reading a story? What does telling do that writing can't do?

2. What do you enjoy most about telling stories? What scares you most about getting up to tell a story?

Lecture 1: Telling a Good Story

Telling a Good Story
Lecture 1—Transcript

Professor Harvey: I tell stories. I first came into storytelling from my grandfather—he would tell me stories about our family history with that wood fire crackling at my back. So at an early age, I was aware of storytelling as the everyday rhythm of our home, and as a public art form.

Most of our lives are spent telling stories. Storytelling is core to the human experience. Your stories are what ground you—what gives you a sense of purpose and identity and continuity between the past and the present.

Story is so much of your life: Oral storytelling is the primary way that you remember and record the peak moments in the life of your family. As it is so core to the human experience, we're going to examine how you can tell your stories better—and by that I mean, tell your stories in such a way that it brings them to life for other people both within and without your own family, or your place of business, or your own community or neighborhood. I'd like to get started by telling you something that's "just a story" in my family:

> I'd like for you to look down at your hands right now. Just take a look at them—how are they feeling? Have you been typing too much today, or maybe working outside with them? One of the things that I remember most about my grandfather was his hands. You see, my grandfather, he learned carpentry from his father, and by the time that I knew him, those hands, they were just gnarled. Those knuckles, they looked like just big marbles had been stuck inside, underneath the skin inside those knuckles, they were so large. He used to come home from work when I'd come to visit them. He'd come in of an evening and he'd take that big hand and he'd just pat me down on the head with it. When I was younger I didn't think about where those hands had been to make them so leathery and so big.
>
> When he was a little boy, my grandfather, he would follow his father out to his workshop. He said, "I was just a-taggin' along behind, you know, wonderin' what he was a-gonna do," and he

would follow him out to his workshop. My great-grandfather, my grandfather said he'd watch as that great-grandfather, he would take these poplar boards, good wood—poplar is good lumber—and he'd take that board and he'd set it down on his workbench, and he would take out a plane and he would start planing that poplar wood. Those shavings, they would just curl up off of that piece of wood, and my grandfather, just sitting there on the ground, he would watch as those shavings curled up and fell onto the floor in front of him.

"I could smell that wood, it smelled so good." He'd take those curled up pieces and he would just stretch them out. He said, "They'd be long, you know," 24 inches or longer and he'd stretch those shavings out and he watched his father. As he watched, he learned. And my grandfather, he took those young hands when he came of age and he started planing the boards himself. And when the war broke out, he took those hands to Guam and he put those hands inside the engines of bomber planes. When the war was over, he came home and he took those hands and he wrapped them around his bride when he came home alive—alive!—from the war. Those strong hands that shook his father's hand and the hand of preachers and young couples in our town, because he built houses and he built churches with his father. And he always said, "Now we don't build homes, we build houses. You can't build a home—you have to make a home. It takes a heap o' living in a house to make it home."

Those hands that he washed and washed so that he could hold his baby girl, that tiny head just nestled in the cup of his palm. Those hands he washed again as he held his second girl, that head just nestled into those fingers. Hands that held the rod, and the reel, and the fish, and the fork, and the belly. Hands that planed like his daddy had. Hands that held a walking stick as he continued to exercise after triple-bypass surgery. Hands that held the walker, held the bed frame—held the tiny foot of his great grandson, that tiny foot, it was just dwarfed in that big hand, but that skin, it was smooth now. A hand that held mine, like he'd done all my life. Like he still does, even though those hands are far away, now. You can tell a lot about a person just by looking at their hands.

Now that's a story about my family, and it's about something so small and everyday—a person's hands—but (and this is key) that story takes us to something larger. It even taps into universal themes about aging and love, and questions such as: What does it mean to make a home? What happens to us when we die?

In the academy, you'll find storytelling studies across a wide variety of programs, because storytelling directly taps into so many different fields—communications, and theatre and performance studies, education. And because of my background, I approach the classroom as a scholar-artist—which means I do storytelling, and I coach storytelling in a very practical way; and as a scholar, I'm interested in understanding the very nature of "story" and storytelling.

My students and I have found that by analyzing how storytelling works—*how* we use stories in everyday life and *why* we tell stories—by asking these "how" and "why" questions about those stories that have staying power, we can become better practitioners of storytelling as an art form.

I'm a professional, but often I'm telling stories to my friends, and neighbors, and on the sofa with my little son. My goal is to show you how professional storytelling techniques can help you in telling your own stories day-to-day.

At this point, I guess somebody would ask us to define our terms. What's a story—what's a storyteller? Someone once posed a challenge to Ernest Hemingway. His friends bet that he couldn't write a story in six words. Here's what he wrote: "For Sale: baby shoes, never worn." So, a story can be very small (about a person's hands—or six words!), or there's an epic history of a nation, a big story.

Let's take a second to distinguish between written narrative (Hemingway's stories, or narrative that we find in print) from oral narrative, (stories that live in conversation, that live outside of writing—stories about your childhood, stories about when you were starting your company). These oral narratives are stories that you know—and they're often *not* written down, the live in here (in your memory), and they come alive through here (through your voice and your body as you tell those stories.) You are a storyteller. We are all storytellers in our daily lives.

But these questions—what's a story, what's a storyteller?—that's not really the interesting question. The question is, what do stories do for us? Well stories do a lot of things for us.

Orally-told stories can delineate relationships and set parameters. Whenever we have a family gathering for Thanksgiving or any holiday, someone has to make the "pink salad." I can't tell you the ingredients for the pink salad because you're not in my family (and if you ever saw this salad, you would probably wonder, "Who would want to know what's in that?")—but it's special to us; it's even sacred to the cooks in our family, because that recipe is a story that we only share inside our family. That story delineates borders between our family and the outside world: the people who know that recipe, and the people who don't. It's a small thing—it's a story about a salad, but that story does something very big for us. It separates us and defines us as a cohesive unit.

Stories make life coherent. They give us a sense of who we are and where we've come from, and they give us a picture of a future that we can work towards—or of a future we don't want (the stories that you tell your children about the mistakes that you've made, so that they don't make the same ones that you did, and you hope that they listen to you). That story about my grandfather, it gives a sense of history and trajectory for his life. And it makes death bearable, because in that story, that's not the end of him: He's still holding my hand. You may have folks in your life who still hold your hand, too. In that story, it's not the end of *his* story when he dies. When you're telling someone a story, you're doing much more than just relaying a message to someone: The story is a container for our deepest longings and hopes and fears.

Stories don't just impart life; they question life. Storytelling forces self-reflection. It puts up a mirror up to yourself and up to culture. Your story gives you access to yourself; it's how you get a handle on yourself—if you don't recognize your story, you can't change your story. That's therapy. What psychotherapy does is it helps someone shape a narrative for a listener.

In hearing yourself tell your own story, and having someone else question that story for the missing parts, or the forgotten parts, you can listen to that story, and you can make change.

Stories reveal human truths—and truth is a different thing from fact. Facts are what happened; truths are about what those happenings meant to people. You may have a story that isn't factual—it could be a completely made-up story, about a man made of gingerbread who runs away from home and gets eaten by a fox. And that may never have happened! But it gives you a way to see the truth of how foolish it is to run away from the wisdom of people who love you, just for the sake of having it your own way, because you could wind up in the middle of a river in the jaws of a fox. Stories give us deep truths.

These stories act on us, often invisibly. Many of the ideas that we have about what is really important in life, they come from stories like these. (Those are the ideas and values that motivate real material decisions for my life, and maybe yours, too—and they come from stories.)

That story, it doesn't live on the page; it lives in the spoken word, and now it lives in the images that you have in your head. That's the primary work of oral storytelling: getting the images in my head into your head. Storytelling is focused on image and storyline, not the memorization of written "lines."

In this course, as I teach you about telling your stories, we'll learn that this art isn't about memorizing—that's the challenge of live theatre, but not storytelling. *This* art is about getting to know a series of images, and knowing them so well that they live in you, that you know them by heart, and you can call them back up—not with the same words every time.

You know this—you *know* this! Think about it. The stories about your mornings as a young child with your mother, or going to games with your father in your hometown where you grew up—they're not written down, most likely. But you don't need them written down. You can tell them by heart—you can call them up because you know them.

I want this course to be useful in every aspect of your personal and professional life, so throughout these lectures, I'll coach you as you try out professional techniques to shape your stories. Some of these are writing techniques, and others are up-on-your-feet exercises to get you ready to tell. These practical bits of advice and exercises, they will prepare you to tell in a variety of situations, and will prepare you for when things don't go according to plan.

For example: There was one time when I was performing at a festival, and I was wearing these pants with an elastic waist—very comfortable, very forgiving, but very stretchy. I move around a lot when I'm telling stories, and I was telling this story and a little girl was running and I ran and I ran and the microphone pack that was hooked onto my elastic waistband, it came flying off into the audience, and the earpiece (which you can see this earpiece on me right now), that earpiece went flying off with it into the front row! There I was, with about 500 people waiting for my next words, and so I walked over to the stationary microphone and grabbed it and came right back and I went right on running.

Maybe you're thinking, "But I don't have any stories! I've lived an ordinary life. Nothing's ever happened to me." But as you hear stories being told—as I tell you stories and as you hear stories from some of my storytelling colleagues, I'll be willing to bet that you'll come up with plenty of ideas. And I'll be giving you prompts. I'll talk about the kind of storytelling journal that most storytellers keep and use to develop prompts into stories that can be told.

We'll start the course by looking at the basics of the storytelling process. It's important to understand that storytelling is a living collaboration. It involves you, and your audience, and the story. The stories you tell are constantly adapting to each different audience that you encounter—they aren't delivered in a fixed, intact form.

We'll examine stories that have staying power. We'll look at the classic stories—from family stories, to traditional fairy tales and myths—and, as you'll see, fairy tales were never just for children. Why have certain stories lasted so long, even across cultures?

We'll practice, using lots of how-to workshops that will help you really develop your stories, and make them more engaging to audiences and even more enjoyable for you to tell. That's where this course may surprise you. How exactly do we workshop to improve our storytelling? Well, it has to do with the very nature of orality: It's very different from written communication, or the dramatic interpretation of the written word.

Let's revisit that "Hands" story for a moment. I want to bring out some of the qualities of oral storytelling in this story. We already said: Storytelling is ephemeral. Oral storytelling is also economical. And by that I mean it's not wasteful. There are many things I could have said in that story, but I trimmed the story down to focus on a few specific things. We'll discuss what to leave in and what to leave out of your stories, and you'll find that some stories are told long for one audience, and short for another.

The story is additive—the story builds on itself: and this happened, and then he planed, and then he went to Guam, and then he built houses, and this and this and this. The story also contains certain oral memory aids—for example, that repeated image of hands, it's a unifying image, but it's also a memory trick for the storyteller. If I'm lost in that story, I just go back to the hands.

When you go back to some of the earliest stories that we have on record—stories that come out of an oral culture—you'll see this same kind of redundancy: repeated modifiers for "Beowulf, son of Ecgtheow" or "Enkidu the faithful companion," in the *Epic of Gilgamesh*. These repeated phrases are memory aids; they highlight the fact that somebody had to remember all those stories.

Like an epic, the "Hands" story is action-centered—we move from planing to working on engines, to building houses. Storytelling is focused on action, on *agon*, or struggle, drama. Those actions happened in a specific context, not some abstract idea of going to war, no, Granddaddy worked on a plane in Guam. And that story that's ephemeral, and economical, and embodied, and full of repetition, and additive, and action-centered—this story *keeps my grandfather alive.*

Storytelling is central to the survival of the family and of specific people. Most people in the world don't exist. My grandfather is gone, and there is nothing except for two kids, and three grandkids, and the stories that we share. Most people, there's nothing left of them. That's appalling to realize, someone so big in your life just passes on!

Now my son never got to meet his great-grandfather. And another wonderful person he will never meet is his great-great-aunt Mae. She died long before he was born, but he will know her through this story.

[Video start.]

> **Professor Harvey:** I wanted to share a story with you all. It's a story that we tell in my family and it's one that I tell to my other family members. It has to do with the card game "Old Maid." Did any of you all ever play this card game? OK, some nods, yes, OK! And you had that special deck of cards. You've seen them? OK. On my special deck of cards—I'm small, right, I wear heels, or I think I'm small—but when I was even smaller, when I was seven years old, the deck of cards just felt so huge to me. They were these big cards and they had these very colorful-looking people on them except for one very special card. And which card was that? The Old Maid.
>
> On my deck of cards, this woman, she was kind of grandmotherly-looking, even though she was the Old Maid, she had on this kind of little dress; she was in a rocking chair. She had this gray hair that was kind of pinned up into a bun and she had two knitting needles, wooden knitting needles that were just pronged in the top of it. She had this little smile on her face.
>
> You never wanted to get the Old Maid. My great-aunt Mae, she was nothing like the woman on that card. Aunt Mae, she wore pants. Only she wore those polyester pants, the kind of scratchy ones, you know? If you saw her in the summertime, if you looked into her house, you'd see this tall, big-boned woman, she was skinny but she was tall. She wore those polyester pants in the summertime and if you happened to pass by her house and look in the window you'd see her in a pair of those pants and her hair up in curlers and nothing on but her bra. She walked around the house that way, she didn't care. I loved Aunt Mae.

That was in the summertime. In the wintertime, she'd put on a sweater and she'd put on one of those pairs of polyester pants and then she'd put another pair on right over on top of it because it got cold in her house. It was an old house, it was from the 1930s. It was the house that she had grown up in. It had two stories and it had one of those wonderful tin roofs that sounded so good in the rain. It got cold in that house in the winter and so Aunt Mae, you may have seen this, she took a sheet and she would drape it over the staircase to trap the heat downstairs. She lived in that house and when I was little, when I was seven and eight years old and whenever I would get sick and have to stay home from school, well my mom, she worked, so she would take me over to Aunt Mae's house and Aunt Mae would take care of me.

We always had to call before we came, because if you didn't call before you came and you walked up to her door and you're knocking on the door, she would answer it, but this tall, big-boned woman, she would answer the door and she would have a hatchet raised in her hand. This tall woman, and once she saw who you were, oh well then she'd set down that hatchet, "Well, come on in." I loved Aunt Mae.

After she knew who we were, she'd set down that hatchet, it was as tall as I was, set it right by the door. We'd walk inside. We'd pass by her kitchen, and this is where she kept her spit cup. I don't know if you people know what a spit cup is. Aunt Mae would take these margarine tubs, you know, parquet tubs, and she would rinse them out and she would keep it in the windowsill. So whenever Aunt Mae had to spit in the day, she would walk into that kitchen, she'd take down that tub, and she'd spit into it and then she'd rinse it out and set it back up.

So I'd walk in and I'd pass by that hatchet, pass the kitchen and the spit cup, I'd walk inside and if I was sick, she would sit me down on her couch. It was that scratchy wool couch that was orange and brown. She'd make me a bed there and I'd pull the sheet up and she would turn on the TV. It had one of those pull dials and one of those turns for channels one through 12. And we could chart our day by the turn of that dial.

Channel five: *Days of our Lives*. And Aunt Mae, during *Days of our Lives*, she would teach me her exercises. This was a 70-year-old woman and she would lay down on her back on the floor and she would kick her legs up and she would just start spinning those legs up in the air like a bicycle, and I'd do that with her, and I taught her my exercises. This 70-year-old woman, I had her get down on all fours and I would climb up on top of her back and I would ride her like a horse all the way around that living room. I loved Aunt Mae.

Channel 11: The news, and it was lunchtime. Aunt Mae, she would go into that kitchen, where the spit cup was, and she would make me a can of chicken noodle soup, Campbell's chicken noodle soup. Only she made it the way that Aunt Mae made it. She made it with a little bit of milk and a little bit of pepper. You've got that face, "Uugh," yeah, that's what I did the first time I tried it, too. I looked at this creamy stuff and I looked up her and I said, "Aunt Mae, that's not how Mama makes it."

She said, "Well just try it. If you don't like it I'll make you something else." I took that first little hesitant sip. [Slurp.] Took another one. [Slurp.] From that day until this, that's how I make my chicken noodle soup. Go home and try it. It's so good. I loved Aunt Mae's.

Channel 12: *Donahue*. When *Donahue* was on it was the afternoon and Aunt Mae, she would get on the phone, and she would call women on her calling circle. Aunt Mae never seemed to leave the house, but she always knew everything that was going on in our community from the women on her calling circle. She would be talking on the phone and *Donahue* was on and that was when I would play with Aunt Mae's buttons. She had this collection of buttons, the ones that had popped off of those polyester pants and the extra ones that came with it, she collected them all in an old powder box, you know, powder for your face.

I dumped those buttons out and I'd play with them on the floor. There were big, shiny buttons with rhinestones on them and little tiny faux pearls and little pink, pink buttons and big, shiny cream buttons, fabric-covered buttons. I'd play with those buttons and I would imagine what was behind that sheet behind me. It covered up that second floor, covered up that staircase, and I'd wonder.

It was years later before I found out what was on that second floor of that house. I grew up, I'd been seven-eight then, I grew up, I got older, went off to college. Aunt Mae, she got older. It was only after I got older and gained some perspective that I realized that Aunt Mae was very nice to me but to the rest of the family, she was the orneriest, most cantankerous, crotchety, mean old woman. She was the Old Maid. She'd never married. She was kind of shy and socially awkward with a lot of adults, and she was tall and skinny. She played basketball when she was younger. She never really knew how to interact with other people. She still lived in that house that she had grown up in, her parents' house. When Aunt Mae got older and she had to be put in a nursing home, we couldn't care for her, give her the care that she needed, she went to a nursing home.

I came home from college for a visit and we all, the whole family, we came into that house and we took down that sheet and we walked upstairs, and I finally saw what was in that second floor. Beautiful antiques. Furniture and carved headboards, beautifully, intricately-carved wooden tea sets, and all of these antiques. Aunt Mae, like many of the women in her generation, she was never financially independent. She was the custodian of many family heirlooms, but she never had any money of her own. She was the Old Maid. Aunt Mae, when I was little, she let me ride on her back like a horse. Oh, Aunt Mae, she wasn't that woman on the card. Aunt Mae was beautiful.

Last time I saw my Aunt Mae, we went to the nursing home. I'd come home from college, I went with my mom and we walked in the door. You know how it is, kind of, in some nursing homes, you open that door and it smells faintly of rubbing alcohol and urine?

We walked in, we were going down the hall to her room, and as I passed by this man in a wheelchair he reached out and grabbed my shirt and I kind of shied away from him and I told my mom. She said, "Well, some people just don't get a lot of visitors in here, and I bet he was just lonely." I was really glad we were going to see my Aunt Mae.

We walked in the door, and *Days of our Lives* was on, and she was on the phone with one of the women in her calling circle, and she was finishing up that conversation so we visited with her for about an hour. When it came time to leave, I bent down and I hugged her. I stood back up, I held her hand, and I remembered all those times when I'd walked into her house. She held my hand, big, tall, strong, big-boned. Now I was the tall one. She looked up at me and she said very firmly, "Don't forget about me."

I thought at the time that she just wanted me to come back and visit, but she passed away soon after that. "Don't forget about me." I keep a jar of Aunt Mae's buttons on my desk, right beside a picture of her. She's got that big smile, all wrinkles. "Don't forget about me." She's one of the most beautiful women I have ever known.

[Video end.]

Professor Harvey: At a certain point in life, you know you have a book in you—will you do it? You may not have the time to write it, but you can call a child over and tell them. Just sit your kid down. Tell them a story. I am so glad that you've joined me for this course. Now let's get started.

Every time I tell Aunt Mae's story, it's slightly different. And that's because of how storytelling works within something called the "storytelling triangle." We'll begin to talk about this storytelling triangle in the next lecture. See you then.

The Storytelling Triangle
Lecture 2

S torytelling isn't about delivering a fixed thing. It's a dynamic process of you shaping the story with the audience. One way of looking at the process of story crafting and storytelling is through the storytelling triangle. In this lecture, we'll set up the triangle, and in the following lectures, we'll look at two aspects of the triangle in more depth: developing your relationship with the stories you tell and developing your relationship with your audience.

The Points of the Triangle

- Telling a story is a three-way relationship involving you, the story, and the audience. We can represent this relationship with the image of a triangle.

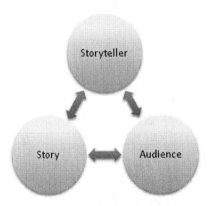

Storytelling is a three-way relationship among the teller, the story, and the audience, with each element of the triangle connected.

- Notice that none of the points on the triangle is independent of the others—they're all connected. Stories are always mediated through a storyteller and exist in relation to an audience.

- Again, storytelling is about connections; in fact, stories exist by virtue of this connection with an audience and the teller.
  - If a story doesn't grab you as a teller, chances are, it isn't a good story for you to tell, because in order to tell a story well, you have to be connected to it. Even if you know a "good" story that others like, ask yourself: Is this a story that means something to me?

  - You should also ask the same question for your audience: Is it a story your audience will connect with? You may have stories that are appropriate for only some audiences but not others, and if a story isn't right for an audience, the connection won't be made.

- Storytelling is also about choices. There is no one "right" way to tell a story because a story isn't an "ideal form" that you are trying to achieve; storytelling is a series of choices that you make in how to connect the audience with a story.

- Storytelling is an adaptive cultural phenomenon. Because of these connections among the story, audience, and teller, stories develop and are adapted based on the needs and desires of the audience and the teller. Many of the stories that we consider "canonized" as great tales, from Greek and Roman myths to fairy tales, exist because they connect with tellers and audiences.
  - Stories survive by virtue of their relationship with tellers and audiences. In this sense, the very idea of what constitutes a story is culturally specific. For example, Western stories (those from the United States and Europe) typically focus on character development and a linear plotline; audiences in these cultures tend to expect that the story will follow events as they happened.

  - But in Bali and Java, there is no such expectation. A story may center on one event, then jump back in time, then move forward

The Old Maid

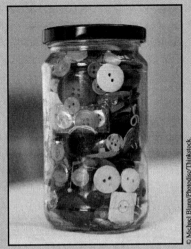

Last time I saw my Aunt Mae, we went to the nursing home. I'd come home from college. I went with my mom, and we walked in the door. You know how it is, kind of, in some nursing homes? You open that door and it smells faintly of rubbing alcohol and urine? We walked in—we were going down the hall to her room, and as I passed by this man in a wheelchair, he reached out and grabbed my shirt. I kind of shied away from him, and I told my mom. She said, "Well, some people just don't get a lot of visitors in here, and I bet he was just lonely." I was really glad we were going to see my Aunt Mae.

We walked in the door, and *Days of our Lives* was on, and she was on the phone with one of the women in her calling circle. She was finishing up that conversation, so we visited with her for about an hour. When it came time to leave, I bent down and I hugged her. I stood back up, I held her hand, and I remembered all those times when I'd walked into her house. She had held my hand—big, tall, strong, big-boned. Now I was the tall one. She looked up at me and she said very firmly, "Don't forget about me."

I thought at the time that she just wanted me to come back and visit, but she passed away soon after that. "Don't forget about me."

I keep a jar of Aunt Mae's buttons on my desk, right beside a picture of her. She's got that big smile, all wrinkles. "Don't forget about me." She's one of the most beautiful women I have ever known.

years later. In these cultures and for these audiences, following a linear timeline is not a requirement for a "real" story.

Lines of Communication

- The three points of the storytelling triangle represent not only connections but lines of communication—and not just one-way communication.

- Consider a situation in which you're explaining the values of your company to new employees. You might share a story with them about the company. We could think of this situation as handing the story over to the audience, as you would a briefing or a document. In a linear diagram, this would be represented with the story first and then the teller, who takes the story to the audience.

- This picture is useful to see how stories are mediated by tellers. Every story we know—whether it's an orally told story or one in print form—was brought to us by storytellers. And the storyteller—the mediator—often has a stake in how the story gets told.
    - The stories you grew up with were probably the stories your parents wanted you to hear. The stories you tell to your children are ones you mediate to them—and you probably craft those stories with careful lessons in mind! My story about my Aunt Mae is mediated by my experiences with her and by my own expectations about how women should act.

    - My story about Mae is different than the stories my grandmother told about her, because my grandmother had a different relationship with Aunt Mae.

    - This reveals something significant about the dynamics of storytelling in any situation. Unlike the experience of reading a story in a book, when you're hearing a story in an audience, you might, for example, laugh at a part of the story, which might prompt the teller to embellish a little bit more. The dynamic of the live encounter influences the story; thus, there's a relationship between the audience directly back to the story itself.

- The directional arrows in our diagram tell us that storytelling is a living thing, a process, an action. As a storyteller, you must be constantly aware of these active lines of communication between you and your audience, the story and your audience, and yourself and the story.

- A sample from the work of award-winning storyteller Bil Lepp illustrates his attention to the audience and the changes it brings to his story about buffalo tipping. Note also the additive qualities in his storytelling as he includes additional examples: "and gator rolling, and elk punting…." Note that Lepp isn't doing stand-up comedy; in that venue, humor is the goal, but in storytelling, humor is a vehicle for the story.

Triangle Review

- Storytelling connects a storyteller and an audience with a story. In this process of connecting the audience with the story, the storyteller makes choices that are specific to that audience and that story. We do this on an unconscious level all the time.

- As a result of these choices, stories are constantly in flux, adapted from one situation to another.

- The triangle image gives us a visual sense of the living, ongoing nature of storytelling. At its best, storytelling is a dynamic dialogue—one in which the teller listens to what the audience needs, the audience listens to the story and the teller, and the story moves back and forth between them.

- An awareness of the storytelling triangle gives us more insight into the process that storytellers use in the moment of telling a story. Tellers don't deliver intact stories to their audiences; at the moment of telling, the story always changes.

Suggested Reading

Conquergood, "Rethinking Ethnography."

Ellis and Neimi, *Inviting the Wolf In.*

Lepp, *Seeing Is Believing.*

———, www.leppstorytelling.com.

Lipman, *Improving Your Storytelling.*

Questions to Consider

1. Your audience will and should affect how you tell a story. Think of a story you've told recently. Whether your "editing" was conscious or not, what is one thing you didn't include in your story because of that audience? Why?

2. We're drawn to stories for different reasons. Can you think of an example of stories you're drawn to because of what or who they represent, how they reflect parts of yourself, or how much you don't like the original and want to retell it differently?

Lecture 2: The Storytelling Triangle

The Storytelling Triangle
Lecture 2—Transcript

Professor Harvey: At the end of the last lecture, we heard a story called "The Old Maid" about my great aunt. In this lecture, we're going to look at that story and some others in more depth to see how storytelling works.

Storytelling isn't about delivering a fixed thing. It's a dynamic process of you shaping the story with the audience. One way of looking at this process of story crafting and storytelling is through the storytelling triangle. In this lecture, we'll set up that triangle. In the next couple of lectures, we'll look at some aspects of the triangle in more depth—developing your relationship with the stories you tell, and developing your relationship with your audience.

Telling a story is a three-way relationship among you, and the story, and the audience. We can represent this through the image of a triangle with each of these points of teller and story and audience all connected. Now, the first idea to consider is that none of these points lies independent of the other—they're all connected. Stories are always mediated through a storyteller and exist in relation to an audience. This is a good place to start, because it lets us know a few things right off the bat.

First: Storytelling is about connections. Stories *are,* they *exist,* by virtue of this connection with the audience, and that connection with the teller. If a story doesn't grab you, chances are it isn't a good story for you choose to tell because in order to tell a story well, you have to be connected to it. So, even if there's a "good" story that other people like, ask yourself: Is it a story that means something to *me*?

It's the same question you have to ask for the audience: Your story should be a story that your audience will connect with. You may have stories that are only appropriate for some audiences, but not for others. If a story isn't right for an audience, that won't make any kind of connection with them, and again, the storytelling falls flat.

Second: Storytelling is about choices. There's not one right way to tell a story, or a right way and a wrong way to tell a story, because a story isn't an "ideal form" (in Plato's sense of ideal forms). There's not an ideal that you're trying to achieve. Storytelling is a series of choices that you make in how to connect the audience with a story.

Now in most cases, there's a real need to get the story right and to tell the truth—I certainly want to tell the truth about my great-aunt Mae. But there are many different ways that you can choose to tell that story and connect with the audience and connect that audience to the truth. There are some choices in storytelling that may be more appropriate for one given audience than another.

Third: Storytelling is an adaptive cultural phenomenon. Because of these connections between the story and the audience and the teller, stories develop and adapt based on the needs and desires of the audience and the teller. Many of the stories that we consider canonized as great tales (from Greek and Roman myths to fairy tales to the jokes you tell that get a laugh every time—that's a way that personal stories get canonized. You've got those jokes and stories in your arsenal that you know nine times out of 10 will land with the people you talk with)—these stories exist because they connect with tellers and with audiences, or at least with a powerful contingent of audiences and tellers.

If a teller has a story, but an audience isn't willing to accept that version of the story, the story either adapts to meet the needs of the audience, or the desires of what the teller wants to tell, or that story dies out. So, you may have a joke that you love, but if the joke doesn't land with your audience, you'll either adapt that joke and change it, or you'll move on completely and not tell it anymore. Stories survive by virtue of their relationship with tellers and audiences.

In this sense, the very idea of what constitutes a story is culturally specific; for example, western stories (from the U.S. and Europe), they typically focus on character development and a linear plotline, and cultural audiences in these locations tend to expect that the story will follow the events as they happened.

But in Bali and in Java, there is no such expectation—your story may center on one event, and then jump back in time, and then move forward a few years later. So in these cultures and for these audiences, following a linear timeline is not a requirement for a "real" story.

Now you may have picked up on something already—these connections between the three points of the storytelling triangle, they represent not only connections, but lines of communication.

It's not just a one-way mode of communication—and this is another important point to consider. Think about it: You're in a meeting, and you're explaining to new employees about the values of your company, and you begin to share a story with them about your company.

Sometimes we think of this as having the story like you would have a brief or a document, and then you're handing that document over to the audience—we could represent this as a linear diagram with the story first, that then comes to the teller, who then takes the story to the audience. We could draw arrows on this linear model, where the story goes to the teller, who goes to the audience. This is useful to see how stories are mediated by tellers. Every story you know (whether it's an orally-told story or one that's brought to you in print form), every story you know was brought to you by a storyteller. Even the books you read, the magazine articles, the news items— these stories are mediated by authors and editors and reporters.

The storyteller, the mediator, often has a stake in how the story gets told. The stories you grew up with were probably stories you heard because they were stories your parents wanted you to hear. The stories you tell to your children are the ones you mediate to them—and you probably craft those stories with careful lessons in mind. My story about my aunt Mae is mediated by my experiences with her, and by my own experiences about how women should act.

My telling about Aunt Mae is very different than the stories my grandmother told about her, because my grandmother had a different relationship with Aunt Mae (who is the subject of the story). My grandmother took care of Aunt Mae, which was no small task, and Mae did not behave like my grandmother thought a proper lady should (she walked around in her bra!). And Nana was so embarrassed because Nana came from a more socially affluent family. She was embarrassed by Aunt Mae, and because of my grandmother's experiences, she mediated the stories about Aunt Mae differently—she rarely ever sang the praises of Aunt Mae's behavior.

This reveals something big about the dynamics of storytelling in any situation, because unlike the experience of reading a story in a book, where the author (or teller) has shaped that story and then (after passing through that mediating gateway of the publishing house), then the story comes to you, the reader, and you read the words that are fixed in print, in storytelling, you're sitting there in the audience (or standing in front of your friend who's telling you a story), and you might laugh at a part of the story that he tells you, which prompts that storyteller to embellish a little bit more. Then you both check your watches and you realize that your break is over, and your friend has to quickly wrap that story up. That dynamic encounter of the live performance influences the story, so there's a relationship between the audience directly back to the story itself, and a relationship with the teller as well.

We learn something else about storytelling from these directional arrows: Storytelling is a living thing. Storytelling is a process, an action, a thing you do. If this is the storytelling triangle, then the "telling" exists in the center of these three lines of movement. The story is a living thing; it exists in the moment of telling to a particular audience. What this means to you, the storyteller, is that while you're telling, you should be aware of these constantly active lines of communication between you and your audience, and the story and your audience, and you and the story.

Because storytelling is a living thing, that means that just like any other living creature, it has the capacity for change. The story may surprise you while you're in the middle of telling it. There may be things that you didn't see before in the story that suddenly become apparent to you because, while you're telling it, your audience makes that realization, and you see them realizing it and, "Ohh!"

I was telling the story of Jacob in the Biblical Old Testament to a group of adults, and when I came to the part where Jacob, he has two wives who are sisters, and he loves the younger one but he was tricked into marrying the older sister, and when the wife he loves can't bear children, she says, "Well here, take my maid and have children with her!"

As I was preparing to tell that story, I was so caught up in that woman's perspective of being desperate, and then of her maid, Zilpah's reaction: "What's going on? What do you mean, you're giving me to him?"

But when I was telling that story, and I came back to Jacob, I had this moment when I was telling the story when Jacob looks at this situation that's being offered to him. When I was telling that story I paused, and the audience started to laugh, and at first I was shocked, and then I realized that there's this whole other moment and perspective where Jacob just got another woman to sleep with—and so I changed the story right there and said, "So she said 'Well, here, sleep with my maid!" and Jacob said, "Well, OK," and he nods comically.

It brought out the humor of it that I hadn't seen before, but of course, it's there—there's some nice potential for a joke about the male sex drive there. And that became a running theme then later in the story, because later in that same story he's offered another maid, and then of course he says, "OK," nodding.

Because I was paying attention to what the audience was responding to, and because I gave myself permission to adapt in the moment, I was able to add in some nice humor and repetition, while playing up the modern-day absurdity of the situation.

Let's look at another example of this, this time from another storyteller named Bil Lepp. Bil is a professional storyteller and he mostly tells comedic stories.

This storytelling clip is a live recording—all the storytelling clips you'll see in this lecture series are live, in order that you would see this living relationship between the teller and the audience. Sometimes you'll see video or audio quality sacrificed to view this teller-audience dynamic, but these examples are useful because you are going to be telling stories live, in front of an audience. From these live recordings, you'll see many techniques that only come out in this storytelling triangle dynamic. Here's just a portion of a story that Bil Lepp tells about buffalo tipping—it's the introduction to his story. Watch how he takes advantage of the audience's reaction to build more humor into the story.

[Video start.]

> **Bil Lepp:** You've probably heard of cow tipping, you know, in some sort of sociology class or somethin' but I'm willing to bet that you've never heard of buffalo tipping. The reason you've never heard of buffalo tipping is the same reason that you've never heard of elk tipping, or moose tipping, or elephant tipping, or alligator rolling. That's kind of superfluous—everybody knows this mean alligator rolling, right? That there is Florida sign language, that's FSL, mm-hmm.
>
> And the reason you've never heard of those things is because you ain't never been to Florida. The reason you've never heard of those things is because they are dumb ideas. Therefore, you know that some man has tried them. It's the way of our people. Some man has tried them, and he has died a horrible death. And his wife told everyone that he ran away with a younger woman, because it was less embarrassing. That's why you've never heard of elk tipping or alligator rolling.
>
> But these guys decided they were gonna do a little buffalo tipping, so they snuck up to that buffalo and put their hands on the side of it and they gave that buffalo a big ole shove. Well, buffaloes are bigger than cows, so that buffalo didn't tip over. Instead, he woke up.

[Video end.]

Professor Harvey: I love that story, and I love how he tells it because he's paying attention to how his audience gets into the humor of things that are foreign to them—it's a change to the story, based on his audience, and it gets the audience connecting with the story all the more.

For example, as we talked about in the last lecture, you can see the additive qualities of oral storytelling—he adds on examples ("and gator rolling, and elk punting") and the story rolls along with a series of "and then this, and then this."

Half of the humor of his timing is his facial gestures and his quick comedic timing during pauses even, and his arm movements to point out towards the tipping of various animals.

What he's doing isn't stand-up—in stand-up comedy, humor is the goal; in storytelling, humor is the vehicle for the story. Bil Lepp's introduction leads into a story that encompasses themes of friendship, and childhood adventure, and larger-than-life drama, and later he rounds the story out to a conclusion. So it's not standup, but it's wildly hilarious because he threads humor through a narrative about an event, and that narrative thread holds the audience from one moment to the next; it carries the audience along. So let's review some things we've learned about the storytelling triangle.

We know that storytelling connects a storyteller and an audience with the story. And in this process of connecting your audience with your story, there are choices you'll make that are specific to that audience and that story. This sounds very self-explanatory. We do this all the time on an unconscious level. But there's a lot going on here with these choices, because storytelling adapts, it morphs. The story changes over time to suit the audiences you come across, so while we may want to think about the story as a set thing—I deliver the story, to you, whole and intact; I deliver it to the audience—no, our stories are constantly in flux, adapting from situation to situation.

What this triangle image gives us is a visual sense of the living, ongoing nature of storytelling because at its best, storytelling is a dynamic dialogue. One in which the teller is listening to what the audience needs, and the audience is listening to the story and the teller, and the story is moving back and forth between them.

To illustrate this sense of dynamism in storytelling, let's look at an example of a story being told to an audience again. We've heard a few personal stories already; let's hear a different kind of story, a folktale. And as you watch and listen to this story, you can start to see this triangle image come to life: There's a story, and it's animated and mediated through a teller (me), and it's told to an audience, and the audience is constantly giving feedback through laughter or participation, and that impacts the storyteller, so I shift how I'm telling the story. So as you listen, think about how these different points of the storytelling triangle are set in motion.

[Video start.]

> **Professor Harvey:** I grew up in northeastern Tennessee and in our part of our country there's a lot of Scottish cultural heritage. We're in the mountains; we actually have a farm back home, we have a working farm. But my family actually married into a clan of Buchannans. In doing some research about those Buchannans, I found a story, several stories, about a man named George Buchannan.
>
> There are actually two George Buchannans in Scotland. There's George Buchannan, he's the historical figure, he lived in the 16th century, he was a tutor to the king, and he was a very smart man. He was a historian and in his spare time translated the entire *Book of Psalms* into Latin verse. He was a very smart man. The story has nothing really to do with him.
>
> This story is about George Buchannan the folk hero. The folk hero George Buchannan, unlike that historical figure, the folk hero isn't limited by time or place. The folk hero of George Buchannan, he hops around in time. You hear stories about George Buchannan placed in a lot of different time settings. As in the story from the 9th and the 10th centuries, not connected with that historical figure. But in all of the stories about George Buchannan, he was always a very wise man, but he often played the fool in public. This story from the 9th and the 10th centuries is no exception. In this story about George Buchannan, he lived on the western coast of Scotland. He lived in a wee crofting village. Can y'all say that with me? "Crofting. Crofting." Crofting—that was very good, that very good—crofting is a fishing village. If you go to some of these towns on the western

coast of Scotland, you'll see some of these crofting houses still preserved there, some of the later versions of them.

The walls on these houses, they're two feet thick. Those walls are built that thick so that they can withstand that salt spray and the winds coming up off the coast. Well George Buchannan, he was a fisherman, and he lived in a wee crofting house and every morning he would take down his herring net—his fishing net—now I'm going to ask you to participate with me. Pretend like you're taking down your own herring net from the walls, reach your hands up and just kind of take that herring net—very good!—reach it down, he would take that herring net, he would take it out on his skiff and he would cast it out on the ocean. Everybody cast your net out, cast your net out, don't hit your neighbor, but cast your net out. He would bring in all of the fish, and he would bring those fish back.

He did that every morning as with this morning, he woke up, took his herring net. Take that herring net down, he'd take it out on his skiff, he'd cast that net out and bring in all of the fish. On this particular day, he brought the fish back in—you can drop your net—he brought those fish in and he was going out after his morning fishing, he was going out to help his father who was working in the fields. So he took that herring net and he hung that wet net up over the fireplace and he always did this so that the net, it would dry out, so that the net wouldn't rot. He always kept his things nice.

He hung that herring up over the fireplace and he went out of that crofting house, he was going out to the fields where his father was. He walked down the lane, and there's a road that passed through that farm, and as he walked through and crossed that road he stood in the middle and he saw something, off in the distance. It was shimmering. He stood there in the road until that thing, it came closer and as it came closer he saw that it was a knight, on horseback. George, he had never seen a knight before. Being a clever man, he wanted to make a good impression but, he's George

Buchannan. He often played the fool in public. As that knight came riding closer and closer, George, he just stood there in the middle of the road, staring straight up in the sky, and he was taking up that middle of the road. That knight, he came riding closer and closer. George stood there, kind of picking at his teeth and picking at his nose. That knight, he came riding closer and closer, finally he was almost right on top of George and he reared back on his horse and he said, "Hey you've got to get out of the way, I'm coming through!"

Well George, he looked up at him and said, "Me? I'll not get out of your way. This is my family's land, it's my part of the road; you get out of my way." The knight wasn't used to being talked to like this.

"You get out of my way or I'll run you down."

"You couldn't run me down."

"What do you mean? I could so run you down."

"Ah, you couldn't run me down."

"What? Me, up here on this big horse and you down there, you piddly little thing."

"Ah, but then it would be your horse running me down and not you, wouldn't it?"

He saw he was dealing with a clever man. "You're a pretty clever man."

"Ah, I am."

"What's your name?"

"George Buchannan, sir."

"Have you got any family?"

"Aye, I've got a sister, she's back home weeping over the fun she had last year." Weeping over the fun she had last year. The knight couldn't figure it out.

"What do you mean she's back home weeping over the fun she had last year?"

"Ah well you see, she's back home having a wee baby. She's weeping over the fun she had last year."

"I see, George, I see. Have you got any other family?"

"Aye, I've got my father; he's out in the fields making bad worse." Making bad worse.

"What do you mean your father's 'making bad worse?'"

"Ah well you see, he cut down a wee bit of hay a few days ago—now will you look up into the sky and tell me what you see?" Sure enough, that knight—have any of you ever been to Scotland? You know if you go to Scotland and you wait in one place for five minutes, the weather will change. And sure enough what had been a beautiful cloudless day, it had started to cloud over. That knight looked up and he started to see those little drops of rain coming down: Plunk, plunk.

They started to drop onto his armor, and he said, "Aye, 'tis a soft day, 'tis raining."

"Aye, and my father's out in the field trying to dry off the hay. He's making bad worse."

"I see. I see," and the knight saw he was dealing with a clever man. He said, "George, how would you like to be *my* man?" George liked the sound of that because, as much as he liked being a fisherman, he liked the idea of being a knight's man.

He said, "Aye, I would."

"George, I'm going down into town, I'm getting out of this rain. You have given me some riddles. You solve three of my riddles and you can be my man. You come down into town tomorrow morning; you come looking and no-looking." That's looking and not looking. "You come into town riding and no-riding." That's riding and not riding. "And you come down into town [Scottish phrase]." That's clothes and no clothes. "You come down, you do those three things, you can be my man," and with that, that knight, cluck cluck, he toodled off around George who was still standing there in the middle of the road with that rain coming down. The knight, he went on, and George he stood there. He tried to make sense of those riddles and he saw his father coming up out of the fields sopping wet, taking his hat off, wringing it out, saying every curse word you can imagine.

Well they went back to that wee crofting house. They sat down, they made themselves a fire, they sat down and they started to eat something. George, he stared off into that fire, and he tried to make sense of those riddles. He looked into that fire. Then he happened to look above that fireplace. And what do you think he saw? That herring net that he had hung up to dry. He had his idea.

"Good night Father. Tomorrow I'm off to be a knight's man," and with that he went over to his bed, he went to sleep, and he woke up bright and early the next morning. He went over to that fireplace and looked up that net. He took off his nightshirt and he took down that herring net and he started to wrap one leg with that herring, and he wrapped the other leg, and he wrapped and he pulled it all up to his waist, and he had invented fishnet stockings.

He kept on wrapping and he slung that excess over his shoulder. "Goodbye father. I'm off to be a knight's man," and he went out the door and he went down the lane. As he was passing out of his father's property he passed by the goat shed. He picked up his father's best goat by the scruff of the neck and he kept on walking. He walked and he walked until he got closer into town where he could start to see those houses that were on the outskirts of town. As he saw those houses, he took that goat and he took one leg and he slung one leg over that goat, and he left the other leg on the ground, and he gave that goat a good lick, and he started walking.

Alollop, alollop, alollop, alollop, alollop, alollop, and down the road. He kept on going and the people in those houses tried to make sense of what they saw as they woke up and saw this man, half on a goat, and wearing nothing—and I mean nothing—but a herring net. They saw him as he walked by. George, he got closer up to that alehouse where the knight was staying and he saw that knight starting to come out of that alehouse. As he did, he kept on going on that goat, but he started to turn sideways. Alollop, alollop, alollop, alollop, alollop, alollop, down the road, and that knight, he tried to make sense of what he saw. He saw a man half on and half off a goat. He was riding and he was no-riding. He was turned profile so he was looking, but he was no-looking. He was wearing nothing—and I mean nothing—but a herring net. He was [Scottish phrase].

"George! George, you've solved my riddles!"

George looked up at him. "Aye, I'm a pretty clever man."

"George, I want you to be my man, but there's something you should know first." With that, that knight, he took off his helmet, and all the people saw that this was no knight. This was the king, in disguise. Because at that time, in the 9th and the 10th centuries in Scotland, the kings of old, they would ride around the countryside and just kind of check in on the nobles, to make sure they were taking care of the common folk like they should, and that's what this king had been doing when he came across George standing in the middle of the road.

He said, "George, will you be a king's man?"

George looked up at him, straightened up, tried to look as dignified as it's possible to look wearing nothing but a herring net, and he said, "Aye sir, under one condition."

"Well what's that, George?"

"Does the job come with a better outfit?" And that is how George Buchannan became the king's fool. Thank you.

[Video end.]

Professor Harvey: On the outside, you see a storyteller telling a story. But with an awareness of this storytelling triangle, you get more insight into that process that storytellers use in the moment of telling a story. I'm not delivering an intact story to an audience—I've prepared and I've learned the story, and then in the moment of the telling, the story changes—it has to. There's a group of folks out there who are going to connect with some parts of the story, and not others. So I've got to pay attention to what that audience needs from the story, and try to adapt in the moment to those needs.

I love that story. But you might be surprised to find out why I love that story. I have a lot of personal connections to that story, and that's what we'll talk about in the next lecture: how to personally connect with all kinds of stories. We'll take a closer look at the George Buchannan story, and the "Moose Tipping" story over the next couple of lectures. And, as you'll see, this personal connection to your story is essential to good storytelling.

Connecting with Your Story
Lecture 3

***

When you start to look more deeply at the stories you tell and ask why you tell those stories—why you connect with those stories—you'll be surprised at how many deeper layers of meaning your everyday stories hold. What those stories say to you at a deeper level is what makes them stick with you. Clearly, we tell many different kinds of stories, such as folktales or family stories. In this lecture, we'll talk about how you personally connect with stories, the genres of stories available to you, and the underlying reasons that explain why we tell the stories we choose to tell.

Personal Connections with Stories
- The personal connection you have with the stories you tell is perhaps the most important relationship in the story-teller-audience triangle. The amount of interest and time you take with a story will certainly vary, but no matter how much time you take in preparation, in the moment of telling, you must care about the story.

- I am drawn to the story about the trickster George Buchannan partly because of what it means to me culturally, as an Appalachian woman.
  - During the Irish potato famine, some Scots-Irish came to America and settled in the mountains of Appalachia, where they were almost always considered members of a lower class. These "hillbillies" were and still are looked down on as being ignorant and backward.

  - But the people of Appalachia know that they're smart, although sometimes they pretend not to be to "have a bit o' fun" at the expense of upper-class society.

  - Being an Appalachian-American in a region with a strong Scottish heritage, I feel cultural, physical, and emotional connections with stories about George Buchannan. I care about

George, and I treat him as if he's a real person, not a two-dimensional character.

Sourcing Stories and Checking Facts

- I also have an intellectual connection to the story of George Buchannan. I'm intellectually challenged by it—the riddles, for example, are delightful—and this intellectual connection means that I have looked deeper into all that the story has to offer. This intellectual connection will vary, depending on how much time you want to spend developing your story.
  - For an impromptu story that occurs to you from personal experience or a recounting of a story you've heard, you may have one level of intellectual connection.

  - But for other stories, you may have a deeper connection. You may spend time getting to know the characters, the plotline, and the cultural context and considering the metaphorical resonances of the story. You may read different versions of a story, learning about cultural context from multiple sources.

- The goal of seeking multiple sources applies whether you're telling a folktale or a personal story. Even if your story is about an event that happened to you, it helps to do some research to flesh out the story for a wider audience. Look for at least three sources to ensure that the details you relate are accurate.

- As someone with training in the methods and ethics of collecting and performing oral history–based stories, I sometimes feel a compulsion to share the stories I learn with others—to start a dialogue about how a story connects outward with wider social and economic issues. You, too, may have access to those kinds of stories.

- If you're telling someone else's story, it's important to get permission to do so, and make sure you're telling the story your subject wants to be told—not turning the story into something that serves your own motives but telling it in such a way that honors that person's perspective.

- In seeking out multiple credible sources, you're seeking multiple viewpoints. This will help you develop the characters within your story. Every character in the story is a potential main character; every character has the potential to be a hero or a villain, depending on the point of view.

- Make sure you do both broad and detailed fact-checking. Details matter; if you get a date wrong in your story, someone in your audience is bound to recognize it, and that misstep immediately distances that audience member from experiencing the story. The details of context are also crucial for you when you're getting to know your story.

Genres of Stories

- Most of the time, the stories we tell come from our personal experience or from the immediate world around us. These are personal narratives—stories you tell about yourself to yourself and to other people. Note that you are always the first audience for your stories. We all test our stories first on ourselves to decide if the stories are worth remembering and repeating.

- Family stories are those passed down to you by family members about your heritage. Stories in this genre include "Hands" and "The Old Maid."

- Some ghost stories are shared in families or in particular regions. Others are part of a wider cultural experience and story-base, shared by larger groups of people.

- Folktales are another kind of cultural story—told by the people of a particular culture, region, or part of the world. They're usually localized; thus, you'll hear about Scottish folktales, such as the stories of George Buchannan, or African folktales, such as stories about Anansi, the spider.
  - In these stories, we can see the dominant cultural values of a region. In the American folktale "Johnny Appleseed," the main character plants and harvests—laying claim to the land as he

A Miner's Story

Buzzy and Dan and Luke, they was all crushed. We carried them out in pieces days later. But Donzel lived. He had 70-some injuries, and where those arms had been pinned underneath him all those hours—14 hours under that rock—it had cut off the circulation, and they had just rotted out from underneath him.

The doctors, they cut off a piece at a time, trying to find something that was living. They left about six inches on each side, but he was alive. I went to visit him while he was in the hospital and then over the next couple of years while he was recuperating at home, and I tell you something, it's true: He and I still go hunting together.

It's true! Now I know I'm not much of a hunter, you know, with my leg and my back, but the doctors, they made Donzel some good arms, prosthetic arms, with metal hinges and a finger that's just about right for that trigger.

We sit out on his back porch and we just wait for them crows to come along.

That night, the night of the accident, I went over, I sat down on my bed when I got home. I unzipped my jacket, took out that fossil. I looked at it; I thought about where it had come from: hole in the earth that's fallen in on itself again, all that coal crushed in with blood and skin where those bodies had stained it. And you look at my knees now, mine where after so many years of working, I got these little spots on them, black coal spots, can't wash them out, can't get them out, can't get them out. The doctors, they pulled me out of the mines a few years back.

> I tell you the truth: I would give anything to go back down there again. The friendships that you make down there... And I was an archaeologist. Given the chance to live over again, I'd go back down every time.

plants seeds across the country. Arguably, these actions relate to some of the values of the early American settlers.

o We generally understand that folk stories aren't true, but they reveal something about a culture, either explicitly or implicitly. It's also true that the culture itself may have changed and adapted away from the values conveyed by the story over time.

o Among the many scholarly sources about folktales, I recommend the online compendium done by D. L. Ashliman at the University of Pittsburgh (http://www.pitt.edu/~dash/folktexts. html), the Pantheon Fairy Tale and Folklore Library, and the books and recordings of August House Press. The versions in these collections usually include cultural context and have been vetted for cultural accuracy or fidelity to oral versions.

- Fairy tales, or wonder tales, such as the stories of Snow White or Sleeping Beauty, are those in which some magical element comes into the story to help (or harm!) the characters.

- Sacred stories and myths deal with gods and mortals and the "big questions," such as: Why am I here? How did I come to be?

- Legends, such as the "Legend of Sleepy Hollow," are stories that may or may not be true. You may also have heard urban legends when you were a child at camp, such as the story known as "The Hook." These legends, as well as other types of stories, serve to communicate cultural values.

- In tall tales, characters or events are blown way out of proportion, perhaps with superhuman strength or size. Often, the joy of these stories is that the person telling them absolutely believes that the story is true, and sometimes they sound so real that you want to believe them, too.

- Finally, there are fables, such as Aesop's fables—stories that teach a moral lesson at the end. Usually, these are short stories with anthropomorphic characters, animals that take on human qualities (the wise owl, the clever fox). But there's always a clear lesson, which is usually stated directly.

- Depending on your background and experiences, you've probably been exposed to several of these genres, but you may not be familiar with some of the others at all. This takes us back to the storytelling triangle in some specific and important ways.
  - We're exposed to stories based on our family backgrounds, our cultural backgrounds, our peers, and our everyday experiences—we're inundated with stories based on the specific contexts of our lives.

  - There are also stories we've sought out because they weren't a part of our background. You may have traveled, for instance, and learned about cultures different from your own. You may have sought out higher education to expand the stories you know; you've chosen to read certain books and watch movies and TV shows that tell stories.

  - At the same time that certain stories press in on us, our own context propels us toward other stories, and the contexts surrounding us and surrounding the stories we seek out are part of how we know the stories we know.

Suggested Reading

Langellier and Peterson, *Storytelling in Daily Life*.

Lipman, *Improving Your Storytelling*.

MacDonald, *The Storyteller's Start-Up Book*.

Pantheon Fairytale and Folklore Library.

Sherman, *Mythology for Storytellers*.

Questions to Consider

1. Story genres often bleed into one another. Do you have a story that has reached "mythic" proportions in your family? Is there a personal story that's really a "tall tale"?

2. Consider your physical, emotional, social, or intellectual connections with the stories you tell. What genre of stories are you most familiar with telling, and what genre do you want to learn more about?

Connecting with Your Story
Lecture 3—Transcript

Professor Harvey: In the last lecture, you heard a couple of stories—one of them was a little folktale I like to tell about George Buchannan. But did you know that the reason that I connect with that story isn't because it's a clever folktale, and it isn't because I think I can get a laugh will all the characters I get into? I connect with that story most because of the countercultural message that the story conveys about rural folk like me.

I'm from the Appalachian mountains of Tennessee. That story tells me, that folk like me may come from the backwoods, but we're pretty clever all the same! That's the real reason why I tell that simple folktale. That's what I'm thinking about when I tell that story to kids in Appalachia—that the folks who live outside of these mountains may hear your accent and they may think you're dumb, but don't let that worry you. You're smart. You're clever. You could be the king's man.

When you start to look more deeply at the stories you tell, and ask *why* you tell those stories—why you connect with those stories—you'll be surprised how many deeper layers of meaning your everyday stories hold. What these stories say to you at a deeper level that makes them stick with you.

Clearly there are lots of different kinds of stories that we tell—folktales like this one, or tall tales (like Bil Lepp's "Moose Tipping" story), or family stories (like the story about my grandfather's "Hands," or my great Aunt Mae, the "Old Maid"). In this lecture, we'll talk about how you personally connect with stories, and the genres of stories available to you, as well as the underlying reasons how and why we tell the stories that we choose to tell.

The personal connection that you have with your story is perhaps the most important relationship in the storyteller-audience-story triangle. The amount of interest and time you take with a story will certainly vary—your relationship with the quick anecdote that you tell will be different than your relationship with other stories that are more meaningful to you. But no matter how much time you take in preparation, in the moment of telling, you have to care about that story. I found several stories about George Buchannan. The story that you heard in the last lecture is one of the many stories out there about this figure in Scottish and Appalachian folktale. George is what is called a "trickster" character, like Brer Rabbit—he gets in and out of mischief.

Let's take this story back to the storytelling triangle. I was drawn to this story partly because of what it means to me culturally, and as an Appalachian woman. This is your social and cultural connection with a story.

My region of the country is steeped in Scottish cultural heritage. Our family actually married into a clan of Buchannans, and those Buchannans were living there in southwestern Virginia because of their cultural history, having to flee Scotland after being kicked out by Bonnie Prince Charlie and then being driven to Ireland. Then, during the potato famine, these Scots-Irish nomads settled in the mountains of Appalachia, and in every place, they were almost always looked down on as being of a lesser class and caste than the more affluent English. Here, the "hillbillies" they became were, and still are, are looked down on as being ignorant and backward.

But most folks in Appalachia know they're smart—like George Buchannan, they know they're clever, and they sometimes may put on that they're not as smart as they actually are, so they can have a bit of fun with the knights and upper castes of contemporary society. So I'm drawn to this story as an Appalachian woman, and then there's this Scottish cultural heritage of my region that presses these particular stories back towards me.

Being an Appalachian-American in a region with a strong Scottish heritage, there's a physical connection that I have with the story. Where you're physically located affects how and if you see something. I've been to Scotland several times, so I've gained a perspective on that place and I've gotten to know the people there, but I'm not a Scottish person.

That affects how I tell the story, because I'm using the accent not the whole time, but only when the characters speak. I took some dialect lessons to try and make the pronunciations as accurate as I could, so that the accent isn't mocking up a culture, but it's one of a number of cultural details that point my audience back to that cultural location.

I have an emotional connection with the story. I care about what happens to the characters, what happens to George. I treat him as though he's a real "person," and not a two-dimensional character. Your emotional connection with your story will be based on how you identify with the story—or not. There may be stories that you have a strong negative emotional reaction to.

I also have an intellectual connection to that story. I'm intellectually challenged by the story—the riddles, for example, are delightful to me—but this intellectual connection also means that I've looked deeper into all that the story has to offer.

This intellectual connection will vary, depending on how much time you want to spend with your story. For an impromptu story that just occurs to you from personal experience, or recounting a story that you've heard, you may have one level of emotional connection. But for other stories, you want a deeper connection, so you spend time getting to know the characters, and the plotline, and the cultural context, and you consider the metaphorical resonances of the story (the connections to Appalachians, for example). You may read different versions of the story, learning from the cultural context from multiple sources.

The goal of seeking multiple sources applies whether you're telling a folktale, or a personal story, or any story. Even if the story you want to tell is an event that happened to you, it's very useful to do some research to flesh out the story for a wider audience.

For one, when you seek out multiple sources, you're fact checking—you're making sure that the story is right, that you get it right, so you're not embarrassed if somebody contradicts you and comes out with the accurate details of the story later. So, it's always good to "triangulate" your research—to look for at least three sources. (You can even do this with family stories, though there are some family stories that just sound great and are worth telling, even if you're not sure if they're true or not.)

Many of the stories I tell are based on oral histories that I've collected—my Ph.D. training is in the methods and ethics of re-performing oral history-based stories. Most recently I've been studying the stories of a community of coal miners. Most of them are disabled, and they live in southwestern Virginia. Here is one of their stories.

[Video start.]

Professor Harvey: I come from coal country, and I know we're officially in Virginia right now, but I wanted to tell a story about more my end. We actually have a farm that straddles the Tennessee-Virginia border, so we have our house in Tennessee, and then you walk about 10 feet off our porch and you're in Virginia, but you're in the southwestern part of Virginia in the mountains. There are a lot of miners who live there; it's coal country. For my Ph.D. training, it's in something called "performance ethnography." It's one of those wonderful multi-syllabic terms; it makes you sound very smart. What it means is that I interview people, and I take those stories, and with those peoples' permission I retell those stories to wider audiences and usually I'm seeking out those stories that don't often get heard in a wider public.

For the past several years, I've been getting to know a community of coal miners in southwestern Virginia, and I'd like to share one of their stories with you today. You should know that this is a contemporary story—all the things that you'll hear are happening right now, OK, this isn't just way back when, all of this, it's a contemporary story. And I have the miners' permission to tell the story, and you need to know that all of these events actually did happen to one man, named Donzel. Isn't that a great name? Can you say that name with me? Don-zel. It's great. All of this happened to one man named Donzel, and I learned, Donzel's the one person who I didn't actually interview myself, his story came to me from a mining training video that the Mining Safety and Health Administration did. It's in public domain, and he wanted his story out there in the public. So it all happened to this one man named Donzel, but the person who narrates this story, it's a composite character, a composite narrator that I created based on these 20-some miners who I interviewed myself, and all of them have given their permission for their story to be heard. The way that this person, this composite character, the way this person tells the story:

Yeah, I was in the mines. Now I was just a red hat when this happened. I'd just started mining, but my friend, Donzel, he'd been in there a little bit longer than me. He was still new, but he kinda took me under his wing, he taught me a thing or two about mining. Now at the time that this happened, we had just blasted and timbered in a new room—timbers are wooden supports you put up to support your roof up above you, 300 feet of mountain up above your head. We'd just blasted and timbered and I went in that room before anybody else got in there, and I switched off my cap light. It was so dark. Ain't never seen anything that dark before, it was pitch-black.

I turned that light back on and, once my eyes adjusted from coming from the dark up into the light, I thought I saw what looked like an outline of ferns all along that wall. Only they couldn't have been ferns because I seen them little-bitty plants out on my mama's front porch and no, these things was huge. 16 foot long arms and leaves this big. Well I went over to it, I had to see if it was real, you know? I took out my knife, that butt end of my knife, I put my hand up there, I tapped that knife up and a little piece of that fossil come off in my hand.

That fossil, millions of years old I found out. It was dark and hard against that gray coal. I could hear the others coming and I didn't want them to see me so fascinated with this piece of rock, you know, so I unzipped my jacket and I put that into my jacket, and the others come and we set to work. Donzel, he was with 'em. Donzel, he run that continuous miner machine. It's a long, low-to-the-ground machine; it's got a rotor on the front of it with carbon-steel teeth.

What you do is you run it with a remote, so he'd turn that remote on, and that rotor, it would start to spinning. That rotor, as it spun, those carbon-steel teeth, they would [growl]. They would dig into that face of coal, they'd dig out that coal and they'd deposit it onto a belt, and that belt, it run from all the way where we were, three miles dug into the mountain; it'd run three miles out to the entrance. Once it got out of that entrance, that coal on that belt, it would tip up on that belt as it arced up into the sky. Then that coal, it would spill off over the tipple and into trucks that were waitin' to take that coal off to those plants to be processed into energy so we can get these lights in this room.

But in order for that coal to get over to those plants, it has to get into that truck and onto that belt, so men like Donzel are down in there, and men like me were down in there. My job, being new, my job my whole shift was to take a shovel, and the coal that fell off that belt, I put it back on that belt. I done that the whole shift. You have to understand this is *low* coal. This ain't like those *high* mines up in Pennsylvania. No, you're talking 28 inches to 36-inch-high tunnels, no higher than a table, so you're crawling.

I always kept one foot under my backside or you had to be on your knees all the time. You say, "Did you get the head up?" No, you worked with your head sideways. Naturally, the top of the roof, it was damp and wet, dusty, and coal would build up on the side of your head or side of it, or water would drip down your ear, down your clothes. Where it was so low, there was no way you could keep your back out of the top of it.

All the time where you're working and moving, by the time the shift was over, you was drenched because you got lakes up above you. You got water, all that water dripping down. It's no dry place.

Once that shift was over, we was cleaning up in that room, and a few boys my age, we were flipping rocks at each other, you know, just horseplay. One of them, he took aim at Donzel. Flipped a rock over at him. Donzel, he brushed it off his cap, he said, "Cut that out! Quit it!" He didn't like that horseplay too much.

But we kept on cleaning up. I looked over at Donzel and he kept brushing his cap, brushing dust off of it, and I thought I saw this little trickle of dust coming from the ceiling. Only the foreman, he hadn't seen it. I thought I was just seeing things, so I went on back and to work and then I heard Donzel again. He's brushing his cap and he said, "Cut that out, quit it!"

I looked over at him and, there was this rock, it come out of the ceiling and it plucked down on his cap and it busted his cap light out. All the lights went off, the foreman, he grabbed me by the shoulders, and he pulled me and him into the next room. There was this huge boom; it was like nothing I'd ever heard before.

We sat up from where we landed, and we saw that whole ceiling had just collapsed in on top of that room. The whole shift, and I was the only one left, me and the foreman. Well, I remembered what Donzel had told me, that them rock falls, that they's deadly.

I couldn't help myself, I just ran over to that pile of rock, and I started pulling them off, hollering, "Donzel! Donzel!" The foreman, he's hollering for help, and me, coughing and hacking, that coal dust is getting in my mouth and down my throat. Well the others come and we set to work, we started tunneling in, trying to find people. I remembered that Donzel, he'd been by that continuous miner machine when his cap light had gone out, so I took a couple of boys, we started tunneling out to where that was, but it took hours.

Ten hours later, that boy down that tunnel—we'd gone in shifts— that boy who was down there, he said he thought he could hear something. It was real weak, but it kind of sounded like breathing. It was my turn to go in that tunnel. I went on through. I picked up a rock and I passed it back.

There he was. Donzel. He had his head pushed up against that miner machine. He found an air pocket in there, that's how he kept alive. But all the rest of him was just covered over in rock, his arms, they was pinned underneath him. I bent down. I was trying to reach his face, getting down to where he was, as I got closer, I could see that he had vomited all over himself. So I cleared that off away from his face so he could breathe a little bit easier, but with those arms pinned underneath him, all that rock on him, he could just barely suck in the air. We kept trying to take that coal off of him; we got all of it off except for one leg.

Then I started to see that same little trickle of dust start to come down. This whole thing was just starting to rib-roll back on top of him again. So we got boards and we covered him over with boards, and we backed out of that tunnel, and me hollering, "We're not leaving you, Donzel, hold on," and then this other huge boom, and that whole thing just came on top of him again.

We went back in. We tunneled through. It took another hour. We got all that rock off. Pulled up those boards. We saw that they had saved him from that second fall. So we worked double-quick, we got all that off of his leg, and I was so tired by that point, I backed out of that tunnel. Another boy, he come in and he grabbed Donzel by the belt and by the collar, and he just lifted him up out of that dark hole and we started passing him, one man to the next.

He come to me, I grabbed onto him. As he passed by me, I saw that there wasn't a cut on him, but his clothes were soaked with blood, where the pressure of being underneath all that rock for 14 hours, it had squeezed the blood out of his pores. Passed him on back, and kept on going. We got three others out that day.

But Buzzy and Dan, and Luke, they was all crushed. We carried them out in pieces days later. But Donzel lived. He had 70-some injuries, and where those arms had been pinned underneath him all those hours—14 hours under that rock—it had cut off the circulation and they had just rotted out from underneath him.

The doctors, they cut off a piece at a time, trying to find something that was living. They left about six inches on each side, but he was alive. I went to visit him while he was in the hospital, and then over the next couple of years while he was recuperating at home, and I tell you something, this is true: He and I still go hunting together. That's true! Now I know I'm not much of a hunter, you know, with my leg and my back, but the doctors, they made Donzel some good arms, prosthetic arms, with metal hinges and a finger that's just about right for that trigger. We sit out on his back porch and we just wait for them crows to come along.

That night, the night of the accident, I went over, I sat down on my bed when I got home. I unzipped my jacket, took out that fossil. I looked at it; I thought about where it had come from. Hole in the earth that's fallen in on itself again, all that coal crushed in with blood and skin where those bodies had stained it. You look at my knees now, mine where after so many years of working, I got these little spots on them, black coal spots, can't wash them out, can't get them out, can't get them out. The doctors, they pulled me out of the mines a few years back.

I tell you the truth; I would give anything to go back down there again. The friendships that you meet down there, make, and I was an archaeologist. Given the chance to live over again, I'd go back down every time.

[Video end.]

Professor Harvey: I'm interested in their stories because of where I'm from, but also because their stories were so compelling, and so often misunderstood by people outside of this region (most people think of mining as an old guy with a pick and a shovel, not a mechanized industry that we're all connected to).

I felt an ethical compulsion to share their stories with others, and to start a dialogue about how this story (as an artistic performance) connects outward with wider social and economic issues that impact all of us. You may have access to those kinds of stories—stories in your history, or your culture, that you want to share, stories that start a dialogue about an issue that matters to you.

It's important if you're telling a story that's someone else's—someone else has told you their story—you need to get their permission to tell their story. You want to make sure that you're telling the story that they want to tell—not turning the story into something that serves your own motives, but telling it in such a way that honors that person's perspective.

In general, try to locate credible sources (people or story versions that can give you differing but reliable perspectives). For instance, this story is based on an interview that was featured in a government-sponsored mining training video (it's in public domain), and I balanced that film perspective with interviews I did with over 20 different contemporary miners (and I had their permission to tell their stories—they knew how these stories would be used).

In seeking out multiple sources, you're seeking multiple viewpoints. This will help you develop your characters within the story because every character has the potential to be the hero or the villain, depending on your point of view.

You're fact checking in big ways, and in small ways, making sure the details are accurate in the story. Details matter, and paying attention to these details is important because if you get a date wrong in your story, you can bet someone in your audience will recognize it, and that misstep—it's not just that it's embarrassing; it distances your audience from experiencing the story. It's a distraction.

The details of context are also crucial when you're getting to know your story, because after all, one of the first questions you usually ask a stranger when you first get to know them is, "Where are you from?" Place shapes us. Pay attention to where are you at any given moment in the story.

Remember the qualities of oral thought—remaining close to the lifeworld, with an emphasis on situated actions and specific locations. Cultural context is important, and as we'll see later, nearly every culture has a Cinderella story, but there are cultural reasons why one story features a woolen bootie, and another story features a glass slipper.

"George Buchannan" is a folktale, and the "Miner's Story" is an ethnographic story (it's based on oral histories)—these are all genres of stories that you can tell. Let's outline some of these different genres. Most of the time, the stories we tell come from our personal experience, or from the immediate world around us. Most of these are personal stories, or personal narratives— those stories that you tell about yourself to yourself and to other people.

Yes, you tell stories to yourself. As we see in this triangle, stories always have an audience, and you are always the first audience for your stories. We are constantly talking to ourselves, and we test out stories first on ourselves to decide if the story is worth remembering, worth repeating. So personal stories are about you and your experiences—they have meaning first to you, and then to your audience.

We have family stories—stories that your family has passed down to you about your heritage, and stories about your family members that members may tell on one another. There's usually a pecking order on who gets to tell stories on another person. It's like we talked about in the first lecture, with the "Hands" story and in the story of Aunt Mae, the "Old Maid".

The sources of these kinds of stories—the personal stories, the family stories—you get these stories from yourself and from family members. Your family may tell ghost stories. Ghosts in your family, I have a few, or ghost stories about your region. Some ghost stories are part of a wider cultural experience and story base They're shared by groups of people; for instance, Japanese ghost stories that have inspired many films.

Folktales are another kind of cultural story—these are tales that are told by the folk of a particular culture or region, or a particular part of the world. They're usually localized, so you'll hear about Scottish folktales (such as "George Buchannan"), or African folktales (such as stories about Anansi, the spider).

In these stories, we can see the dominant values and cultural values of that region coming through. So in the American folktale "Johnny Appleseed," the main character, he plants and he harvests—he even lays claim to the land in this way, planting seeds all over the land. Arguably these were some of the early American settlers' values.

Now, we generally understand that the folk stories aren't actually true—there may never have been a person Johnny Appleseed, although that's an interesting story. But folktales still reveal something about a culture, either explicitly or implicitly, although the culture itself may have changed and adapted away from those values over time. Folktales tell about the folk.

There's an excellent online compendium of folktales. It's been arranged by type and by topics. It was done by D. L. Ashliman at the University of Pittsburgh.These stories are arranged topically, according to a cross-cultural referencing system that was created by the folklorists Aarne and Thompson. So, you can look up—on this database—you can look up stories under headings such as "Bald Stories: Folktales about Hairless Men," and "Stories about Humans with Animal Ears and Horns." All of these are tale types and topics.

Another source is your library's 398.2 section. Three ninety eight point two is sometimes called the "storytelling section" among storytellers, because it's this section that houses written records of stories that, on the whole, originated in the oral tradition.

Another great resource is the Pantheon collection; it's called the Pantheon Fairy Tale and Folklore Library. It's a good idea to veer towards scholarly presses for folktale collections, such as the Oxford collections, because these versions provide cultural context and they've been vetted for cultural accuracy, or fidelity to the oral versions of stories, rather than a literary "prettying up" of oral stories—the Victorians were famous for this.

August House is another publishing company that specializes in the dissemination of the work of professional storytellers. It's a great resource for reading and for listening to professional storytellers at the top of their craft. But as with any other source, make sure you're crafting your own versions of stories from multiple sources, and putting them into your own words because plagiarizing a professional teller's story is as much a sin as academic plagiarism.

In these sources, you'll find folktales and also fairy tales, or wonder tales—such as "Snow White," or "Sleeping Beauty"—they're fairy tales because some magical help comes into the story and aids (or tries to harm) the characters in the story.

Then there are sacred stories and myths—they deal with gods and mortals and the big questions such as, "Why am I here? How did I come to be?" You may have your own stories from your own faith tradition, your own sacred stories.

Just a note: We tend to talk about ancient myths such as Greek mythology or Roman mythology, and we tend to use the term "mythology" to separate our own belief system as sacred stories, from the "just stories" of other cultures. It's important to remember that other people's myths are just as sacred to them as your own sacred stories are for you.

Some sources for finding myths are your own sacred texts, and the sacred texts of other world religions. D. L. Ashliman's website also contains myths, as well as another very good book, Josepha Sherman's book *Mythology for Storytellers*.

Legends are another great genre. Legends may or may not be true. There are old legends, such as the "Legend of Sleepy Hollow," about the poor teacher Ichabod Crane who happens to cross the path of the headless rider on that lonely road and he was never heard from again.

You may have heard urban legends when you were a kid at camp, like the story called "The Hook"—it's one of my favorites. It's that story about the kids who were out necking in the boy's car at make-out point, and then the girl, she keeps putting the guy off, and he grabs for her, and she puts him off, until finally he's so frustrated that he just lays on the gas pedal and speeds home. On the way home they hear on the radio that a murderer is on the loose right out from where they were making out, and the murderer has a hook for a hand, and when the boy, he drives that girl home and he comes around the car to let the girl out at her house, he sees a hook still dangling from the door handle—dun dun dun!

Of course, the lesson of that story is that they got away just before the murderer opened the car door and would've slashed them, and by implication it was the girl putting the guy off from his sexual advances that got them away in the nick of time, and there's the model for the stereotypical young American couple. The guy tries to get as far as he can, and the girl is supposed to put him off, and if she doesn't put him off the "hook" will get them both!

There are values that these legends carry with them. We're seeing that stories do a lot of work in cultures to communicate values. Some good sources for urban legends are Jan Van Brunvand's works, her books. Or, just volunteer as a leader at any Girl Scout or Boy Scout campout, you'll hear plenty of these.

There are tall tales, with characters that are blown way out of proportion, they have superhuman strength that's attributed to an ordinary person. Of course the joy in these stories is that the person telling them absolutely believes that the story is true: "Yes, I really did catch a fish this big!" Bil Lepp specializes in tall tales, or "liar's stories"—they're fictions (like "Moose Tipping"), but they sound so real that you *want* to believe that they're true! Tall tales.

The last one I'll mention are fables, such as Aesop's fables—stories that teach a moral lesson at the end, and usually these are short stories with anthropomorphic characters, animals that take on human qualities, so the wise owl, the clever fox. But there's usually always a clear lesson that's tied to the story and stated directly: Two crows work together to drop pebbles into a jar of water until they can reach the water with their beaks and they both can drink. A clever crow will never grow thirsty.

Depending on your background and your experiences, you've been exposed to one or a number of these genres, and there are other genres you may not be as familiar with. This takes us back to the storytelling triangle in some interesting and important ways. Because there are stories that press in on us due to our cultural context. The family stories that you grew up with, the childhood fairy tales that you heard (and depending on what country that you grew up in, you'd hear different stories).

Even the stories that your peers tell you, even stories that you're exposed to because you stumble on them—that person you didn't expect to run into, but all of a sudden you hear his story or her story, and you're pulled into this whole other world.

For example, I was shopping one day in the grocery store, and at this time it was right after our baby was born, and a relative was watching the baby so I had a few precious seconds on my own to stock our pantry, and so as I rushed from aisle to aisle, this older man started talking to me. You know how this is, it's the person who just needs to talk with someone, and you just happen to be that person they've trapped into a conversation—and that's how I thought of it at first. I was stuck there and when I didn't really have a lot of time to waste, but as he talked he told me about how he had just lost his wife. And then I stopped, and I put my own day aside for a second, and I asked him about her, and he said, "I only had 49 years with her." For the rest of that day, and whenever I think about that story, I think about how he phrased that: "I *only* had 49 years with her." Now *that's* a love story.

We're exposed to stories based on our family background, our cultural background, our peers, even the grocery store we happen to go to! If you look at the storytelling triangle, here's the story pressing towards you—we're inundated with specific stories based on the specific context of our lives.

Then there are stories that we've sought out because they weren't a part of our background. You may have traveled and learned about cultures that are different from your own—travel is a wonderful way to learn new stories. Isn't that what draws us to travel: to explore, to learn, to expand? You may have sought out education that expanded the stories you knew. You've chosen and read certain books and you watch movies and TV programs that tell stories.

Back to the storytelling triangle, at the same time as certain stories press in on us, here's our own context propelling us towards other stories—and the context surrounding us, and surrounding the stories we seek out, are all a part of how we know the stories that we know.

The stories we know and choose to tell, there are really a lot of factors that weigh on these choices. And there is a context that weighs on your audience as well. This context impacts how your audience will interpret and respond to your story. It impacts if they're even ready to listen to you in the first place. See, there's a lot going on in this storytelling dynamic than we give it credit for.

In our next lecture, we'll talk about how your relationship with your audience affects the stories that you tell.

Connecting with Your Audience
Lecture 4

In this lecture, we will focus on the second aspect of the storytelling triangle—your relationship with your audience. We'll talk about some of the different contexts of this relationship (physical, social, emotional, and intellectual), and then we'll consider how stories bring audiences together. At the end of the lecture, you'll start keeping a storytelling journal, recording three events that happened in the recent past that might hold meaning for others.

Physical and Social Contexts

- Think for a moment about the contexts of the performance of the George Buchannan story. First, there's the physical context of storytelling. As the teller, you're in a room with other people and, perhaps, you're at a microphone. One of the first things you'll do is make eye contact with the audience.
  - Psychologically, this acknowledges the presence of other people; eye contact is the first way you invite the audience into a relationship with you.

  - Try to make eye contact with everyone in the room, and as you speak, continue to do so.

- Making eye contact acknowledges that you're speaking with your audience, as opposed to speaking to them or having them overhear your conversations onstage. You're in a social relationship with your audience. Speaking with someone is very different than delivering a monologue; it means you're entering into a conversation with that person.
  - Remember that communication is a two-way street; the audience is feeding you information (through body language, reactions, and so on) while you are feeding them information (telling them about the different places and people in your story).

- Many effective storytellers constantly evaluate how their audience is communicating with them, incorporating that information into how they develop the emotional arc of the story and their choices in telling the story.

- If children in a group are starting to fidget and talk to their neighbors, they're telling you that they need more help getting into the story. Ask them to physically do something to draw them back in.

- Note, too, that sometimes physical cues can be misleading. If a listener is looking off into space but seems focused, it could be that he or she is imagining the story you're painting with words.

- The truth is that you never really know how a story is resonating with an audience. But if you're in tune with the audience and look for obvious cues, you can adjust your story to suit their needs. Telling a "dynamic" story means you're able to change and adapt what you say in the moment to communicate the story effectively.

Audience-Centered Storytelling

- In audience-centered storytelling, you put the needs of the audience first. Part of adopting this perspective is acknowledging that every audience is different—every audience has a different background and different needs.

- As we discussed, each point on the storytelling triangle represents a different sphere of context and interaction; each audience member comes from one context, and that context influences his or her understanding of the references you make and the symbols you use.
  - In cross-cultural storytelling, audience members may have completely different interpretations of what we might think of as "universal" references and symbols. For example, the sociologist Laura Bohannan was corrected in her telling of *Hamlet* by the elders of the Tiv people in West Africa. If the dead king were a ghost, they said, he wouldn't be able to speak; thus, he must have been an omen sent by a witch.

o   Such cultural differences may influence how your audience understands and accepts your stories.

- In storytelling, your job isn't to dictate conclusions to your audience. It is, instead, to help your audience see inside a situation—the world of the story—and the situations of the characters. Stories help us see inside the decisions of other people in such a way that they open us up to other perspectives.

Establishing Trust with the Audience

- Part of the social connection with an audience also has to do with trust. In order to really hear a story, you have to trust the person who's telling it. You have to trust that the teller is telling the truth, which again, is different from relating facts. Remember, facts are about what happened, and truths are about the meaning behind what happened.

- One way to establish a trust relationship with an audience is to speak in a conversational and approachable way, as Bil Lepp did in his telling of the buffalo tipping story. Don't be afraid to laugh at yourself, which gives the audience permission to laugh with you.

- It's also important to pay attention to how you physically interact with an audience. Standing in an open posture invites others to approach you. Closed or negative postures close you off from your audience and tend to focus your energy in and down.

Emotional Context

- Connected with the social context is the emotional context between you and your audience, because everyone you come into contact with brings along his or her own emotional baggage.

- It's your job to put everyone in the right mood to hear the story, to try to tune out the emotions of previous contexts and tune in to the emotional context of the story.

- Much of that emotional tuning happens in your introduction—those first moments with the audience. This means that you must be emotionally committed to the story you're going to tell. You must believe the words that you are saying. You must take the time to let the words and the truth of those words resonate with you; in doing so, they will most likely resonate with your audience.

Intellectual Context

- The intellectual context of storytelling requires you to gear your story's language, content, and length to the needs of a given audience.

- This doesn't mean that you "dumb down" the story for an audience any more than you would intentionally talk over their heads. Neither of these approaches accomplishes anything. You want to meet your audience members where they are.

- Especially with children, don't underestimate your audience. When you talk down to children of a certain age, they tune out, or worse, they start to mock you! Talking a little above children can be a good thing—it keeps them on their toes.

How Stories Bring Audiences Together

- Sometimes, your relationship with an audience may be mixed. Maybe you know some people in a group better than others. Stories are a way to bring the group together. One of the best ways to do this in everyday conversation is to look for ways that your own human moments connect with the struggles that everyone faces.

- A story about losing patience with a store clerk demonstrates this point. At the moment the incident took place, it didn't seem as if it would make a great story. But later, sharing the story with friends was cathartic—allowing the group to laugh at shared frustration—and it was healing—illustrating how understandable it is to get angry and snap.

- Finding a connection with your audience sometimes means finding the story that connects your common struggles. It's a good idea to reflect a few times a week on those "human moments" that you've experienced so that when you're in an everyday conversation, you can plug those stories in.

The "Universal Singular"

- In stories, your small triumphs or stumbles serve as metaphors, which is what makes storytelling such a powerful way to relate to people. In life and in everyday conversation, stories often become metaphors for larger issues: the explosion at the store clerk—the small moment—that stands for more universal struggles with patience, kindness, and self-control.

- Stories can help us see a real situation in a different setting. And that separation out of the everyday helps us return to our current situation with new eyes, because we've started to see our own world through the lens of the story-world. This is why stories work so well in difficult conversations and why humor in stories can help relax a tense situation.

A small story about frustration outside of work might be useful in counseling an employee who is frequently angered in the office.

- Of course, this can work in reverse, as well; as you listen to the stories of others, you see the universal moments in their situations.

- The cultural theorist Norman Denzin uses the term "universal singular" to discuss the fact that each of us represents both singular and universal experiences. We are singular—there are things that are unique to our own backgrounds, upbringing, choices, and personalities—and, at the same time, we each represent something universal about our cultures and, indeed, the human experience.

- With this in mind, I invite you to target your own experiences—big and small—and begin to see the thread of universal experience in them. Start a storytelling journal, and as a first exercise, write down three things that happened to you this week that stick out in your mind.

  o These events don't have to be significant—just occurrences that were meaningful to you. It could be hugging your child after you came home from work or making a difficult choice at the office.

  o Think of the details surrounding each of those three events. If you hugged your child after coming home from work, what was work like that day? What was the commute like? What was the expression on your child's face? Where were you when you hugged your child? Take time to write down as many details as you can.

  o Then, look at those three rough stories and see if you can identify one universal struggle or feature in each of them—something that goes beyond the individual circumstances that you just wrote down.

  o Remember those three universals and look for opportunities later this week to tell one of those stories in a situation in which your audience might need to hear it. The audience might be your son or daughter, your spouse, or a couple of co-workers.

  o If you find the right situation to tell the story, pay attention to the ongoing needs of your audience as you're telling it. Do you need to tell a shortened version of the story (because of the physical or social contexts)? Do you need to stress some details and not others because those are the ones that would matter most to this audience?

  o Finally, if you get a chance to tell one of those stories, record how you adapted the story to your audience. And hold onto that notebook—you'll need it for the lectures to come!

Suggested Reading

Breen, *Chamber Theatre*.

Lepp, *Seeing Is Believing*.

———, www.leppstorytelling.com.

Lipman, *Improving Your Storytelling*.

Questions to Consider

1. How, specifically, does an audience communicate its needs to you as you're telling a story?

2. Think of three events or moments from your past week. Can you see threads of universal experience in those events?

Connecting with Your Audience
Lecture 4—Transcript

Professor Harvey: In this lecture, we're going to focus on the second aspect of the storytelling triangle—your relationship with your audience. We'll talk about some of the different contexts of this relationship (the physical, social, emotional, and intellectual contexts). Then we'll move to consider how stories bring audiences together.

At the end of this lecture, I'd like to get you started keeping a storytelling journal. We'll start your journal off with an exercise that ties together this storytelling triangle. This exercise will help identify stories that will connect with a variety of audiences. I keep a journal like this for myself. Most professional storytellers and writers do.

To begin with, there are multiple contexts in the audience-performer dynamic. Let's go back for a moment to the "George Buchannan" story—think about the context of this storytelling performance.

In this performance, there's the physical context of storytelling. You're in a room with other people, you're looking at them—maybe you're with a couple of people, or maybe you're with a crowd and you're at a microphone. So one of the first things that you're doing is making eye contact with people. As we said in the first lecture, the storyteller breaks the "fourth wall." You're looking your audience directly in the eye.

Now, this has some very specific physiological and psychological effects. Psychologically, you're acknowledging that the other person is there—your eye contact is the first way that you invite your audience into a relationship with you. It's a good idea, if you're talking with more than one person, to give everyone a good dose of eye contact as you begin your story. Acknowledging each person draws them in. As you speak, continue to make that eye contact—we'll talk in a later lecture about how you can use specific choices in where you look during a story to paint a picture of that story—but for now we're working on establishing this relationship with your audience, and drawing them in from the beginning.

Making eye contact also acknowledges that you're speaking with your audience (as opposed to speaking to them, or having them overhear your conversation onstage). You're in a social relationship with your audience—the social context of storytelling. Speaking with someone is very different than delivering a monologue—it means you're entering into a conversation with them, communicating with them.

Communication is a two-way street (as we've already illustrated in the storytelling triangle)—your audience is feeding you information (through their body language, how they sit, how they react) while, at the same time, you're feeding them information (you're telling them about the different places and the different people in your story).

Many effective storytellers are constantly looking for how their audience is communicating with them, and they're incorporating that information into how they develop the emotional arc of their story and on their choices on how they tell the story. What it means is, as a storyteller, you're willing to let go of any preconceived notions about "the best way" to word something or to describe something. You exchange that in favor of paying attention to what your audience really needs.

For example, in some versions of the "George Buchannan" story, especially if I'm telling to kids, and if I see a few of them start to fidget and turn and talk to their neighbors, in doing that, they're telling me that they need more to help them get into the story.

Now, instead of interrupting the story and calling them out for their inattentiveness, if I notice the kids' attention wandering, I'll ask them to physically do something to draw them back into the story—so here's a clip from a telling of that story to adults with audience interaction.

[Video start.]

> **Professor Harvey:** Well George Buchannan, he was a fisherman, and he lived in a wee crofting house and every morning he would take down his herring net—his fishing net—now I'm going to ask you to participate with me. Pretend like you're taking down your

own herring net from the walls, so reach your hands up and just kind of take that herring net—very good!—reach it down, he would take that herring net, he would take it out on his skiff and he would cast it out on the ocean. Everybody cast your net out, cast your net out, don't hit your neighbor but cast your net out. And he would bring in all of the fish, and he would bring those fish back.

He did that every morning as with this morning, he woke up, took his herring net. Take that herring net down, he'd take it out on his skiff, he'd cast that net out and bring in all of the fish.

[Video end.]

Professor Harvey: That's an example of using interaction to bring your audience back, and we'll give you more tips like this during in our last couple of lectures on keeping your audience's attention.

It's worth noting here, as you listen to the physical cues that your audience is feeding you (if they sit attentively or if they're looking away), that sometimes the physical cues can be misleading. Someone may get up and leave in the middle of your story if you're telling to a group—and it probably has nothing to do with your story, it just means they have to go to the bathroom.

Someone, if they're looking off into space, but they're focused, it may (and it probably) does mean that they're imagining that story that you're painting with your words. Also remember that most people get their entertainment from a TV screen, and it doesn't hurt their feelings if you stare at it, with your mouth hanging open and a blank expression on your face. It doesn't hurt the TV's feelings if you're doing that as an audience member. Not every audience is going to look as interested as they really may be.

It's important not to expect them to always act interested. If you're telling a story solely to see the look of admiration in your audience's eyes, you might want to reevaluate why you're telling that story. The truth is, you never really know how a story is resonating with an audience. But if you're in tune with that audience, and you're looking for the obvious cues, then you can adjust your story to suit the needs of that audience—that's the definition of "dynamic," it's change. Telling a dynamic story means you're able to change and adapt what you say in the moment to communicate the story effectively.

It's also what we mean by being "audience centered" in your storytelling—you put the needs of your audience first. Part of adopting an audience-centered perspective is acknowledging that every audience is different. This gets to the social context between you and your audience. Every audience is going to come from a different background, and have different needs. As we talked about before, each point on that storytelling triangle represents a different sphere and context of interaction. The audience (and really, each member of that audience) is going to be coming from their own context, and that context will influence how they understand the references you make, and the symbols you use.

Two examples, from cross-cultural storytelling, and these are true stories. A sociologist named Laura Bohannan went to study with the Tiv people of West Africa, and she took along with her a copy of Shakespeare's *Hamlet*. After a while, the natives asked her to tell them a story, and she thought, well what could be more universal than Shakespeare? But when she tried to explain about how the dead king Hamlet appeared to the sentinels, the natives, they corrected her and said, "No no no, it wasn't a ghost—he must have been an omen sent by a witch," and they continued to correct her in the story, that ghosts can't talk, nor can omens, so the dead Hamlet must have been a zombie.

Eventually, the natives said, "That was a very good story, and you told it with very few mistakes. Sometime, you must tell us some more stories of your country. We, who are elders, will instruct you in their true meaning, so that when you return to your own land, your elders will see that you have not been sitting among the bush, but among those who know things and who have taught you wisdom."

Second example: A couple who were working with the Summer Institute of Linguistics International, they were doing research in Nepal. And while they were there, they were learning about the dialect of this certain region, and the people there asked her to tell them a story that meant a lot to them, and so this couple, the man and the woman, they decided to tell the Biblical account of the birth of Jesus. They told about Mary, who wrapped the baby in swaddling clothes and laid him in a manger.

The Nepalese audience members were shocked, and they told the couple that Mary was a terrible mother. They went on to explain how you never lay an infant down—in that culture, you always wear the baby on you, with cloth tying the baby to your body, and when you work and when you rest the baby is right there, touching you.

Now these examples of cultural differences may impact how your audience understands and accepts your story. There are other potential differences to be aware of in everyday storytelling. Your job isn't to dictate conclusions to your audience. It's to help your audience see inside a situation—the world of the story—and the situations of the characters. Stories help us see inside the decisions of another person, and in that way they open us up to see different perspectives.

Part of that social connection with your audience has to do with trust. In order to listen to a story, and really hear the story, you have to trust the person who's telling the story to you. You have to trust that they're telling the truth, which is different than giving someone facts. Remember, facts are about what happened, and truths are about the *meaning* behind what happened.

This is why you can listen to a good liar's tale—like the one that Bil Lepp tells, you heard part of that on his "Buffalo Tipping" story in the second lecture. You can really enjoy them because there are humorous truths there about how people interact with each other, even though the circumstances (the happenings, the facts) may be very different.

Part of what Bil does to establish that trust with an audience is he speaks in a conversational and approachable way. He laughs at himself a lot, which gives the audience permission to laugh at him. He definitely has a storytelling persona (he's usually got his hands in his pockets; he stares off into the sky sometimes; he'll sway a little bit, like a kid)—and this persona is approachable.

That's something else to consider when you're telling a story—developing that trust relationship with the audience—and one of the first ways that you do that is to pay attention to how you physically interact with them. So ask yourself, is your posture open? Standing in an open posture invites someone to approach you. Or do you have negative posture and a closed position? Your hands are crossed, your feet are turned away from that person, or you're looking at them from the side. These are closed postures, negative postures, and they close you off from your audience. So, open up your posture.

Open posture also has another effect on you as the storyteller. Closed postures tend to focus your energy in and down. You'll see that my arms are folded, it curves my spine down and my body, it slumps, my energy is thrown down. But when I have open posture to my audience, it throws my spine back, and my energy is up, and I can focus that energy into sharing a story out to the person in front of me, rather than down.

Connected with this social context is the emotional context between you and your audience, because everyone you come into contact with is coming with their own emotional baggage. You might be on your way to work with others in the car, and some of them are frustrated because their car wouldn't start and they had to bum a ride with your carpool.

Or you're in a meeting, and one person had a fight with his wife the night before, and this one's dog died, and that one's exhausted because she stayed up all night with her sick daughter. Everyone's coming from different places, and it's your job to put everyone in the right mood to hear that story, to try to tune out all of the emotions of their previous contexts and tune them in to the emotional context of the story.

A lot of that emotional tuning happens in your introduction—those first moments with your audience. In our last two lectures we'll workshop in-depth about how to remove emotional barriers for your audience, and how to use introductions as a kind of "emotional on-ramp" for your stories. But for now, let's focus on that moment when you're sharing the story itself with your audience.

This means being emotionally connected to the story you're going to tell. It doesn't mean that you break down in tears if you're telling a sad story—it doesn't mean getting "emotional" in that sense. It means that you believe the words that you're saying. It's the difference between saying, "I had a cat for seven years, and she died," and, "I had a cat for *seven years* ... and she died."

It means you take the time to let the words and the truth of those words—the meaning—resonate with you, and in doing so, they will most likely resonate with your audience.

Lastly, there's an intellectual context in your relationship with your audience, and it's the same question of listening to your audience's needs. The intellectual context of storytelling requires you to gear your story's language, and content, and length to the needs of the audience at hand.

Now this doesn't mean dumbing down a story for any audience, in the same way that intentionally talking above someone's head doesn't accomplish anything. In some ways, these are really problems of over- or under-identification with your audience. We've all seen the speaker who over-identified with us ("Oh, I understand where you're coming from!"), or someone who under-identified (with no comprehension of their audience's background or interests—so, the doctor who speaks in specialty-specific language to someone outside their field). You want to meet your audience where they are.

And give your audience some credit—they're smart! Especially bear this in mind with children: When you talk down to children of a certain age, they tune out—or worse, they start to mock you! With kids, talking a little bit above them can be a good thing—it keeps them on their toes. We'll talk a lot more about relating to children in a later lecture.

We've talked about some of the different contexts in the audience-storyteller dynamic (the physical, social, emotional, and intellectual), and how that might affect your storytelling. Let's talk now about how stories work to bring audiences together, and how you can identify stories that will connect with a variety of audiences.

Sometimes, your relationship with your audience may be mixed—you're standing around, maybe with a good friend, and along come some other people who you've just started to get to know better. And you want to bring the whole group together. Stories are a great way to make connections with and among people, and one of the best ways to do this in everyday conversation is to look for those ways that your own human moments connect with the struggles of everyone else.

A few of my friends got together—some I knew well, and some I had just started getting to know—and we got to talking about patience, and what it takes to be patient with other people, and what makes us lose our patience. It occurred to me that just that week I had had a similar circumstance that tested my patience:

> I'd had a few extra minutes in the day, and I was driving my son back home, and we passed by a local bookstore. I had been wanting to pick up this specific book for him. So I get him out of the car seat (he's almost two), and I unbuckle him, and we're going in for just a minute so I didn't take in the diaper bag. I just walk with him into the bookstore, we're all excited, and he's looking at the books, and I'm having a hard time trying to find this particular book that I want.

> He starts playing with the toys in the toy section, and I tell him, "No, we're looking for a book," and I'm trying to entice him away from the toys to look at these others books down the aisles. This clerk is trying to help us, and my son, he starts going back to the toys, and I say, "No," and I try to get him going down this right aisle to find this book. By now, he's fussing, and he's running around with his Thomas the Tank Engine toy. When we finally get the book, we need to get to the front, and he's running around with the toys and I tell him, "No."

> I start to take him up to the front and, "Wuh, wuh, wuh!" and the tantrum starts. So I'm picking him up and I'm trying to get him to the front of the store. I should have just left the store right then, but I'd been really wanting to pick this book up and I thought, "OK,

I won't reward him right now, but I'll keep it for when he's been good. I'll just get the book right now."

So I make it up to the front, and by now he's "Waaah" and he's struggling in my arms, and I have one arm around him, and the other is reaching for my credit card, and the clerk behind the counter says, "Do you have your store rewards card?" and I say, "No"—and I know what's coming.

She says, "Would you like to buy a rewards card?" and I paused, and he's still wriggling in my arm, and I said "I have neither the time nor the energy to sign up for a rewards card right now. No."

And she keeps on going—like a two-year-old.

"But it only takes a few minutes and you'll save such and such percent on your purchase and it practically pays for itself within a few purchases—"

Before I knew what I was really doing, I had taken my only free hand and I thrust it out in front of me and I said, "Stop! I don't want the card, I don't need the card, I said 'NO!'"

And I looked out in front of me at my hand, and I thought, "What am I doing? This poor girl, she doesn't want to press in on me like this—she's *required* not to take no for an answer—and what yahoo of a manager is making her act like this?! This is not helping your sales; it's making me want to storm out of the store and not buy anything!" And "waah" he's excited and crying, and I put my hand down, and I could see that I had hurt her, and I said, "I'm sorry. I know that you're required to say all that, and I know you don't have a choice in this particular situation to read the situation and stop talking—and I'm sorry that someone makes you say all that," and by now I'm giving a fierce look to the large man who's looming off to the side who seems to be her manager.

It doesn't help, and she's still hurt, and I take my book and I walk out, and "waah," and we get home. I think, "patience." Patience is the presence of mind to keep your hand down, and to see the whole situation, (and to ream out the *manager* if need be but not this poor girl), and just walk out the door.

This was not a story that I thought, "Oh, that will make a great story" when I was in the moment of it—because I was at my wit's end! But later, I started thinking (with my friends) about what a human thing it is to lose your patience. And how everyone experiences that, having your patience tested again and again (because this poor sales clerk wasn't the first one to press me to try to buy something that week).

A day earlier it was the cable company calling me when I was in the middle of grocery shopping (with my two-year-old) saying, "Don't you want to sign up for this new bundled service?"

"No."

"Well, you'd save so much money—"

"No."

"OK, well I see this is a bad time for you, we'll call back." Click.

Arrgh, and it just exploded later the next day on this poor book clerk! There's humor in that story that I didn't see at the time at all—self-deprecating humor. Because the horror was in what I said and did ("Stop!"). The humor was recognizing the absurdity of what I said and did, and the context of the screaming baby, and the succession of "no's," and the climax (where the poor woman stumbled into my bad day), and my fault (which is so human). Everyone has been to that brink of your patience.

And the story was cathartic. It let us all laugh out the frustrations, and it was healing (we each saw each other laughing at that story, and how much we all related to that, and how understandable it is just to snap, even though it was rude and it was wrong). That story brought the group together.

Finding that connection with your audience sometimes means finding the story that connects your common struggles, so it's a good idea to reflect a few times a week on those "human moments" that you've experienced, so that when you're in an everyday conversation you can just plug that story in.

You might want to jot these ideas down in a journal, and I encourage you to start this now, start a storytelling journal, because in later exercises and lectures we'll be doing do some more writing workshops to help you organize and remember your stories. Pay attention to your stumbles, to those epiphanies—those times when you have your "a-ha!" moments. Pay attention to the small revelations, the small things.

In stories, these small things serve as metaphors, which is what makes stories such a powerful way to relate to people. In life and in everyday conversation, stories often serve as metaphors for larger issues—the hand stuck in someone's face, it's a small moment, but that stands for more universal struggles with patience, and kindness, and self-control. This is a small story that you could use in your work, or when you've got an employee who keeps losing his cool.

Stories can help us see a real situation in a different setting (either in another place, or even in a fantasy world). That separation out of the everyday helps us return to our present situation with new eyes, because we've started to see our own world through the lens of the story world. This is why stories work so well when you're in the middle of a difficult conversation, and why humor in stories (even a joke) can help break up a tense situation in a room. They get us into another setting, and they break us out of the (perhaps more painful) setting that we're stuck in, to help us see issues through a different lens.

This can work in reverse as well. You listen to others' stories; you see the universal moments in their situations. This happened to me a few days ago—I was at a meeting with some people, and we were all acquaintances either from work or from other associations. One of the guys came dressed up to this meeting, and he said, "I just came from court." He told us briefly about how he was going through a divorce, and how he hadn't been able to see his kids as often as he wanted to, and how his teenager was acting out.

This bundle of stories had to do with situations that were painful and frustrating and hard (and as the story details got worse, you could just feel that we were all trying to reach out to him, but we didn't know what to say—and he's in the middle of all this, so he doesn't have a conclusion for the stories either). There was this pause in conversation, and then one of the men in the group, who was a friend of this guy, said, "Well gosh, somebody up there is trying to teach you about patience!" And he laughed, and the guy this was happening to, he laughed, and we all laughed. It was funny because that was such an understatement to all that was going on, but also because it was true.

That friend bridged the man's struggles (which were unique and extraordinary in some details). He bridged them out to something that embraced the whole group—a universal—and it brought the group together. So it's useful to see the resonance your small moments can have with universal struggles, and it's useful to listen to the universal moments in other peoples' stories.

There's a cultural theorist named Norman Denzin who used a term called "universal singular." He uses this term to talk about the fact that each of us represents both a singular and a universal experience. We are singular: There are things that are unique to our own background and upbringing and choices and personalities—singular experiences. At the same time, we each represent something universal about the culture out of which we come, and indeed universal about the human experience.

With this in mind, I invite you to target your own experiences—big and small—and begin to see the thread of universal experience in them. Try this: Take out a sheet of paper or a notebook that you can keep as a journal for your storytelling exercises and ideas.

Write down three things that happened to you this week that stuck out in your mind. It doesn't have to be anything big, just something that was meaningful to you. It could be hugging your child after you came home from work, or a difficult choice that you had to make at the office, or how you've been wanting to do this one thing all week and something keeps getting in the way. Just jot down three things.

OK, think of the events surrounding these three things—if you hugged your child after coming home from work, what was that workday like? What was the commute like? What was the expression on your child's face? Where were you when you hugged him or her? Take time; write down as many details as you can.

Then look at those stories, because that's what you've identified; you've come up with three stories. They're in rough form, but they're stories. Look at those stories, and see if you can identify one universal struggle or aspect in each of them—something that goes beyond the individual circumstances that you just wrote down.

Remember those three universals, and this week, see if there is a situation when you're with an audience that might need to hear one of those stories. Your audience might be your daughter, or your spouse, or a couple of coworkers. If you find the right situation to tell that story, as you're telling it, pay attention to the ongoing needs of your audience. Do you need to tell a shortened version of that story because of the physical or social contexts? Or do you need to stress some details and not others because those are the ones that would matter the most to this audience?

If you get a chance to tell one of these stories, later on that night, write down how you adapted that story to your audience. Keep that notebook—you'll need it in the exercises to come!

One last thing about the storytelling triangle: You'll notice that we've talked about the relationship between you and the story, and you and the audience, but the relationship between the audience and the story isn't something that you have any direct control over.

That's an important thing to recognize. You can't force your audience to relate to a story. You can invite, and you can entice, but you can't force. And classic stories contain time-tested characteristics that have enticed audiences for generations. So let's turn to some of these traditional stories—from your own family stories, to fairy tales and myths. We'll ask how these stories became classics, and how you can use classic storytelling techniques to make your own stories more enticing, and inviting, and memorable.

Telling Family Stories
Lecture 5

In this lecture and the next two, we'll talk about time-tested stories: family stories, fairy tales, and myths. Of course, there are many other kinds of stories, but these are some of the foundational ones. In fact, one of the first places we encounter stories is in our families. The stories we hear as children shape family continuity, creating a sense of connection to the past and sending that connection on through future generations. This lecture will help you identify more of your own family stories to tell. We'll also talk about the hidden meanings of this story genre: why we tell family stories, how stories organically emerge from families, and what remembering these stories entails.

Why Do We Tell Family Stories?

- Many repeated family stories are about small things: the time you skinned your knee, or built a tree house, or your father told you something wise after you'd done something foolish. Some of the most meaningful stories we pass along to our children are about small occurrences that amount to big truths about who we are and who we want to be.

- A story about my two-year-old son's reaction to a dramatic weather forecast on TV serves several purposes for our family. When we tell this story to our son later, we will be shaping his sense of self and identity; he'll grow up knowing that we know he's smart, that we were charmed by his innocence, and that he's central to our family. According to Professor Elizabeth Stone, family stories tell us "who we are and how we got that way."

- We tell stories within the family to shape identities—for ourselves and for other family members. We also give others outside the family a sense of who the family as a unit is through our stories. The very fact that we think of families as being cohesive is the

86

result of stories. Families are linked by blood, of course, but we make that blood mean something through our stories.

- Family stories give us a sense of continuity with the past and buoyancy in the present—they give us a foundation for where we stand in history.

- Further, it's not just what we say (the content) but how we say it (the telling) and who speaks. Your sister may tell a story about when you were children, and it may irritate you when she tells it, but she can tell it because she's your older sister. Her telling that story is a sign of her authority and position in the family.

- There may also be stories that aren't told to newcomers in the family, as a way of keeping them out and securing the family borders, or stories that are only whispered among family members.
  - The next time you're at a family gathering, observe how the stories emerge. Going back to our first lecture, you can see many of the qualities of oral thought in these scenes.

  - For instance, family stories are co-constructed in vibrant, complex contexts. You've got Uncle Joe telling a story about his first wife, and his current wife shushing him under her breath, and the cousins whispering side comments to each other, and all the while, people are adding to other people's stories. All of these activities add to the emergence of the story.

  - Stories hang in this web of social relations, and they're edited and in constant flux depending on the audience they're told to.

  - We can take all of this back to the storytelling triangle: Here is the physical and social context in which you're telling many of your stories—in the midst of family bustle or in quieter moments with just one other family member.

Family stories are often co-constructed in complex contexts, with multiple tellers and activities contributing to the emergence of the story.

Family Stories and Memory

- Family stories are usually about memory—remembering other family members who have come before us or remembering childhood experiences.

- In telling a story about a family member, we're often choosing how to remember that person. That choice may not be a conscious one—you're just telling your son about his grandfather—but even in that context, there are deep relationships going on in the storytelling triangle.
  - You're telling stories to an audience—your son—and you want your son to think of his grandfather (and, by association, himself) in a certain way.

  - You have a relationship to the story subject (your father), and that affects what you want to tell, how you want to remember that person.

- There is no such thing as an objectively told story. There is a power dynamic at play when you are the storyteller. You decide what gets into the story and what gets left out, whose voices are privileged, whose experiences matter enough to be worthy of mention, and how the story concludes—who gets the last word.

Your Canon of Family Stories

- Start a list in your storytelling journal of people in your family who exist now only through stories. Are there family members for whom you are the sole bearer of their stories? How do you remember those people? How do you want your children to remember them? What do those closest to you need to know about these family members? How do you want those people to survive?

- Write down three characteristics that you know about yourself. Can you connect any of those characteristics to other family members or to the opposite of other family members?

- Think about the stories you know because they were repeated to you many times by family members. Write down a few quick phrases or topics to help you remember.

- Think about the stories you have passed down to your children. Again, jot down just a few topics or phrases.

- Also consider how small a family story can be. What is one thing that happened to you this week that typifies a value for your family or yourself?

- Consider whether there are family stories that you intentionally don't tell. Why not?

- Finally, think about how you want to survive. What stories do you want your family to tell about you?

- These questions are wonderful for jumpstarting ideas about the family stories you already have, and they can help you think about stories you might want to share with others. Family stories and personal stories are a wonderful place to start when you're working on developing your storytelling because you often know these stories so well already.

Bridging Personal Stories to Public Audiences

- One difficulty in telling family stories to audiences outside the family is that you know the characters so well that it may be hard to contextualize the social connections and to distill the characters.

- In the sample story from Elizabeth Ellis about her grandson, note how the characters are introduced, how the context is set, and how the particular story relates to wider issues facing many other people. Ellis uses several techniques to make the story accessible to an outside audience.
  - First, she clarifies who she is and her relationship with her grandson. She also sets the context of the story well. Much of the story is relatable to us; many of us have children, and we understand the difficulties of trying to get out the door with a child.

  - Then, Ellis takes us inside her own perspective, and the humor of the story becomes what isn't clear to her. From this moment of humor, we get to the meaning of the story—it expands out from the particular situation to the wider struggles that many people face. The story is about much more than a conversation in the bathroom; it's about love, and investing time in the people you love, and taking care of each other.

- Revision and editing are crucial when you're adapting family stories for a public audience. Such a story as "Hands" is what Ellis would call an "accordion story"; it can expand or contract to suit the needs of the audience. In fact, there was much that I had to distill into that story.
  - The idea for the story began with the image of my grandfather's hands. Their size, his tough skin, the signs of arthritis—all those details spoke to many other parts of his life. I thought

outward to other stories that connected to his hands, but at each of those mini-stories, I had to maintain an awareness that they came back to his hands.

- o The image of my grandfather cupping the heads of his baby girls in his hands is an imagined one, but it encompasses many other stories that relate to the unquestioned love my mother felt from her father. The audience doesn't get to hear those stories but gets the point that moves this particular story along. The editing retains the focus on the central character and allows the narrative thread to hang together.

- When you're doing your own editing of family stories, keep the following tips in mind.
  - o Look at the story as a whole, with all the tangents, and try to identify what the story is really about for you. With "Hands," the story was about my grandfather's deep love for me. He loves a lot of other people and ideals in the story, but ultimately, the story came back to him and me—with the central image being his hands.

  - o Consider what parts of the story your audience can relate to.

  - o If possible, limit yourself to three main characters. If you include more than that, an audience may get overwhelmed.

  - o Pair these editing suggestions with the questions we asked regarding Elizabeth Ellis's story to help bridge your story to an audience unfamiliar with your family dynamics. Introduce the main characters, set the context, and relate the particular story outward to wider issues facing your audience.

- Keep in mind that family and personal stories are most effective when the particular dramas of your own life animate and illustrate the wider dramas in all our lives. Make your story relevant by identifying your own moments of human struggle or triumph and giving your audience the language to voice those dramas that we all face. Give them a story they could live in.

Suggested Reading

Ellis, "Storytelling and the Development of Ethical Behavior with Elizabeth Ellis."

———, *Elizabeth Ellis: Storyteller*, www.elizabethellis.com.

Ellis and Neimi, *Inviting the Wolf In*.

Meyerhoff, *Number Our Days*.

Stone, *Black Sheep and Kissing Cousins*.

Questions to Consider

1. Do you have a family member who exists now only through stories? How do you want others to remember that person?

2. Think of one of your favorite family stories. What would an outside audience need in terms of context and character descriptions in order to understand the meaning of that story? How might that specific story relate to wider issues facing many other people?

Telling Family Stories
Lecture 5—Transcript

Professor Harvey: In this lecture and in the two that follow, we're going to talk about time-tested stories: family stories, fairy tales, and myths. There are many different kinds of stories to talk about, but these are some of the foundational ones. An analysis of these stories will help you to start thinking about the sorts of stories you want to tell, and how you can tell them better in any context.

One of the first places we encounter stories is in our family. I want you to think about your own family for a moment. Have you ever seen your own child exhibit behaviors or traits that you connected with yourself or with other family members? Did you ever tell them about that? "Oh, you are exactly like your father—he never listens!" or "You get your mechanical mind from your grandfather—he was an engineer." Have you ever had someone in your family say something similar about you? "You're just like Aunt Abigail, she was so stylish."

We shape family continuity through storytelling. We create a sense of connection to the past that sends that connection on through future generations through these stories, about Aunt Abigail's sense of style, or a grandfather's ability to build and create—even those stories that we spend our lives fighting against ("I will never be like my mother—she was never satisfied with me, and I will be different, I will love my child for who he is").

Family stories are our first stories. We're born into them, and we edit and retell them in our own lives, and then we send them on into our children to shape their sense of who they are ("You're a strong girl—you come from a strong family").

This lecture will help you identify more of your own family stories to tell, whether it's a story about a beloved family relative or a family character. We'll start by talking about the hidden meanings of this story genre: why we tell family stories, and how stories in families organically emerge, and what remembering these stories really entails.

With these hidden meanings in mind, then we'll launch into how you can tell your family stories in such a way that it captures your audience's attention (whether you're telling to your child or to someone outside of the family).

Many repeated family stories (the stories you tell again and again) are about small things—the time you skinned your knee when you were a child, or when you built a tree house (and set it on fire with your brother), or when your child took his first steps, or when you did something foolish when you were little and your father told you something wise. Some of the most meaningful stories that we pass along to our children, they're about small things and small happenings, but they amount to big truths about who we are and who we want to be. I want to tell you a small story of ours:

> We had a tornado warning in my part of the country a few months ago, and it was unusually warm weather in the late winter. We live on top of a hill on a farm. You have to understand we'd just built our house and moved in a year ago. This is our dream house; blood, sweat and tears went into this thing. We found ourselves, our little family, my husband and me and our two-year-old son, we were sitting in this darkened basement (there was still construction dirt all over floor). And it's eleven o'clock at night, and we're bundled on the couch, and we're watching the emergency weather broadcast, and it's preempted regular programming, so that TV light is the only thing on in that room, that flickering light.
>
> These warnings are scrawling across the bottom of the screen, and at the top, at the Doppler map, there's this red, angry patch of storm coming nearer—and then the screen goes black. And this typed message comes up across it saying, "Seek shelter now."
>
> And our son points at the screen, and he says, "Uh-oh."
>
> It was this wonderful moment, because we were so scared, and then we all laughed, and we rallied our spirits, and about an hour later the storms passed and they didn't touch down on us—they did in neighboring counties, but not right on us. We were safe.

That's a little story, but we love telling it. My husband and I, we told it to our friends who'd been through the tornado warnings, and we tell it to other family members.

Stories about that night could be about so many different things, but for us it was all about that moment when our little two year old son said, "Uh-oh." It's a fun story, because of that moment of dramatic irony when you as the audience know more than the little boy in the story knows.

We tell these little family stories for lots of reasons. With this story, as with all stories, the story does something for our family: It not only communicates how adorable our son is, it's stories like these that actually shape and create that idea of his cuteness. I mean you look at him and he's adorable (and yes, I'm biased), but it's these stories that we tell about him that go before him. The stories precede him. And so people who haven't even met our son—you—you know several things about him: You know he's smart (he knew that the screen meant something bad was happening), and he's got that childlike innocence (he doesn't know how bad it really is), and he's fun to be around (you get those moments of dramatic irony).

That's sweet to share with others, but it has a foundational effect when we tell this story within the family, especially to our son. When we reinforce that story to him, we're shaping his sense of self and his identity—so he grows up knowing that we know he's smart; and we praise his innocence through the story; and he's the key turning point of the story. He's the center of it, and by association he knows he's central to our family.

Family stories tell us who we are, and they tell us how we got that way. We even put our bodies into these stories; we make our bodies mean things through these stories. For example, my cousin, she has a widow's peak in her brow. Our Nana, our grandmother, always told us, "Oh, you've got Nana's brow," and in our family we all knew what that means because you believe that this means beauty. It's what Nana always taught us. That's what the widow's peak means. And we believed it because someone told us that story, and whenever we see that feature, you see yourself as beautiful because of that story. We tell stories within the family to shape our identities—for ourselves, and for other family members. We give others outside of the family a sense of who the family is as a unit through the stories that we tell about it (the very fact that we think of families as being cohesive is due to stories. Think about it. It's a bundle of people linked together by words—"I do," and yes, they're link by blood, but we make that blood mean something through our stories: "Oh, you've got Nana's brow"). It's not just the genetic feature; it's what we make that feature *mean* through our stories.

So when you're telling your daughter about that family feature that she has, you're doing a powerful bit of intergenerational storytelling. You're linking her with a past, and a past person that she may never have known—but there's that person coming right through that feature in her face!

Stories give us a sense of continuity with the past, and buoyancy in the present. They give us a foundation for where we stand in history. Family stories make us mean something. It's not just the content of what we say, not just what we say, but how we say it (the telling of that story), and who can tell stories on whom. Now your sister may tell a story about you when you were children, and it irritates you when she tells it, but she can tell it because she's your older sister.

Her telling that story is a sign of her authority and position in the family. The story is a sign of her power. Or if you're a newcomer to the family, the in-laws might have stories in the family that they don't tell you, as a way of keeping you out, of securing borders and designating who's really "in" and who's really "out."

There are some family stories that we whisper among the family—stories everybody knows but nobody talks about. And there are stories that we tell right out in the open, at the Thanksgiving table.

The next time you're at a family gathering, sit back and watch how these stories emerge. This goes back to our first lecture: You can see many of the qualities of oral thought in these scenes. For instance, family stories are co-constructed in vibrant, complex contexts. You've got Uncle Joe telling a story about his first wife, and then his current wife is shushing him under her breath, and then the cousins who have radically different politics from everyone else in the room are whispering side comments to each other, and all the while food's being passed, and people are adding to people's stories, and maybe there's a football game going on in the background. And it adds to the scene of how the stories emerge. They're contingent on so many things (who is there to talk to, and if the other cousin is there to talk politics with).

Stories hang in this web of social relations, and they're edited and in constant flux depending on the audience that they're told to. So when you have your mother and you get her by herself after dinner, and she tells you about what it's like to be in an aging body—a story that could only be told away from the bustle of that crowded table.

We can take all of this back to the storytelling triangle, because there's the physical and the social context in which you're telling many of the stories that you tell, right there in the midst of family bustle or in the quiet moments with just you and your daughter.

Family stories are usually about memory—remembering other family members who have come before us, or remembering my son's childhood expressions ("Uh-oh").

Sometimes we struggle with memory. I wish I remembered more of my grandfather's stories, and my mother has told me that she wishes she remembered many specifics about my own childhood. Sometimes memory fails us. But a lot of the time, we're choosing how to remember someone— now, that choice may not be a conscious one (you're just telling your son about his grandfather). But even in that context, there are deep questions going on in this storytelling triangle scenario. You're telling stories to an audience—your son—and you want your son to think about his grandfather (and, by association, himself) in a certain way. You have a relationship with the story subject (your father), and that affects what you want to tell, how you want to remember that person.

There is no such thing as an objectively-told story. There is a power dynamic at play when you are the storyteller. You decide what gets left in the story, and you decide what gets left out, whose voices are privileged, whose experiences matter enough to be worthy of mention to this particular audience, and how the story concludes—who gets the last word. That's a huge responsibility.

Family stories work very hard to do a lot of things for us, and they work in very artful ways to bind the family together and give a sense of cohesion for that family to the outside world.

So how can we apply all of this to improving your own storytelling within and outside of your family? Let's first look at all of your own family canon of stories because some of you, even now, may be saying, "But I don't have any family stories!" Last time, we talked about your storytelling journal. In that journal now, for this lecture, I'd like for you to start a list.

Think of one person in your family who exists now only through stories— someone who's not with you now, but who lives in your memory. Are there any family members for whom you are the sole bearer of their story? How do you remember that person? How do you want your children to remember that person? What do those people closest to you *need* to know about this person? How do you want that person to survive?

What are three characteristics that you know about yourself? Can you connect any of these characteristics to other family members? Your feisty personality being similar to one of your parents? Or your stubbornness, which is a family trait that you share with an uncle? Maybe one of these characteristics is the *opposite* of a family member. Maybe you're very patient, in a way that some of your other family members are not?

What are the stories you know because they were repeated to you over and over by family members? I'd like for you to write down a few quick phrases or topics to help you remember. What are stories that you have passed down to your children already? Jot down just a few topics or phrases.

How small can a family story be? What is one thing that happened to you this week that typifies a value for your family or for yourself? Are there family stories you intentionally don't tell? Why don't you tell them? How do you want to survive? What stories do you want your family to tell about you?

These are some wonderful ways to jumpstart ideas about the family stories that you already have. And these questions can help you think about the stories you might want to share with others. Family stories and personal stories, they're wonderful places to start when you're working on developing your own storytelling, because you often know these stories so well already.

But sometimes that can be a difficult thing, in telling that story to audiences outside the family. You know the characters so well, and it's hard to contextualize the social connections, it's hard to distill those characters, and it's hard to bridge the story of your particular family experience out to people on the outside of your family. So let's spend some time thinking about how to bridge your personal stories out to public audiences.

Here's is example of a storyteller telling a story about her family, to a general audience. This is Elizabeth Ellis. And I'd like for you to pay attention, during this story to a few things: How the characters are introduced (how do you get a sense of who they are?). How the context gets set. How the particular story relates to wider issues facing many other people. This is professional storyteller Elizabeth Ellis.

[Video start.]

> **Elizabeth Ellis:** Sittin' at my desk, years back, I realized all of a sudden I was getting ready to make one of those horrible mistakes a storyteller always hates to make. I was about to forget a performance. One of those after school ones, starts about three thirty in the afternoon. I jumped up from my desk when I realized what I was doing, and I ran for the bathroom. And there was my little grandson that I was raising. One-bathroom house.
>
> Christopher, who had only recently graduated from trainer pants to what he thought of as being big-boy underwear, was ensconced on the porcelain throne. I came running in the door and I said, "I'm not looking at you, and you don't have to look at me. You can pretend like I'm not there but Granny has to get ready to go to a gig."

He didn't say a word. He's looking down between his legs. I said, "Just pretend I'm not here. I've gotta brush my teeth. I've got to go."

I'm scrubbing at my teeth, and I hear this little voice say, "I have grapes."

I thought, well, being raised by a woman, it's entirely possible that there are parts of his anatomy for which he has no words yet. I have to fix that, but not right now. I'll tend to that tomorrow; right now, I've got to get out of here. I keep on brushing my teeth.

He says, "Pretty grapes." I thought, well, he's proud of his body, that's a plus. He says, "I have an apple too." I went—

He was very carefully examining his Fruit of the Loom underwear. But even when it's the second generation that you have raised, they grow up so fast, that in the blink of an eye it seemed to me like he was leaving home. No, it didn't seem to me like he was leaving home. He was really leaving home. It seemed liked it had been the blink of an eye.

I never had a child leave home before. Not really *leave home*. The generation before him, they just rolled out the door down the street a half a block or so, and took up residence quickly enough and soon enough and close enough that they could just come home and raid the refrigerator and use my washing machine. I never had a child really *leave home*. I was unprepared.

I wondered why we have all those stories about Jack going to seek his fortune, and not a single story about his mama staying behind. Why is that, I wonder. Hmm. And so Christopher, who had gotten a wonderful graduate assistantship at the University of Tennessee, rented the biggest U-Haul truck they make, and behind it he attached a flatbed trailer on which he was hauling his car. And the end result of that was longer than the average 18-wheeler. Having never driven a truck before in his entire life, but with the absolute certainty of a young man in his 20s, he got on the interstate and set off from Dallas, Texas to Knoxville, Tennessee without a backward glance.

We had the biggest fight we've ever had in our lives just as he was going out the door over whether or not he should take the paperwork for the rental truck with him on the trip. Because I am who I am, when he went to the bathroom one last time, I sneaked out to the truck, opened the glove compartment, and stuck the paperwork in it, then ran. So I was standing on the front porch, and butter wouldn't melt in my mouth by the time he came out and got in his car and I watched him drive away.

Five hours later, the phone rang. "Granny?"

"Yes, Chris?"

"The truck has a flat. What do I do?"

"Well if you open the glove compartment, you will find the paperwork for the rental, and on the bottom there is an 800 number, and if you call that number they will come and change the tire. That's their responsibility."

"Oh. Cool." Click.

Because I thought it was more dignified to write a poem than it was to run after that truck, I wrote this that day:

And so Jack goes to seek his fortune. His mama stands and waves him out of sight.

Child of her old age, an unbidden gift. She sheds no tear until he moves beyond that first bend in his bright road.

He is a good boy, and knows those things that can be taught by telling. Nine nines are 81. Yes ma'am, no sir, and where those elbows do not go. She has seen to that.

But does he know those things you cannot tell, but only teach by living?

How forgiveness and gratitude can flow across your heart like water over stone? That a dream is always worth the risk?

And can he learn to love himself enough to make a sweet life in that new place? A place she cannot go. A place he will soon call home.

Thank you.

[Video end.]

Professor Harvey: In this story, Elizabeth Ellis does several things to make the story accessible to an outside audience. First, she establishes the characters. She clarifies who she is, and she clarifies her relationship with her grandson, and she sets the context of the story well. We're clear where we are (we're in the bathroom), and what the situation is (she's getting ready to head out the door). So much of this is approachable to us. Many of us have children in our lives or we remember being children, and you may have been there when a grown-up is trying to get out the door, *with a child*!

Then, she takes us inside her own perspective, and the humor of that story becomes what *isn't* clear to her—what her grandson means by "grapes" and "fruit." And then this lovely moment of humor, from that, we get to the meaning of the story, that expands out from the particular situation to the wider struggles that many people face. The story is about so much more than that conversation in the bathroom. It's about love, and investing time in the people you love, and taking care of each other.

There's so much more that Elizabeth Ellis could have said, but she edited that story down. There are lots of reasons why we edit stories—we talked about oral storytelling being "economical" in the first lecture.

Most of the time, it goes back to that relationship between the storyteller and the audience. You as the storyteller recognize that your audience only has so much time to hear the story (that's the physical context), or they have a limited attention span, so you shorten the story to fit the time frame that you have. There are longer and shorter versions of the stories you tell, depending on your audience.

You have to edit your stories down. We're constantly revising and editing the stories that we tell to craft that "best version" of the story for a given audience—a version that is acceptable, and coherent, and hopefully compelling.

Let's think about this process of revision and editing for a minute because that's really the crux of the issue when you're adapting family stories for a public audience, for people outside your own family. Let's go back to that story "Hands"—it's a family story. And it's what Elizabeth Ellis would call an "accordion story." It can expand or contract longer or shorter depending on the needs of that audience. There is so much that I had to distill into that one story.

For that story, I started with the image of my grandfather's hands. It's such a strong image for me: the lines that were cut deeply into his palms, his tough skin, and the way his hands cupped inwards because of arthritis. They were just so big. All those images, they spoke to many other parts of his life, and so I started thinking outwards to all of those stories that connected to each part of his hands. But at each one of those little mini stories, I had to maintain an awareness that they were coming back to him, and to that part of his body. I'll give you an example of this.

"He holds his baby girls in his hands, cupping their heads in his palm." The stories about my mother's birth and infancy, those stories came mainly from my Nana. And in Nana's time, the women were completely anesthetized—so my mother's birth story comes from my Nana, and it goes from my Nana planting potatoes in the garden with my grandfather (trying to get her labor started), to my mama being a toddler in the house! My mother, she was the second child, and the second girl, and the last child—and my mother said she of course had the thought, "Well, had my parents wished for a boy?" But she never wondered this about my grandfather. She never doubted the love from her father.

While that's such an interesting story to me, it's too long to fit into this narrative about my grandfather. So I distilled that story into one image, and it's an imagined image, because my grandfather never talked to me about holding his baby girls, but I know from the context of other stories, like the one I just told. I know the truth of that moment. The unquestioning love that my mother felt from him all of her life, and that sense of approval and deep love from him. I condensed that longer story into an image: cradling that little head in those strong, big hands. Even though the audience doesn't get to hear the rest of that story, you get the point that moves the story at hand along. And the focus stays on that one person, and the narrative thread hangs together.

I edited out a great deal just in that one moment of that "Hands" story, and that story was better because of it. You can see this in Elizabeth Ellis's story about her grandson, too: There is so much more that she could have said. She could have talked more about the storytelling gig she was going to in the beginning, or about the family situation that led to her grandson having to live with her, or later, when he moves away, about why he chose the college that he did. But the story was better for her editing.

The "Hands" story also uses the device of chronology—it follows my grandfather's timeline chronology, his lifeline. And this is a device that you can use as well, but you can *choose* to use it. You're not limited to chronology when you're shaping your stories (and we'll talk about that more in a future lecture), but chronology is a device that can help keep your audience with you as the story progresses. When you're doing your own editing of family stories, there are a few ways to quickly edit:

Look at your story as a whole, with all of the tangents, and think: "What is this story really about for me?" For the "Hands" story, it was about my grandfather's deep love for me. He loves a lot of other people and ideals in the story, but ultimately it came back to him and me—with the central image being his hands.

What part of this story can my audience most relate to? (Simply put, everybody has a pair of hands, but it's what you do with them that makes this story.) Who are the main three characters in this story? Try to limit yourself to three main characters—more than that, and the average audience starts to get overwhelmed. (There are many exceptions to this, but in a typical everyday storytelling scenario, three is the magic number.)

You can pair these editing suggestions with our questions for Elizabeth Ellis's story, to help you bridge your own story out to an audience that may not be familiar with your own family dynamics. Introduce the characters; set the context; relate your own particular story outward to the wider issues facing your audience.

Family and personal stories are most effective when the particular dramas of your own life animate and illustrate the wider dramas in all of our lives—you make your story relevant by identifying your own human moments of struggle or triumph, and by giving your audience language to voice those dramas that we all face. You give them a story they could live in.

This doesn't mean that family stories have to neatly wrap up in a bow at the end, like a fairy tale. Family stories are messy. And as we'll see in the next lecture, fairy tales—the *real* fairy tales, before the Grimm brothers—fairy tales can be pretty messy, too.

The Powerful Telling of Fairy Tales
Lecture 6

airy tales have staying power. We have many versions of these basic stories because, like myths, they contain something that speaks to us at a core level. As we'll see in this lecture, fairy tales relate to everyone—not just children—because they reveal the human condition; they are, in fact, deeply personal. In this lecture, we'll talk first about how we come to know fairy tales; then we'll discuss what fairy tales do psychologically for children and why the themes of these classic stories can be just as appealing to adults.

"Cinderella"

- Most of us know the story of Cinderella in one form or another, but did you know that nearly every culture has a Cinderella story? There are hundreds of variants of this story from around the world.

- One of the oldest versions of the Cinderella story comes from China, where the ancient practice of foot binding reveals that culture's association of small feet with beauty. From this, we get the idea that Cinderella must have a dainty foot to fit inside the slipper.

- This detail carried over into the German version that the Grimm brothers collected. In fact, in the Grimm version, the stepsisters, whose feet are too big for the slipper, cut off their big toes to try to make their feet fit.

- The idea of a glass slipper comes from a French collection done by a man named Perrault; his is the only version that has the slipper made of glass. In Russia, it's a fleece-lined boot, and in Kashmir, it's a nose ring. Perrault took the common versions of the story and elevated the raw materials—from common skin to glass—because his versions were written to suit the salons and courts of 17th-century Paris.

- Of course, the Cinderella story is also repeated in modern films, such as *Pretty Woman*. This fairy tale is even embedded in *The King's Speech*, in which King George VI enlists the aid of a speech therapist (his fairy godmother) to help him overcome his stuttering so that he can announce on the radio Britain's declaration of war on Germany (his magic-slipper moment).

"Little Red Riding Hood"

- Let's look at another fairy tale you're probably familiar with: "Little Red Riding Hood." Many versions of this story also exist around the world, all forms of a tale type called the "Grandmother's Tale," which originated in Asia. The different versions of this story animate earlier cultural mores and psychological preoccupations.

- Perrault's version, for example, is a reworking of the story from a 17th-century perspective, shaped by the court of Louis XIV, a reign known for sexual excess and intrigues. In earlier versions, the girl figured out a way to escape from the wolf's clutches. But in Perrault's version, she is an unchaste girl, draped in red, who dawdles in the woods and is eaten. The didactic fable ending tacked on tells little girls not to associate with wolves.

- The Grimm brothers in Germany called their version "Little Red Cap." They were the ones who introduced the huntsman into the story and the idea that the grandmother and the girl are eaten whole but then brought back out of the belly of the wolf.

Contradictory Desires

- Over the years, this story has been handed down and revised to suit the cultural values of the time and location of the telling. But throughout these versions, the theme of contradictory desires comes through: Should Red Riding Hood talk to the wolf or go on her way; stay on the path or wander and pick flowers; talk to grandmother, even though she seems odd, or run away?

- Of course, as adults, we deal with conflicting desires all the time. In Freudian terms, we're dealing with the reality principle and the pleasure principle. The reality principle (what we know we should do—go to work, take out the trash) stands in direct contrast to the pleasure principle (what we want to do, even at the expense of others).

- At age five, these contradictory desires can seem very basic, but they are real and even heightened, so children who get into trouble really do feel as if a wolf has swallowed them whole!

- It's important to recognize the reality of these heightened feelings in children. They need to know that their feelings are valid; that even though they struggle with contradictory desires, everything will be fine in the end; and that when they enter the woods again, they can overcome the temptations and desires the woods present.

- Bruno Bettelheim was one of the first scholars to note the real work that fairy tales do for children's psychological development. Fantasy provides an "unreal" world where a wolf can be cut open and a grandmother and child can remain alive in its belly! Although that world is a fantasy, it still reveals powerful truths, and it reveals them in a heightened way that meets children right where they are—in the heightened emotional state of childhood.

In the heightened emotional state of childhood, a child who gets in trouble or is put down may believe, "Nobody loves me!"

- When you're telling a fairy tale to children, keep these three points in mind:

  o Such characters as the wolf represent a "real" temptation and problem to children. When I tell "Little Red Riding Hood" to children, I believe that the wolf is real. This helps draw the children into the story because they see that I'm taking it seriously.

o   As a storyteller, you have to clearly picture the story you want to tell. You need to have specific visual images that you "see" when you talk about the wolf, or the path, or Red Riding Hood. We'll discuss this visualization in depth in later lectures.

o   Finally, the happy ending assures children that their real conflicting desires are valid and that it's acceptable to have those desires. As they grow and mature, they will work through those conflicts. As a storyteller, you take children into the belly of the beast—because their fears of the beast are real—but you leave them in a safe, reassuring place at the end.

A Medieval Version of "Little Red Riding Hood"

- A French version of the "Little Red Riding Hood" story from the Middle Ages is more representative of a majority of the older oral versions across cultures.

- In this version, we find no huntsman, no "resurrection" for the grandmother, and no little red cape for the girl. In fact, this story presents some curious and mature themes.

- For instance, the wolf asks the girl if she wants to go the path of the pins or the path of the needles. Conducting research in rural France, the scholar Yvonne Verdier found that traditionally, young girls were sent away to spend the winter with a seamstress. Ostensibly, this practice was meant to teach the girls about sewing, but in effect, the ritual winter away was more about preening the girls for womanhood.

  o   Girls were said to be "gathering pins" until they reached the age of 15, when they could go to dances and be "pinned" by the boys; thus, pins symbolize the bridge to maidenhood.

  o   Needles, with the thread going through the eye, are symbolic of sexual maturity. When the girl in this story faces the fork in the road with the wolf—and he gives her the choice of maidenhood (pins) or sexual maturity (needles)—she picks the pins, but the wolf (a clear sexual symbol in the story) goes the path of the needles.

- When she gets to the house, the girl drinks her grandmother's blood and eats her flesh. According to Bettelheim, this is a symbolic act of maturity and puberty; the girl is coming into womanhood, replacing the older woman of the family and conquering her by consuming her. The gore in these stories seems to give form to the psychological disarray in our minds as we sort through the steps into a new phase of life.
  - o Literature and the media often feature stories of aging women having difficulty with young women. "Snow White and the Seven Dwarves" is about that theme: the age-old "war" between younger women and older women. The theme relates to fears of both young and old alike.

  - o As I'm telling this part of the story, I'm narrating about blood and flesh, but in my mind, I'm thinking about that step into maturity. In theater terms, this is the difference between my spoken lines and my "internal monologue," the voice inside that motivates what you say.

  - o You can apply this technique to add nuance to your storytelling. Symbols are very powerful, and you can communicate them powerfully to audiences, not by explaining what they mean but by thinking about the deeper meanings of them while you tell.

- The wolf crawls into grandmother's bed and draws Red Riding Hood closer to him; he seduces her toward the bed. And she is drawn to him; even in the more sanitized Perrault version, she jumps into bed with the wolf. This points to the human fascination with things that are bad for us.
  - o But the idea of literally "getting in bed with the bad boy" is never explicitly stated; it's handled through metaphor and fantasy. That's the crucially unique thing that fairy tales do for us: They handle universal themes that stick with us.

o For a five-year-old girl, the metaphorical wolf may be the temptation to eat all the cookies from the cookie jar when mom isn't watching. But when that girl gets to be a teenager, the story is still there as a part of her memory, whether she consciously brings it to mind or not, and it may remind her not to associate with the bad boy or to veer off the path that leads to college and wander through the woods.

Telling Fairy Tales to Adults

- I apply many of the same lessons about storytelling for children when I'm telling adult versions.

- As a storyteller, you have to believe in the truth of what you're saying. Even though they may be fantasy, fairy tales reveal truths. Explore the deeper themes and truths that a story offers; even as adults, such stories help us sort through contradictory desires.

- Again, clearly picture the story you want to tell. You need to have specific visual images that you "see" when you talk about the wolf, or the path, or Red Riding Hood.

- As a storyteller, you must have the "dark" in order to have the "light" of the happy ending; that is, Red Riding Hood must get swallowed by the wolf in order to see the goodness of not wandering from the path again. Explore the possibilities that the dark and light places in these stories offer.

Suggested Reading

Bettelheim, *The Uses of Enchantment*.

Pantheon Fairytale and Folklore Library.

Windling, "The Path of Needles or Pins: Little Red Riding Hood."

Zipes, *The Brothers Grimm*.

1. Fairy tales take us to a fantasy world. Things are possible in this world that aren't in the real world (for example, animals talk and magic exists), but there are still rules that govern that fantasy world (if you don't obey, a wolf might get you). How does "fantasy" still represent a kind of "reality," and how can reality be enhanced by our experiences in fantasy?

2. Name one metaphorical "wolf" in your own experiences—something or someone that you're drawn to (the pleasure principle), but you know you shouldn't act on that desire (the reality principle). Can you retell a short version of "Red Riding Hood," still using the fantasy characters and scenes but thinking about your own personal "wolf"? How does that enhance your telling?

Lecture 6: The Powerful Telling of Fairy Tales

The Powerful Telling of Fairy Tales
Lecture 6—Transcript

Professor Harvey: You may be thinking, "I don't tell stories to kids. Why do I want to hear about fairy tales?" Fairy tales don't leave us when we enter adulthood. Most of us know the story of Cinderella, in one form or another: There's a girl, and a ball, and a glass slipper, and a prince. Some versions of this story are more popular than another in American culture, but did you know that nearly every culture has a Cinderella story? There are hundreds of versions and variants of this story from all over the world. For instance, the slipper: Why is it that she must have a dainty foot in order to fit inside that slipper? It's because one of the oldest versions of that story comes from China, where the ancient practice of foot binding reflected that culture's desire for women to have small feet. It was a sign of beauty.

This detail carried over into the German version that the Grimm brothers collected. And in this version, the stepsisters, whose feet are too big for that shoe, they take scissors and they cut off their big toes in order to fit into the shoe.

And we get the idea of a glass slipper from the French collection done by a man named Perrault. He is the only person who made up the version of the slipper being made of glass. (In Russia, it's a fleece-lined boot, and in Kashmir it's a nose ring.) Perrault took the common versions of that story and elevated the raw materials of the story—from common skin, to glass—because he wrote his versions of the story to suit the salons and courts of 17th-century Paris.

If you think about it, you'll realize that you see this same Cinderella story repeated in modern films, such as the movie *Pretty Woman* (from 1990), which is a Cinderella story about a hooker who finds the love of her life, but who also teaches him what it means to be a compassionate human being. (Incidentally, Julia Roberts, who earned an Academy Award nomination for that film, she's been featured in a number of Cinderella stories, including *My Best Friend's Wedding* (from 1997) and *Runaway Bride* (from 1999)—it's as if she's typecast for this role.)

But we find this fairy-tale frame embedded even more secretively. In the movie *The King's Speech* (in 2010), it's its own version of a Cinderella story. Now, this is an Oscar-winning British historical drama about King George VI, who suffered from stuttering. He enlists the aid of a speech therapist (who is his "fairy godmother"). That therapist helps him to overcome his stuttering in order to give a radio address in which Great Britain declares war on Germany (this is his magic slipper moment—he gives the address, he transforms into someone else who's able to play the part of royalty, and he wins the hearts of a nation). Fairy tales are everywhere.

Fairy tales have staying power—we have all these different versions of the same basic story because, like myths, there's something in fairy tales that speaks to us, deeply, at a core level. And when you understand what fairy tales really do for us—what's underneath the story, what the story speaks at both a conscious and subconscious level—you can more effectively tell the story, because you understand what it is about that story that makes it resonate with audiences of children and adults.

You may also better understand what it is about that story that makes you want to critique it, and then to retell it in a different way—so what if Cinderella saves the prince in the end?

There are two underlying principles that thread through this lecture. One: Fairy tales relate to everyone, because they reveal the human condition—they are in fact deeply personal. Their themes run deep.

Two: Fairy tales use fantasy to help us work through very real troubles and contradictory desires. We struggle with contradictory desires all throughout our lives, but perhaps most keenly when we're children (which is part of why fairy tales are so appealing for kids). Fairy tales speak powerfully through the language of fantasy and symbol to show children (and adults) that there is a way through their troubles.

First we'll talk about how we come to know fairy tales (some of the cultural history of fairy tales). Then we'll talk about what fairy tales do psychologically for children. Lastly, we'll discuss why the themes of these classic stories can be just as appealing to adults, and we'll identify some tips for telling these kinds of stories to children and adults.

I'd like to begin by guiding you though a bit of the cultural history for just one fairy tale, because the versions that you know may just scratch the surface of the older versions out there. Let's start with one you're probably already familiar with: "Little Red Riding Hood." You probably know some version of this story.

But did you know that in many other versions of this same story, that girl never dressed in red? And there never was a huntsman? We have lots of different versions of "Red Riding Hood" from all over the world— they form a tale type called "The Grandmother's Tale," and it actually originated in Asia.

The different versions of this story, they animate cultural mores and psychological preoccupations of the time. For example, there is a French version by Perrault. Perrault is the one who gives the little girl a red cap and calls her "Red Riding Hood." Older versions had no mention of a red cap or a cloak. Perrault's version is a reworking of the same story from an 17th-century perspective, and it was shaped by the courts of Louis XIV, who had a reign that was known for sexual excess and intrigues.

Perrault reframed the story. In older versions, the girl figured a way out of the wolf's clutches herself. In his version, she's an unchaste girl who's draped in, of all colors, red—scandalous. And she dawdles in the woods, picks flowers and she's eaten, and she should have known better. In Perrault's story, Little Red dies, the end—and there's this didactic fable ending tacked on the end that tells little girls not to mess with wolves.

The Grimm brothers in Germany called their version "Little Red Cap"— they were the ones who introduced the huntsman into the story, and they made up the idea that the grandmother and Little Red are eaten whole, and then they're brought back to life out of the belly of the wolf.

The Grimms actually derived their version of the story from a housekeeper who had French Huguenot ancestry. Their version is a retelling of Perrault's version. The Grimms kept rewriting the version that they heard—first for the adults in Victorian salons, and then for increasingly younger audiences. Their version, perhaps more than any other, has the characters all live happily ever after in the end.

Over the years, this story has been handed down and revised to suit the cultural values of the time and of the location of the telling. Remember what we talked about in our previous lecture: Stories are constantly being revised, and stories adapt to the particular context they're in—that's how stories survive. If "Little Red" hadn't adapted, we wouldn't know it today.

Throughout these versions, the themes of contradictory desires come through in this story. Do I talk to the wolf, or do I head on my way? Do I stay on the path, or do I wander around and pick flowers? Do I talk to my grandmother who seems a little strange today, or do I listen to my gut and run away? Even for the wolf: Do I eat Little Red right off, or do I try and get a two-for-one and eat her grandmother as well?

You deal with this as an adult, too. We all deal with contradictory desires. We deal with it all the time. In Freudian terms, this is the "reality principle" and the "pleasure principle." So there's the reality principle (what we know as adults what we should do—we go to work, we take out the trash). And the reality principle is in direct contrast to the pleasure principle (what we want to do, even at the expense of others—"I don't want to go to work, I'll take out the trash tomorrow").

At age five, these contradictory desires can seem very basic: "Please, just give me another cookie! I want another cookie!" Those desires are very real for children and they're even heightened, so the child who gets into trouble really does feel like a wolf has swallowed her whole!

It's important to recognize the reality of these heightened feelings because it highlights how "real" the fantasy world of wolves, and deep woods, and the goodness of the grandmother, and the life-saving valor of the woodcutter, how they're so important to children because children need several things.

They need to know that their feelings are validated. It really does feel like a wolf has eaten you when you're in a bad mess. They need to know that even though they struggle with these contradictory desires, it'll all be OK in the end. They need to know that even when they enter the woods again, they can overcome the temptations and desires that the woods present.

Bruno Bettelheim was one of the first scholars to note the real work that fairy tales do for children's psychological development. Fantasy provides an unreal world where wolves can be cut open and still stay alive and asleep, and the grandmother and the child remain alive in its belly!

While that world is a fantasy, it still reveals powerful truths, and it reveals them in a heightened way that meets children right where they are—in that heightened emotional state of childhood. And in that heightened emotional state, when you get put down it feels like, "Nobody loves me!" And when you are afraid of something, it feels like you're being "swallowed by a scary monster!" What this means is, when you're telling a fairy tale to children, it's important keep in mind three things:

Characters such as the wolf represent a "real" temptation and problem to children. When I tell my children's version of the story of Red Riding Hood, I believe that wolf is real, and it helps children to be drawn into that story because they see that I'm taking it seriously!

It means that you as a storyteller have to clearly picture the story that you want to tell. You need to have a specific visual image that you see when you talk about the wolf, or the path, or Little Red. This is what we mean by "visualization," and we'll talk about that in depth in some of the workshops in later lectures.

The happy ending assures children that their real conflicting desires are valid and that it's OK to have those desires, and that as they grow and mature, they will work through those conflicts, and that everything will be OK. You take them to the scary belly of the beast, because their fears and experience of scariness are real, but you leave kids in a reassuring, safe place at the end of the story.

Most of us think of "Little Red Riding Hood" as just a children's story. Let's listen to another version of this story. This version is based primarily on one from France, and it has one detail from an Austrian version. It's an old version, and try to put aside any preconceived notions you have about how this story is supposed to go, because this version is more representative of a majority of the older oral versions that are out there across cultures. This is the oral version, before the writers got hold of it.

[Video start.]

Professor Harvey: The woods were deep, and they were full of life. That girl as she walked through the woods, she could see that canopy of leaves up above her, a hundred feet up above her, those oak trees stretched that high. She looked up; she could see those leaves were golden underneath where that sun was shining up above. That sunlight, a hundred feet above, it would pierce down and she stretched her arm out and she would see those pieces of light dapple across her arm as she walked.

She knew the way; she'd been here many many times before with her mother, but this was the first time she was going by herself. She walked along; she followed that path. The path, it wound around a boulder. She went around that boulder and she saw what she expected to see. The road, it forked off in two directions, but there standing in the middle of that fork in the road, was a man. He was tall; he had that scraggly hair on his chin and on his arms. He asked her where she was going, and you know how it is when you see somebody you kind of like, and your heart starts going, and your breath starts kind of picking up a little bit? That was what happened with her and she just started saying the first things that came out of her mouth and into her mind.

She said where she was going, that she was going to that house that was in the clearing on down that path. That man, he asked her, "Well, those legs of yours look fast. Why don't we race there?" She thought that sounded good. He said, "Are you taking the path of the pins, or the path of the needles?" because he knew that both of those paths—the pins and the needles—led back to that clearing in the woods.

She looked up at him and she said, "Well, I'm taking the path of the pins," because she was a good girl, "I'm taking the path of the pins."

"Oh, well I'll take the path of the needles and we'll see who gets there first." She was off; she raced, and she had those young, long legs and she raced. But that man, he raced, and he got down on all fours and he went faster. Because he was *bzou*, he was werewolf, he was wolf-man. He ran and he got to that clearing in the glen and he saw that house that that girl had described, that house by the oak tree.

He went and he knocked up onto the door, he knocked and he heard a voice: "Open the latch, pull that latch and come on inside," and he pulled that latch; he came on inside; he saw that old woman over there on the bed. He ate her up. [Snarling.] He ate all of her flesh. [Snarling.] He ate some of her bones. [Choking.] She was very stringy; she was very old. [Snarling.] That meat, it was very tough, and then he had an idea. He ate some of that meat, but he took some of the rest of that meat and he put it onto a plate, and put that plate on the table. Then he took some of that old woman's blood; he poured it into a carafe, and he put that carafe by that meat on the plate.

Then, he went to that old woman and he took out part of her intestine, [ripping], and he went over the door and he hung part of that intestine up in place of the latch on the door. He looked and that was just in time because he could see that girl starting to come down the path of the pins, coming towards the house. So he went back inside—it was very dark inside this house, compared with the glen in that clearing—and so he went over and he took that woman's bonnet, he pulled that bonnet onto him. His fingers, they were sticky from all that blood. He pulled that sheet up over him and he waited.

That was just in time because that girl came down the path of the pins and she [heavy breathing] had raced. She looked around and she thought she'd gotten there first. She was a little disappointed not to see that man. She knocked on that door, and she heard that voice, "Pull on the latch and come in," and so she grabbed onto that latch and it kind of squeezed strangely in her hand, but she pulled on that latch and it opened the door. She walked on in and it was dark inside, compared with that glen.

She heard a voice coming from the bed, "Oh you must be hungry. I set out something to eat, just for you. Go and see it on the table." She went over to that table, and what did she see? That meat on that plate and that carafe full of something liquid. She took that meat, she picked it up with a fork and she put it into a skillet, and she started to cook it, stoked the fire, and she seasoned it. Then she put that meat back on that plate and she got a fork and she started to cut herself a slice and she raised it up to her mouth, and a cat that was curled up in the corner of that room, he spoke up. He said, "The slut, she's eating the flesh of her grandmother."

That girl, she put her fork down; she said, "Well, what was that?"

"Oh just throw your shoe at that noisy cat and keep eating." She put that fork up to her mouth, and she ate it all down. But it was stringy and it was tough and so she got very thirsty, so she saw that carafe and so she poured herself a glass of what was in that carafe. She raised that up to her lips and right as she did she heard a bird outside and it was tweeting. It said, "You're drinking the blood of your grandmother."

She turned and she said, "Well, what was that?"

"Oh just throw your shoe at that noisy bird and keep eating." She threw both of her shoes at the cat and the bird and she kept drinking. She drank all that down. And she was full. She heard that voice coming from the bed.

"Oh, you must be tired. Come into the bed and rest awhile."

She went closer to that bed and she got a feeling in her stomach; it was a queer, strange feeling, and she thought, "Well that's odd, I've never felt this way in my grandmother's house before."

As she got closer to that bed, that feeling, it started to grow a little bit. So she got ready to get into bed and she took off her apron and she asked and she said, "Well what should I do with my apron?"

"Oh, just throw it in the fire; you won't need it anymore." She threw it in the fire

She took off her bodice. "What should I do with my bodice?"

"Oh just throw it in the fire; you won't need it anymore." She threw it into the fire; she did the same thing with her skirt. She did the same thing with her stockings until there she was. She got into bed, and she felt over and she felt something with her leg.

She said, "Grandmother, how hairy you are."

"Oh, the better to keep you warm with. Come closer."

She scooted a little bit closer. "Grandmother, what long arms you have."

"Oh, the better to keep you warm with and hold you tight with. Come closer."

"Grandmother, what big teeth you have."

"Oh, the better to eat you with. Come closer." She looked and she saw, and she looked down at herself, and she realized where she was. Her heart started going, and her breath started picking up, only it was a little different than it had been in that fork in the road. She said the first thing that came to her mind.

"Grandmother, I have to go the bathroom."

"What?"

"Grandmother, I have to go to the bathroom."

"Well just do it in the bed."

"Grandmother, I have to go to the bathroom! I have to go outside."

"Well very well," but that wolf, he took a thread, a red cord, and he tied it around her ankle. "This is so I'll know where you are."

She left, and as she was walking out with that cord tied onto her, she grabbed a parcel that she'd left on that table and she ran out into that clearing, that cord trailing behind her. She ran over to a plum tree and she took, out of that parcel, she took her sewing scissors, and she took those scissors and she cut that cord. She took that red thread and she tied it around a plum tree that was growing there in the glen. She ran. She ran off through those woods until she came to another clearing and there was a river coming through this clearing and there were laundresses, three laundresses, who were washing these white sheets in the river. They turned and they saw this girl, naked, running through the woods. They took one of those sheets and they wrapped it around her shoulders. They listened to her story and right about that time that wolf, he was sitting there in that bed, growing very impatient.

He hollered out to her, "Well are you watering the trees or are you feeding the grass?" After awhile his impatience grew to where he threw down the sheets—they were still kind of stuck to his fingers—but he threw down the sheets and he went out and he [sniffing], he followed that cord and he came to that plum tree. [Sniffing.] He started to sniff her out. He got down on all fours and he started to follow her scent through the woods. About that time, that girl had explained to those laundresses what had happened. The laundresses, they took that sheet, one of those sheets that they were washing, and they stretched it out over that river; they held it taut. That girl, she walked across that sheet bridge. She got to the other side and she turned around—that was just in time because she could see that wolf coming, raising up from all fours and walking through that glen.

The women, too, they were old, and they were wise. They looked and they saw something kind of comical: a wolf-man who had a blood-covered bonnet slightly askew. He was trying to walk towards them, and he said to them, he said, "You make that bridge for me so I can get across."

So they said, "Very well." They took that sheet and they stretched it across that river and that wolf-man, he started to walk across that bridge but as it got to the center, his paws, his feet, started to get a little damp. He looked down and up to his ankles were covered in water, and that sheet was starting to get squishy. He looked over at one of those laundresses right in time to see her say, "Oop." That sheet, it swallowed over him, and that girl, as she ran off up the hill on the other side of that river, the last thing she saw of that wolf was that sheet swallowing him whole and sinking underneath the ripples. She ran off with that anklet, red, around her, that white sheet, ran off home.

That wasn't the last of the girl, and it wasn't the last time that that girl came across a wolf in the woods, and raced with him, and beat him. But it was the last time she ever ate meat. She became a vegetarian after that, because after all, no one ever leaves a fairy tale unscathed.

[Video end.]

Professor Harvey: No huntsman, no grandmother hopping out of the wolf's stomach, and no little red cape for the girl. (It's somewhat ironic that this is called the "Grandmother's Tale"—that the tale type is the "Grandmother's Tale"—since the grandmother irrevocably dies in this account.)

There are some curious and mature themes that are present in this story that are worth bringing up. For instance, the wolf asks the girl if she wants to go down the path of the pins or the path of the needles. Yvonne Verdier conducted research in rural areas of France, and she found that traditionally, young girls were sent away to spend the winter with a seamstress. On the outside, this was to learn how to work with needles and pins, with sewing. But in effect, that ritual winter away, it was about preening the girls for womanhood: learning how to dress, how to hold herself. In effect, it was teaching them how to be appealing and proper.

The seamstress would say that the girls were "gathering pins," until the girls reached the age of 15 when they could go to dances and be "pinned" by the boys. Pins symbolize the bridge to maidenhood. Needles, with the thread going through the eye, those are symbolic of sexual maturity. When the little girl faces that fork in the road with the wolf—and he gives her the choice of maidenhood (the pins) or sexual maturity (the needles)—well, in this version, she picks the pins. But the wolf—a clear sexual symbol in the story—he goes down the path of the needles.

When she gets to the house, the little girl drinks the blood of her grandmother, and she eats the flesh and meat of that grandmother. (These details were all in the French version. In the Austrian account, she eats the jawbone and even more—the intestines that the wolf hangs on the door-pull, that detail came from the Austrian account.) Bettelheim says that this is a symbolic act of maturity and puberty—she's coming into womanhood, and replacing the older woman of the family and conquering her by consuming her. She's coming into her own. It's an albeit gory way to symbolize it, but let's face it—these rites of passage aren't pretty in reality, either. Getting older isn't a ride in the park! The bridge to womanhood is marked itself with blood (menstruation). The gore in these stories gives form to the psychological mess that goes on in our heads as we sort through these steps into our new phase of life. She's not eating her grandmother; she's dealing with growing up.

We see a lot of literature and media that feature an aging woman having difficulty with young women—fearing being cast off for a younger woman. *Snow White and the Seven Dwarves* is about that—about the age-old war between younger women and older women. You see it in beauty treatment ads: Collagen injections are literally about taking younger cells and inserting them into an aging body, the old consuming younger flesh. These are themes for young and old alike—fears of young and old—and so, these themes are useful, and useful in stories for young and old.

So, as I'm telling this part of the story, I'm narrating about blood and flesh and meat, but in my head, I'm thinking about that step into maturity. In theatre terms, this is the difference between my spoken lines and my internal monologue, that voice inside that motivates what you're going to say. You can apply this to telling your own fairy tales to add nuance to your telling. Symbols are very powerful, and you can communicate them powerfully to audiences not by explaining what they mean, but by thinking about the deeper meanings of them while you tell. It adds another layer to your telling.

The wolf crawls into the grandmother's bed and then draws Red Riding Hood closer—he seduces her towards the bed. And she is even drawn to him. Even in the more sanitized Perrault version, she jumps into bed with him. There's this lovely illustration by Gustav Dore of Red Riding Hood in bed with the wolf/grandmother, and you can see the wolf's tongue hanging out of his mouth, with his eyes, they're shaded by this frilly nightcap. It has a velvet bow. He almost looks comically asleep—and Little Red has the covers drawn up to her chin protectively, and she's got this look on her face that's this mixture of fascination and fear. It's as if she can't look away.

Isn't that how it is with some of us and of the metaphorical "wolves" in our own lives? It's this fascination with the bad boy, or the bad girl, or the bad habit—you know you shouldn't, but you're drawn to it. It's such a human theme and it's all there, in that story!

But the whole idea of literally "getting in bed with the bad boy" is never explicitly stated—it's handled through metaphor and fantasy. And that's the crucially unique thing that fairy tales do for us. They handle universal themes that stick with us, and they stick with us because, for a little five-year-old girl, the metaphorical wolf may be the temptation to eat all the cookies from the jar when mom isn't watching.

But when that little girl gets to be a teenager, that story is still there as a part of her memory, and whether she consciously brings that story to mind or not, it's sitting there in her unconscious thought, and that wolf by this time may be the bad boy that her mother always warned her about, and warned her not to crawl in bed with, or the temptation to leave the path that leads to college and wander through the woods.

But if you tell this story as a strict morality tale to your teenager, nine times out of 10 it's going to fall on deaf ears, because children and teenagers don't want to be preached to any more than adults do. (There's that "listening to your audience" part of the storytelling triangle.)

That's where the lure of fantasy and metaphor comes back in: If you explain the metaphor, it kills the story because it reduces that wolf that has so much possibility in the imagination. It reduces it to one thing, and it limits the power of that image. It's the same with the symbolism of the flesh and the blood—if you explain it, it flattens the power of that moment. I apply many of the same lessons about storytelling for children as when I'm telling the adult version of this story.

As a storyteller, you have to believe in the truth of what you're saying. Even though it's fantasy, stories reveal truths. And they explore the deeper theme and truths that the story offers—even as adults, these stories help us sort through contradictory desires.

As a storyteller, you have to clearly picture the story that you want to tell. You need to have specific visual image that you see when you talk about the wolf, or the path, or Little Red. This is what we mean by visualization.

As a storyteller, you have to go to the "dark" in order to have the "light" of the happy ending. She has to get swallowed by the wolf or get into bed with him in order to see the goodness of not wandering down the path and wandering away again. Explore the possibilities that "dark" and "light" places in these stories offer.

You may also have noticed a pattern in this story: The story went from a common place into something darker and more removed from the everyday world (and in this dark place, wolves can talk). And in the end she came back whole, but changed for the experience.

We can read a formula for storytelling in this fairy tale—it's called the "hero's journey." The hero is called into a quest (often unwittingly), and the hero descends into this other world, where he's challenged and helped by others, and eventually the hero emerges and returns to the world from whence he came, but he's forever altered. He's changed somehow by the experience.

The well-known mythologist Joseph Campbell identified this formula, and he traced that formula through a variety of international myths. It's this hero's journey that we'll study further in the next lecture. It's a pattern that you can apply in your telling of myths or fairy tales, and you can even apply it to your own telling of personal stories. We'll see you next time for the hero's journey.

Myth and the Hero's Journey
Lecture 7

In the same way that patterns in art are repeated across cultures, so are patterns in stories, including repeated structures and archetypal symbols. The tale of Red Riding Hood, for example, followed a kind of pattern: start in the "real" world, descend into a dark place, and emerge from that place as a new and different person. Many traditional stories symbolically connect with the needs of the human spirit through archetypal figures and by following a specific trajectory of events mapped out as the hero's journey. Everyday storytellers can apply these concepts that scholars have gleaned from studying myths across cultures to make their own stories more lasting and compelling.

Joseph Campbell's "Hero's Journey"

- The trajectory of events identified by the mythologist Joseph Campbell as the "hero's journey" follows a pattern of separation from the world, initiation into new understanding (usually through trials), and return to the known world. This is the same formula that we all experience in life in "rites of passage."

- This type of journey doesn't happen only in adolescence. Life is marked by continual rites of passage, points when we leave the known and enter something new. When your parents pass away, for example, you are flung from your known world into an unfamiliar and frightening place. After a time of wrestling with your new position, you emerge with a new understanding of who you are.

- This pattern of separation, initiation, and return is one way to think about structuring the stories you tell. This structure is evident in the story of Kyazimba, the East African man who set out to find the land of the rising sun.
  - The separation occurs when the mythological hero is unwittingly called into danger. At the very moment that Kyazimba is about

to give up his search, he meets the old woman, who gives him her cloak, with which he is whisked away.

o   As his initiation, Kyazimba casts himself into the unknown and faces powerful forces that have the potential to destroy him. He must earn the favor of the sun god.

o   Finally, Kyazimba returns home, and with the sun god's blessings, he prospers. When the hero emerges, he is not the same person who once descended into the dark—the journey has transformed him.

- Think about applying the hero's journey to pivotal moments in your life, at which you had a choice to either stay where you were or go into the unknown. Consider events that transformed you in some way, even though they may not seem significant to others, such as the first time you rode a bike or traveled in a foreign country.

o   In your storytelling journal, write down a few details of the events surrounding this pivotal moment. See if you can identify the point of departure, and circle the word or phrase that most pointedly marks this moment.

o   Next, circle the word or phrase that marks the point of initiation. Note that this may or may not be the emotional peak of the story.

o   Finally, identify the word or phrase that marks the moment of return.

The Inanna Story: Separation

- The Inanna story is one of the most ancient stories we have on record. In it, Inanna descends into the underworld and is transformed into a corpse. When she is finally rescued, she is told that she must find a replacement for herself. Ultimately, the replacements she names are her husband and his sister, who divide the time they must serve in hell each year. When her husband is in hell, Inanna mourns, and her sorrow brings winter to the earth.

- Even in the truncated version of the Inanna epic, we can see the structure of the hero's journey emerging in more detail.

- At the moment of departure, Inanna receives aid from her servant; Ninshubur promises to come for Inanna if she doesn't return.
  - Usually in myths, there is some form of helper (an old woman, a servant) who nudges the hero further along the path. Symbolically, this is the moment of overcoming the ego, when the hero lets go of what is secure and exhibits the willingness to take a risk in order to change his or her life.

  - Go back to the story from your life in your storytelling journal and try to identify the person or thing who nudged you into your journey. What part of you might have needed convincing to take the journey? What desires or fears might you have needed to overcome in order to dive in to your adventure?

- In the Inanna story, the hero reaches the threshold—the gates of hell—where Neti is the gatekeeper. This is the edge of the earth, beyond which is the unknown.
  - Psychologically, this is a moment of self-annihilation; if what has come before is the self you've known, crossing this threshold is passing into the potential for a new self—which risks a kind of death of your old self.

  - Inanna is the concrete form of this psychological risk; she knows she risks literal death. For your story, the gatekeeper may be those desires or fears that you had to push past as you set out on your journey.

- When Inanna passes through the seven gates of hell, she descends fully into the underworld—fully surrounded and encompassed by this dangerous place.
  - Such stories as Inanna's give us a trajectory for our own experiences; they map out those times in our lives when we feel swallowed whole by an overwhelmingly impossible task,

and they map out the inner struggles that take place when we're in the midst of those outer, physical realities.

o In your journal, write down a few descriptions of what it felt like for you to be in the midst of a new and unfamiliar place. In some cases, your journey might be a grand adventure (such as a trip overseas), but it can still be overwhelming; you're still making yourself vulnerable by leaving home.

The Inanna Story: Initiation

- In the second phase of the hero's journey, the hero is initiated into some new knowledge and way of being. As Inanna passes through the seven gates of hell, she must give up some part of herself or her former life at every gate.
    o Psychologically, this is the point when you decide to put the comfort and security of your former life aside in order to risk change or transformation—it's the point when you let go.

© Digital Vision/Thinkstock.

The "dragon" in your story may be physical exhaustion in a race or fear of taking a risk in business.

    ○   In the story, Inanna is literally stripped bare, and to some extent, that's what it feels like when you're in the midst of an overwhelmingly challenging experience and you commit yourself to complete that challenge. The process is one of both letting go and opening up to meet what awaits you.

- In that state, you face your dragon. For Inanna, the dragon is the judges and death. In your story, the dragon could be a point of utter exhaustion in a race, a point of depression, or a moment of fear. Write down your thoughts on your "dragon," including the physical events of the moment and the mental challenges you had to overcome.

The Inanna Story: Return
- In Inanna's story, she has a magical helper, one who fought for her in heaven. In your story, you may have a very real spiritual moment when some greater power saved you as you faced your dragon. But remember that traditional stories give us a way to deal with different aspects of our own personalities.

    ○   According to Carl Jung, the images and characters in our dreams don't represent us versus the evils of the outside world but different aspects of ourselves. And myths are our collective dreams. They bring up archetypal figures—shared symbols, such as the mother figure or the servant-helper—who tap into our collective unconscious and connect all of humanity.

    ○   Archetypes link humanity laterally; for example, everyone has a mother figure, although she may be embodied by someone other than your biological mother. They also connect us horizontally, up and down the family line, to the line of mother figures who have come before us.

    ○   We feel the power of archetypes perhaps most keenly when we lose an archetypal figure in our lives, such as a parent or grandparent. You're not just losing the person, but you're losing the physical trace of all that figure represents, both laterally and horizontally.

- Look back to your story to see if you can identify any archetypal figures.

- Perhaps in your story, you found some inner strength to overcome the dragon you were facing and return to the known world with new knowledge about yourself.
  - If the complete story is an attempt to reconcile all the parts of a whole person, then the helper represents that strong part of ourselves that we know exists, the part that steps in to save us when our former selves have been eviscerated.

  - The helper brings growth, change, and renewal. And in Inanna's story, she herself prepared this help before she descended; she knew she would need a way out, and even though she dies in the story, she helps herself out of death.

- Inanna leaves the underworld as a new person, with new power. She has, after all, just frightened the judges who rule over death. She exerts this power over all the earth to give us the seasons.
  - Campbell describes the ability Inanna now possesses as being the "master of two worlds." She has one foot on earth and the other in the realm of the spirit.

  - In your story, your journey may have brought you to some new insight about yourself, have given you access to a different way of being, or have brought a spiritual revelation. You can keep your feet in this world, but you also have access to cross into another place that you've journeyed through and survived.

  - In your journal, write down what facing the dragon led you to. What did you find when you were in the belly of the beast? You may have gained something physical (a new ability or renewed physical strength), as well as something mental. When you returned, how did you understand your world differently as a result of your journey?

Your Hero's Journey

- What you've sketched out in your journal over the course of this lecture is probably a fairly compelling story for others.

- You've looked not just at your own experience but at the deeper psychological journey that the experience took you on. And you've looked for those archetypal figures in your story that connect with our collective human experiences and struggles.

Suggested Reading

Bodkin, *The Odyssey: An Epic Telling.*

———, www.oddsbodkin.com.

Campbell, *The Hero with a Thousand Faces.*

Campbell, Moyers, and Lucas, *The Power of Myth.*

Sherman, *Mythology for Storytellers.*

Wolkstein and Kramer, *Inanna.*

Questions to Consider

1. Discuss the hero's journey story you sketched out in this lecture. What is your "dragon," and how did you overcome it?

2. When I told my hairdresser the Inanna story, I drastically shortened the separation and initiation sections in order to get to "her" part at the end: when, in Inanna's return, she sends her husband to hell instead of her beautician! You may want to focus on a specific part of your journey story, either because of your audience or your own connection to the story. Which part (separation, initiation, return) interests you most in the story you just sketched out? Why?

Myth and the Hero's Journey
Lecture 7—Transcript

Professor Harvey: If you go to the British Isles, there are several ancient structures that you can visit. The best known of this is probably Stonehenge, but there's an even older one. It's in Ireland. It's an ancient tomb called Newgrange. It was a temple 5,000 years ago. And perched outside of the entrance of this burial mound, with the [River Boyne] flowing nearby, there's an enormous stone. And carved deeply into that stone are these swirling patterns—a triple spiral. It's repeated inside the tomb's passageway.

That image of the spiral is archetypal. You see it across cultures, from Viking ships with these giant swirls on the prow, to Malta, and the megalithic Tarxien Temple that has raised swirls—they look embossed into the stone. And then in Arizona to the Homolovi Ruins State Park (where the ancestors of the Hopi Native Americans carved double spirals into the stones there).

These patterns are there across cultures—and in a similar way, you can see repeated patterns in stories across cultures. Repeated structures for stories, and archetypal symbols that appear in the spoken word of traditional stories. The last fairy tale we heard followed a kind of a pattern: You start in a world that you know, and you descend into a dark place, and you emerge from that place as a new and different person.

Joseph Campbell said that many traditional stories symbolically connect with the needs of our human spirit through archetypal figures, and by following a specific trajectory of events that he mapped out as the "hero's journey." (His model is now textbook for many filmmakers—Campbell himself worked with George Lucas in developing the *Star Wars* films.) In both novels and films—*The Lord of the Rings*, *Harry Potter*, *The Hunger Games*—all of these stories, they all follow a hero's journey, and they contain archetypal figures.

In this lecture, we're building on what we talked about before: In traditional stories, the physical trials and the triumphs of the hero aren't really the point; it's how those physical battles give form to our internal battles. And then, how we struggle to make them into compelling stories. Myths use symbols to make us face our inner demons.

For the everyday storyteller, you can take these concepts that scholars have gleaned from studying the great myths, and you can apply the same concepts to make your own stories more lasting and more compelling. You can apply these concepts also to how you tell your personal stories, your family stories, business stories, because we are all the heroes of our own life journeys.

Let's start by laying out the structure that Campbell identified as "the hero's journey." Then, we'll go even deeper into what this journey really means and why it resonates so deeply with the human spirit. We'll end with some exercises that will help you shape your own stories as a hero's journey. (Bear in mind, this structure may not work for every story; there are plenty of valid critiques of Campbell's work. This is not a prescriptive way for how you should tell every story you have, but it's a great place to start.)

The hero's journey follows a pattern of separation from the world, and initiation into new understanding (usually through trials), and then we return to the known world. It's the same formula that we experience in life if you think about any major "rite of passage," those pivotal moments that we all face in life. This doesn't just happen in adolescence; life is marked by these continual rites of passage, when we leave the known and we enter into something new altogether. And maybe it's not a change that we asked for: when your parents pass away, and you're flung from your known world into an altogether unfamiliar and frightening place, and you wrestle with your new position in life, and in your family.

After a time of wrestling (that may in some ways continue for the rest of your life), you emerge with a new understanding of who you are. You're back in the world, but not in the same way, and not as the same person you were before.

So this pattern of the hero's journey—separation, initiation, and return—is one immediate way that you can think about structuring the stories that you tell. (It also sets up a nice beginning, middle, and end.)

You can see this structure best through illustration, so, let's look at a few example stories from a few different mythic cultural traditions. We'll start with a story from East Africa:

In Tanganyika, the Wachago people tell the story of a man who was desparately poor. He was named Kyazimba. And Kyazimba was desperate for a better life, so, one day he set out to seek the land of the Rising Sun. And he walked for days, across hot ground and dry grass. Then, one day as he was walking along, he came across an old woman. She came up to him, full of wrinkles, and asked him where he was going and why was he going there?

He told her, "I'm trying to get to the home of the Rising Sun," and the old woman, she took her cloak, and she took her old arm and she flung one side of that cloak around Kyazimba, and that cloak, it lifted Kyazimba and the old woman up, up, into the sky, to the very zenith of the sky where the Sun rests each day. There, they looked to the east and they saw the great Sun-chieftain riding towards them. There were other great men who were following behind him. And the old woman, she took Kyazimba over to the Sun-chieftain, and the Sun blessed Kyazimba, and sent him on home. Forever after that, Kyazimba, the pilgrim, he prospered in his homeland.

Now, in this story, you can trace the basic structure of separation, initiation, and return. First, separation: The mythological hero is unwittingly called into danger. He doesn't ask to go on this trip, he's called into it; he's desperately poor. At the moment he's about to give up in the wilderness, at that very moment Kyazimba meets the old woman, the crone, and she mysteriously appears to help him along the way, and he gets what he needs from her to head into the unknown—in this case, she gives him her cloak that whisks them away.

Second, initiation: The hero casts himself out into the unknown, and he faces powerful and terrifying forces, and those forces have the potential to destroy him. In this case, Kyazimba shoots up through the air, and he meets this Sun-god, and he has to earn the favor of that Sun-god. Sometimes, the hero can't make it, so in some stories you see this lair of the beast that's littered with the skeletons of people who've come before this hero—but you usually don't hear their stories! This hero is victorious (he wins the blessing of that Sun-chief).

Lastly, return: He comes home with the Sun-chieftain's blessing, and he prospers. When the hero emerges, he is not the same person who once descended into the dark—the journey has transformed him.

This basic structure of separation, initiation, and return, it's one that you can apply to your own personal stories as you think about how to tell them to others. You can take something as simple as your day yesterday and you can tell that story through this model. Separation: You faced a mountain of deadlines—that's initiation through trials. And then you came home (return). This works well with the hero's journey, but the hero's journey works best if you think about the pivotal moments in your life, the real turning points in your life.

When you had a choice to either stay where you were, or to go into the unknown, and you chose one path and it took you somewhere. Those events that transformed you in some way, and it may not be a way that seems big to anyone else, or through events that would seem big to anyone else, but it radically changed you. The first time you rode a bike, or traveling for the first time in a foreign country.

Think about one of those pivotal moments in your life right now. Think about the circumstances surrounding that event. On a piece of paper—maybe in your storytelling notebook—write down a few of the details of that set of events. Don't worry about writing out a full story; just write down the things that immediately come to mind and that you remember most. What you remember might be the look on someone's face, or how you felt when you first left that place that you knew.

Take a few moments to remember those events on paper, and see if you can identify the point of departure, and circle that word or phrase that most pointedly marks that moment of separation.

Look again: At what point on your journey were you fully immersed into this other place or experience? Circle a word or phrase in your description that marks that point of initiation into this new experience. You may note that this may or may not be the emotional peak of your story. That's something we'll discuss in a later lecture on emotional arc.

Now, do you have any descriptions of what happened to you right after you returned from this other place? Again, choose a word or phrase that marks that moment of return, and circle it. That's the basic structure of the hero's journey—now let's go a little bit deeper into this structure, and let's think about what this journey is really all about.

Let's look at another story—this time, it's one of the most ancient stories we have on record. This time as you listen I'd like for you to pay attention to some particular aspects of this separation, and initiation, and return. As the hero separates from the known world, look for the role of a magical helper (in the "Kyazimba" story, this was the crone).

In the initiation phase (when the hero dives into this adventure), look at how this story literally takes you down into the "belly of the beast" (that's what Campbell called it), when you take a flying leap from all that's known and you come face-to-face with something powerful and dangerous.

Like the last story, the hero in this one that I'm about to tell, from this other place, he emerges, this hero does, with help. With Kyazimba, he was helped with the Sun-chieftain's blessing; in this story, the hero requires a different kind of magical assistance to get home:

In ancient Sumeria, there were two sisters: Inanna, the Queen of Sex and of Love, who lives in heaven, and Ereshkigal, the Queen of Death in hell. One morning, Inanna above, she draped herself in jewels and fine robes and she descended into the netherworld of her sister. She knew that this thing that she was doing was risky, so as she left, she turned to her servant in heaven, to Ninshubur, and she said told her servant, "Wait for me three days, and if I do not return in three days, send for me."

She descended, and at the first of the seven gates of the netherworld, the gatekeeper, Neti, she asked her why she had come, and she said, "I am the queen of the place where the sun rises, and I have come for the funeral of my sister's husband."

And Neti, she went and told her sister, the Queen of the Dead, and Neti came back and she started to open those seven gates of hell for Inanna, and at the first gate Neti told Inanna to remove her crown.

"But why?"

"Oh Inanna, do not question the rites of the underworld."

At the second gate, Neti made her lay down her rod; it was made of a deep blue stone, lapis lazuli.

"Why should I lay down my rod?"

"Oh Inanna, do not question the rites of the underworld."

At the third gate she took off her lapis necklace, and at the fourth gate, the stones that sparkled at her breasts; and at the fifth she took off her gold ring; at the sixth gate she took off her golden breastplate; at the seventh gate, she was made to remove all the rest of her garments.

"Oh Inanna, do not question the rites of the underworld."

So there she stood at last, completely naked, and they brought her to the judges that rule over hell, those seven judges. When those seven judges, they fixed eyes on her, she sickened, and she turned into a corpse, and Inanna's corpse, it was hung on a stake. There she hung for three days and for three nights. On the third night, back up in heaven, Inanna's messenger, Ninshubur, she cried for her; she went to the gods up in heaven.

The first god shook his head, "In the netherworld, the decrees of the netherworld prevail." The second told Ninshubur, "No, in the netherworld, the decrees of the netherworld prevail." But the third god that Ninshubur sought out, the god Enki, Enki had a plan.

He took dirt from underneath the fingernails of the gods, and from that dirt he made two creatures. To one he gave the food of life, and to the other he gave the water of life. And he told them how to go to the underworld and how to get the corpse of Inanna, and to sprinkle the food and water over Inanna's corpse 60 times—and they went. The two creatures, they soothed Ereshkigal, and they got Inanna's corpse, and they sprinkled, again and again, and at the 60th time the food sprinkled, and the water, Inanna rose.

The judges of the underworld, they fled, but the tiny demons, they followed her as she left, and they went ahead of her. Demons the size of tiny reeds, the size of a pen, they went out in front of her, and at Inanna's side. When Inanna rose, all of those souls who had descended peacefully into the underworld, they rose again with Inanna, and so this company of spirits and demons, they walked with Inanna on the earth in the land of Sumer. The demons, they told Inanna that someone must take her place in the underworld.

First they came across Ninshubur—and Inanna said, "No, no, Ninshubur has mourned me properly. You cannot take Ninshubur."

And second they came across Inanna's beautician (which I think is hilarious, because I think of this most ancient Mesopotamian text, and then I think about my hairdresser whom I love, and no, I would not let the demons take her to the underworld either!)—and Inanna, she said, "No, no, my beautician has mourned me as she should; you cannot take her."

And then they came at last across Inanna's husband, and when they found her husband, he was sitting under a tree and draped in lovely robes and not appearing to mourn the loss of his wife in the slightest. And she said to the demons, "Well, take him!"

So they did, but as they were about to take him away, her husband's sister, she pleaded for him, and she said that she would take his place.

And so they divided the time they would serve in hell. Inanna's husband spent six months of the year in hell, and the husband's sister the other six months, and then it was Inanna's husband's turn to go back, and they went back and forth throughout the year.

Being the Queen of Sex, and associated with fertility, Inanna mourns for her husband while he is still in hell (and on earth, life seems to grow cold, and to die away). And when he returns from the underworld, she celebrates with him (and on earth, life is warm and fertile and abundant). That is how we know the seasons on this earth.

Now this is a highly truncated version of the "Inanna" epic for the sake of getting us into the world of myth. But you can see this story structure pattern emerging for the hero in more detail. If you look at the moment of departure, Inanna receives aid from her servant. Ninshubur promises to come for her if she doesn't return.

Usually in the great myths, there's some form of helper (there's the old woman, the servant) who comes along to nudge the hero further along the path. Psychologically, this helper is there to nudge the hero into the task, and symbolically, this is the moment when you as a person overcome your ego. You let go of what's comfortable, of what's secure, and you're willing to make the risk and make a change in your life.

In your journal, go back to that story from your own life that you wrote about, and think back: Was there someone or something along the way that helped nudge you into this journey? Try to name that person or thing. Just jot down a few quick notes about that part of the story. Think about what part of you might have needed convincing in order to go along on this journey. What other desires or fears might you have needed to overcome in order to dive into this adventure?

Now, back to Inanna. There's a point at which she reaches the threshold—it's the gates of hell, and there's Neti the gatekeeper (this is the edge of the earth, where beyond it, the guardian of this threshold, beyond that guardian there's the unknown). Psychologically, this is the moment of self-annihilation—if what's come before is the self you've known, crossing this threshold is passing into the potential for a new self altogether, which risks a kind of death of your old self.

For Inanna, she knows she risks literal death (she is the concrete form of the psychological risk—shattering the old self to be made into something new). For your story, this gatekeeper may be what you just wrote down—those desires or fears that you had to push past as you were setting out on your journey. "Am I up to this task? Can I risk my fear of failure in order to dive into this journey?"

Inanna, passing through these seven gates of hell, she descends fully into the underworld. She's in the belly of the whale (for those of you who know the "Jonah and the Whale" story).She's fully surrounded and encompassed by this place, it's dangerous (for Little Red Riding Hood, it's the moment when she's there in bed with the wolf).

What these myths do so powerfully for us, is they give us a trajectory for our own experiences—they map out those times when we really feel swallowed whole by an overwhelmingly impossible task, and they map out the inner struggles that are going on when we're in the midst of those outer, physical realities.

So, in your journal, write down a few descriptions of what it felt like for you to be there in the midst of this new and unfamiliar place. For some of us, it's like a grand adventure (it's like a trip overseas), but it can still be overwhelming: You're still making yourself vulnerable by going there. Take a few moments to sketch out what this new point in your journey looked and felt like.

Phase two initiates the hero into some kind of new knowledge, some new way of being. It's radically transformative. For Inanna, she goes through these seven gates of hell and at every gate, she has to give up some part of herself, some part of her former life. Psychologically, this is the point when you decide to put aside your comfortable old life and to really risk change, to risk that transformation—it's that point when you let go. In the story, Inanna, she's literally naked, she's stripped bare, she has to lay it all aside.

Isn't that what it feels like when you're in the midst of a really overwhelmingly challenging obstacle, and you decide to just go for it? When you're in a race, and you've accepted that you're going to do this race, and you start going, and you're picking up speed (you're passing through those gates) and with each mile that you clock you're exerting yourself more and more, and you're pushing yourself to your limits—you're giving yourself completely over to that challenge. You're committed.

It's a process of letting go and of opening up then to what you meet and what you find in the midst of this challenge. In that vulnerable state, you're ready, you're charged, but you're still vulnerable. There, you face your "dragon." For Inanna, she faces these judges, and she faces death.

In your story, the dragon could be that point of utter exhaustion in the race; or the lowest point of your depression after your parents' passing; or your fear of not measuring up to other peoples' expectations. For the founder of a company, it could be taking a risk and trying for a new client or a new direction in your business. For a failing company that's trying to make a comeback, the dragon could be the challenge of encouraging employees to stay committed to the company.

Take a moment and write down a few thoughts on what your dragon was in your story. You may want to write down what you physically were facing at that moment, and then, what the mental challenges were that the physical event made you come to terms with.

For Inanna, this dragon eats her—death itself swallows her—and she becomes a corpse. But that's not the end of her, and that's not the end of the story, because there's the magical helper, the one who fights for her, and fights all the way from heaven down into hell to save her, and who brings her back to life.

Now, for some of us, there may be that real point in your story, a very real spiritual moment, when some greater power comes in to save you at this moment when you face your dragon.

But let's also remember what we talked about in our study on fairy tales. Traditional stories give us a way to deal with these different aspects of our personality.

Carl Jung said that, when we dream, images and characters come floating up from our subconscious, and these images don't really represent us versus the evils of the outside world, no, in fact we are all of the characters in our dreams—all the characters represent the different aspects of ourselves.

Myths—these great stories shared across cultures, surviving over thousands of years, with the same figures, the same images welling up in these stories across cultural divides—these myths are our collective dreams. They bring up archetypal figures—shared symbols, like the mother figure, or the servant-helper, and these archetypal figures tap into our collective unconscious, that subterranean stream of images, and desires, and symbols that connects all of humanity.

Archetypes link humanity not only laterally (everyone has a mother figure, even if you don't particularly get along with your mother, you have a mother figure, an idea of a mother, and that may be embodied best by an older female relative or a step-parent). So archetypes connect laterally, but they also connect horizontally, up and back down the family line, the line of mother figures that have come before you.

We feel the power of archetypes most keenly when we lose an archetypal figure in our lives, so the death of your father or the death of your grandmother. You're not just losing the person; you're losing the physical trace of all that that figure represents, both laterally and horizontally. Look back at your story. See if you can identify a few of these archetypal figures in your own story.

So this journey that Inanna takes through these shared archetypal symbols, the story taps deep into the experiences that all of us have. And you've been there. Even though this is a story from thousands of years ago in another culture, and dealing with metaphysical demons that have been long past, you can understand what it's like to be rescued when you think that all hope is gone.

Maybe, in your story, you found that strength somewhere inside you, where you, maybe with help, you found your way back to life again. You found the strength to overcome the dragon you were facing (the exhaustion, the depression, the fear), you beat it, and you returned (phase three); you made your way back, and you took with you some added knowledge about yourself.

Because if the complete story is an attempt to reconcile all of these parts of the whole person, then the helper represents that strong part of yourself that you know is in there. That part that steps in to save you, when that old self you used to be has been eviscerated. The helper brings growth, and change, and renewal—and, in the story, Inanna herself prepared this help before she descended. She knew she would need a way out. Even though she dies in the story, she helps herself out of death.

Inanna, she leaves the underworld—she walks out of hell and onto the earth, and not as the same person she was; she's been reborn, she's got new power, she's just frightened away the judges the rule over death. There is no fear. Only a kind of whimsical mourning over her husband (who *she* put in hell, by the way)—and she exerts this power over the earth to give us the seasons. She's transformed by the end, and she has this ability that Campbell describes as being the "master of two worlds"—she has a foot, one in the earth, and a foot in the other world (the realm of spirit).

For your story, your journey may have brought you to some new insight about yourself, or some new access to a different way of being, or a new spiritual revelation. You come back to the world you knew, but you're changed by the experience you had. You can keep your feet in the world you were in, but you also have access to cross over to this other place that you've journeyed through and survived—so you can be here at your home in Seattle, and you can talk knowledgably about what it's like to be in Paris.

So, going back to your storytelling journal, write down what this dragon *led* you to—what did you find there, when you were stuck in the belly of your own whale? Again, you may have gained something physical. (You may have learned to play a difficult piece of music? Or you built something? Or you survived a serious surgery, or you regained physical strength after an illness?) You may have gained something physical as well as something mental. (You realized that life isn't what you expect it to be? Or you earned a degree? Or you learned a new skill? You earned a promotion?) When you returned, how did you understand your same world differently as a result of this journey?

If you look at what you've sketched out over the course of this lecture, you've mapped out the start of what will probably be a pretty compelling story for people *other* than those who you know, and have an emotional connection to you, and to your life, because you're not just looking at your own experience; you're looking at the deeper psychological journey that the experience took you on. You're looking for those archetypal figures in your story, the ones that will connect with our collective human experiences and stories.

When you share this story with others, it doesn't have to be long. You could tell a version of that story in a minute and a half (that's about as long as it took for me to tell you the first myth, the "Kyazimba"). Or you could go into even greater detail and tell a longer version. (The "Inanna" story was about five minutes, and storyteller Diane Wolkstein has developed an hour-long telling of that one story!) You could tell your story during a coffee break, and by incorporating these aspects of the hero's journey, you can increase the chances that your story will connect with your audience.

We've talked about family stories, fairy tales, myths and the hero's journey—the classic stories that contain classic storytelling structures. But remember, when you tell a story, you're not just reciting a story that you heard; you're making that story your own. Finding your own way to tell it, your own voice as a storyteller. That's where we're headed in these next lectures. How to take these basics, and these lessons from the classics, and find your own voice as a storyteller.

Tensive Conflict and Meaning
Lecture 8

Thus far, we've talked about mythical journeys, psychological themes, and family dramas. But what about the beginning, middle, and end—isn't that what a story is all about? Many stories follow that structure, but as we'll see, some stories don't. Locating a beginning, middle, and end isn't the way you discover a story's meaning. In this lecture, we'll think about a story as a set of interconnected pieces, and we'll look at how these pieces relate to one another to create drama.

Story Pieces

- Let's begin by looking at the hero's journey we sketched out in the last lecture and identifying some of the different pieces that are present in that story. If you like, get out your storytelling journal and take some notes.

- Start by listing all the characters in your hero's journey story and consider whether there are any tangential characters or people who could be included. Next, list all the places that are present in your story.

- Every story takes the audience out of the "here and now" and into a "there and then"—a different time. What moment in time does your story transport your audience to? Is there a radical shift in time from one scene to the next?

- All of these pieces of your story stand in relation to one another. The people are connected in some way, but there's also a kind of dynamic tension that's possible between characters in a story. This kind of relationship is known as "tensiveness."
  - This is not the same kind of tension that we think of as a negative in our daily lives. In the storytelling context, tensiveness is the dynamic quality in stories that reveals pulls between opposing forces.

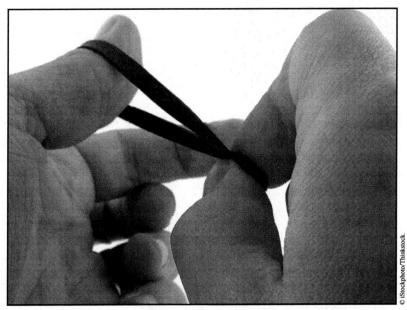

Think about tensive forces as a rubber band; there's a connection between the two ends of the band, but each side is moving in a different direction from the other.

- o These opposing forces are everywhere in stories: The main character wants to go somewhere, but she's stuck somewhere else. Another character is getting older but feels and acts much younger.

- o Literary scholars sometimes use the term "juxtapose" to talk about contrasts in a story, but that term has a static quality to it. In "Snow White," the juxtaposition of the old queen and the young princess tends to make both ends of the age spectrum clearer, but it doesn't reveal the dynamism or interaction between those opposites.

Tensive Forces in Action
- • The story told in an earlier lecture about the coal miner trapped underground for 14 hours was based on interviews with more than 20 miners, most of whom were disabled, and most of whom said

they would go back to the mines again if they could. In the process of stepping back and seeing all the pieces of mining life that could make a story, I noticed many tensive desires at play:

- o The pain of disability and the longing of the miners to go back to the work that had made them disabled

- o The constant danger of daily work in the mines and the horseplay that made the daily work bearable

- o The underground work of the miners and their lives with their families aboveground

- o The connection to parents who had been miners and a strong desire for the miners' own children to do a different kind of work.

- • Tensive possibilities were also present in the concrete environment of the mines and my own thoughts about mining in the wider scope of American life:
  - o The blackness of coal and the fact that we get the brightest and most valuable gem—diamonds—from coal

  - o The dirt and dust of the mines (and the stigma that attaches to dirtiness in American culture) and the clean, bright places that coal enables us to create

  - o One miner's observation: "We work with our hands so other people can work with their heads."

- • From those tensive pulls, I started to locate the real point of these stories—the connection between audience members' aboveground lives (powered by coal energy) and the bodies working underground to make that lifestyle possible.

- • From my interviews with miners, I saw what they stressed in their stories—the fascination with fossils, the relationships with friends, and the real need for horseplay as a kind of relief from the tension of their difficult and dangerous work.

- I began to see that the story of the one trapped miner, Donzel, could be the spine for all the tensive pulls that existed in the mining culture. Instead of retelling the mining company's version of Donzel's story, I stepped back and looked at the real tensive pulls at play.
  o The story couldn't be one of doom and gloom, because that's not how the miners view their lives; as I said, many of them dream of going back to the mines.

  o The real story is about relationships, about the fact that the "rescue team" is the person working beside you, and about survival. The moment when Donzel made it out of the mine was the climax for the story.

  o Looking at these tensive forces is how you locate conflict in your story, and conflict is what drives a story.

Maintaining Tensiveness in Telling
- Of course, people often tell stories once the "real" conflict is resolved, but it's important, while you're telling the story, to be in the moment of each scene, because the characters don't know what's going to happen!

- Telling a story as if everything that takes place is a foregone conclusion diffuses all the tensiveness that you worked so hard to identify.

- Living and telling in the moment, as if you don't know how the story will turn out, will help draw your listeners closer to the characters. They'll empathize with the characters more, because they're right there with you, following your lead, not knowing what's going to happen either. Your audience becomes curious to hear more.

- Examine one of your own stories to try to identify one tensive pull between locations. Is one place darker, more threatening than another? Is one place more vibrant or full of life? Again, it's not just a juxtaposition that you're looking for—it's not just labeling opposites. Think about how these places relate to each other. Next, try to identify one tensive pull between two different characters in your story, two times, or two emotions.

- Along with these tensive pulls, stand back from your story pieces and identify any repeated images or themes, such as patterns of light and dark. Both the tensive pulls and the common themes help you locate what's really going on in your story—what your purpose is in telling the story and the meaning you find in it.

The Cycle of Story Development

- As we said, a storyteller's work does not start with identifying a beginning, middle, and end; rather, it starts by identifying the tensive potential—between characters, between places, between times, or between combinations of those elements.

- The idea of stepping back from your story, seeing the story pieces, and looking at the tensiveness and relationship between those pieces is all part of the cycle of story development.

- Stories live with us, and the more we get to know a story, the more we see in that story and the more dimensions open up. The more we tell the story to audiences (formally or informally), the more we see how others see that story, and that opens up more dimensions. Then you step back again and see other relationships between the pieces.

- For the professional storyteller, creating a story performance is an alchemical process that usually involves an interconnected cycle of talking, writing, imaging, playing, and rehearsing. The process of developing a story could begin at any of these points.
  - Talking is a crucial part of story development because stories often come up as a part of conversation and are initially "rehearsed" in conversation. Talking—practicing the story as

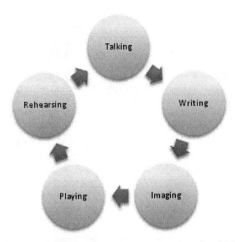

The story development process is an interconnected cycle of talking, writing, imaging, playing, and rehearsing.

part of a shared conversation—prevents you from crafting a story in isolation, which may result in telling that feels forced. Talking also reveals aspects of a story, such as humor, that you may not be initially aware of.

o   In the story development process, writing does not mean scripting; it means journaling, sketching out ideas, or free-associating on paper. Writing works in tandem with telling the story aloud to help you piece together the parts of your story. Writing also helps you remember, but it's important not to get tied to the wording you use in your journals and sketches. Writing can give you a certain comfortable distance from your audience and your topic, but in telling, you are fully immersed in the scene.

o   This immersion is equivalent to imaging. You should be able to see the story all around you; the places and people of the story become real to you because you are "in" the story. In turn, your audience will be drawn into your story and will believe it because they can see the reality of those people and places for you.

o One of the best parts of storytelling is playing with stories, that is, exploring all the possibilities that a story can hold. When you play with your story, you're testing the characters: How loud can the giant be? How frightening can the witch be? You can play with the order of events or the appearance of characters. You're also testing possible meanings; is the story really about power or love, revenge or forgiveness? Finally, you're testing your own limits as a storyteller—your gestures and delivery.

o Rehearsing is really the process of learning the story, which is what you're doing when you're talking, writing, and so on. To rehearse is to get comfortable with a story so that it lives inside you.

• Again, because this cycle is interconnected, you can start at any one phase of it and jump to another. Stories come to us in different ways, and you will develop your own preferred way of developing stories. This is a much freer, more creative approach than trying to find a beginning, middle, and end.

• Keep in mind, too, that this is a repeating cycle. You don't just play once with a story and that's it. As you develop and refine a story, you'll go back to each of these parts of the process, and each time, you will deepen your understanding of the story and reflect on the meanings it can hold.

• With each audience and each telling, your relationship with the story changes; another layer of meaning and experience is added. Sometimes, this process of story development can be its own hero's journey, going deeper into the story until you emerge with a story that feels comfortable to you and that you enjoy telling to audiences.

Suggested Reading

Ellis and Neimi, *Inviting the Wolf In.*

The Folktellers (Regan-Blake and Freeman), *Storytelling.*

Questions to Consider

1. Story development is a process. What part of this process (talking, writing, imaging, playing, rehearsing) seems most natural to you? What part might be a different experience for you?

2. Think of a story you like to tell. What are some tensive pulls in this story?

Tensive Conflict and Meaning
Lecture 8—Transcript

Professor Harvey: Thus far, we've talked about mythical journeys, and psychological themes, and family dramas, and you may start to think, "Well what about beginning, middle, and end—isn't that what a story's all about?" Yes, many stories follow that pattern of structure, but as we'll see, some stories don't. Locating a beginning, and a middle and end isn't the way you discover a story's meaning.

You might discover, as you play with your story, that the most interesting part about that story to you, and the real *meaning* of the story, lies in the perspective that someone else had on events; or the more that you think about it, the story really revolves around this one place that you loved as a child; or you start out hearing a family story about one person, but what you, as a storyteller, connected to most was that small thing that your grandmother said in the middle of someone else's account—and that small thing made all the difference to you.

If you start out thinking about finding a beginning and a middle and an end, you might wind up copying someone else's opinion of what the story really means, and you circumvent your own opportunity to discover your own voice as a storyteller, your own version of the story, and your own way of drawing out what really matters in the story.

The structure of your story charts where the story goes, so you really need to know the meaning that you want to arrive at, perhaps even more than the eventual destination that your main character arrives at in the end.

So I want for you to think about story development, from the get-go, not in terms of beginning, and middle, and end, not right away—not in terms of nailing down a structure from the outset, and not in terms of memorizing a story. But to look at the whole process of developing a story in terms of seeing all the pieces, and all the different dimensions, and taking a good look at these different pieces, before you even start to put them together into a structure and to learn them. You want to figure out the meaning of the story to you, because this will determine not just *how* all the pieces fit together, but *why* they fit together for you.

In this lecture, we're going to think about how your story is a set of connected pieces, and look at how these pieces relate to each other to create drama (that's the real crux of a story—the friction between opposing forces). We'll look at this process of stepping back from a story as just that—a process. We'll talk about the different parts of the overall process of crafting a good story.

Let's take that hero's journey that you sketched out in the last lecture, and let's start to identify some of the pieces that are there in that story. We'll start with characters—who all is in that story that you mapped out? If you like, you can go ahead and get out your storytelling journal, and take some notes. Try to list out the characters in that story. Think beyond what you wrote about in the initial sketches. Are there any tangential characters or people who could be included in this story?

Places—where all does this story take you? List the places in your story, and try to be specific. If you're moving from one room to another, those are two different places.

Times—your story may move you from one time, to another, and then back again. Every story takes your audience out of here-and-now time and into the then-and-there of another experience. What moment in time do you take us to—and do you jump around in time? Is there a time in life that you talk about, and then another time in life that you take the audience to? Is there a radical shift in time from one scene to the next?

All of these pieces of your story stand in relation to one another—the people are connected in some way (they're connected by the story, to the main event of the story; or they may be connected to each other by blood or by friendship). So there's a connection, but there's also a kind of dynamic tension that's possible between the characters in a story, and it's a kind of a relationship that's known as "tensiveness."

In this context, it's not the same thing as tension. When we think of tension, we think of it as a negative thing: "Oh, I have a tension headache," or seizing up because we're tense. "Tensive" is literally defined as "stretching or straining." In this context, "tensiveness" is that dynamic quality in stories that reveals contrary pulls, or pulls between opposing forces.

Opposing forces are everywhere in stories. Where your main character wants to go, but she's stuck somewhere else entirely. When a person is a particular age in a story (maybe she's 62), but the character feels and acts much younger (like she's a 20-year-old stuck in a 62-year-old body).

In literature, we use the term "juxtapose" to talk about contrasting opposites that are put side-by-side in a story—so, in *Snow White* you can look at the queen, who is older, and then this younger princess. And one edge of this age spectrum, it's clearer because we see it alongside this other end of the spectrum.

But the term "juxtapose" has a static quality to it—you look at these things side by side, and it's revelatory, but "juxtaposing" doesn't imply the dynamism or interaction between these opposites. Looking for "tensive" forces in your story helps you see these opposites not only there (and each time more apparent for the presence of the other, as with juxtaposition), but also that there are contrary pulls between them in the story. You can think about this as a rubber band, this tensive pull—there's a connection between the two ends of this band, and each side is moving in a different direction from the other.

Let's look at an example of these opposing forces in action. When I crafted that story about the coal miners, the story was about the man trapped underground for 14 hours. That story was based on interviews I'd done with over 20 different coal miners, most of whom were disabled, and most of whom also said they'd go right back down there in the mines today if the doctors would let them—they miss it.

It was surprising to hear that in a way, but it gave such depth to their experiences to know how much many of them enjoyed their work. In the process of stepping back and seeing all the pieces of mining life that could make a story, there were many tensive desires at play. There's the pain of disability on one hand, and there's their longing to go back to that work (that made them disabled).

There's the constant danger of work in the mines, and then there's the horseplay (like flipping rocks at each other) that made that daily work bearable, that broke the tension. There's their work underground, and then their lives with their families above ground. There's their connection to fathers or mothers who had been miners (they were following in the family footsteps), and then this strong desire for their own children never to do that kind of work (because they knew how hard it was on you).

Even the concrete location of the mines, and thinking of this work in the wider scope of American life, even there, there were tensive possibilities. The blackness of coal, and the fact that we get the brightest and most valuable gem from that same coal—diamonds! The dirt and the dust of that place (and how stigmatized "dirty bodies" in American culture are), and that clean bright place that coal enables us to create (bright rooms filled with light, created from energy that we got from coal, bright rooms where clean bodies work).

Then, another tensive pull: As one miner said, "We work with our hands so other people can work with their heads." He meant they dig coal out of the ground so that people can have coal power to work with their computers. This miner's name was Bill, he was an engineer in the mines. He said, "I was with a bunch of people one day, they were just talking about coal miners, y'know, like we was ignorant people and I said, 'Let me tell you something,' I said, 'we had million dollar remote-controlled miner machines before you ever had any of your little remote-controlled cars. So really, we are a little bit more advanced than what you all are!'"

There were all these tensive pulls present in mining culture, and it's from those tensive pulls that I started to locate the real point of these stories: the connection between audience members' above-ground lives (powered by coal energy) and the bodies working underground to make that lifestyle possible. They were heroes—in their own eyes, and in mine.

When I encountered Donzel's story, he was the one miner whose story I tell whom I never met personally. Donzel's story was featured on a film made by MSHA—the Mining Safety and Health Administration. They used the film to train new miners on the need for safety in the mines; that's how they couched Donzel's story.

While his accident was tragic, there were these other parts of the story, too. There was his survival, and his life (as a hunter) even after his amputation! (The film showed him with his gun in the backyard!) And sitting there beside him during his interview in this film was his wife, who was in tears by the end.

From my interviews with these 20 other miners, I saw what they stressed in their stories—their fascination with fossils, and their relationships with friends, and the real *need* for horseplay as a kind of relief from the tension of that kind of work. The horseplay served a purpose.

As I looked at these pieces, I started to see how Donzel's story could be the spine for all of these tensive pulls going on around mining culture. Instead of telling the mining company's version of Donzel's story (and their point was that the miners were at fault—if they had just been paying attention and not horseplaying, this never would have happened). I could have just retold that story.

But instead, when I stepped back, and I looked these pieces and the real tensive pulls at play, I was much more drawn to this human story of mining life, and how these accidents are directly connected to how I'm able to live and work and operate in my above-ground world.

It's not as simple as saying, "Oh, mining culture is hard and life is hard for them, or bad," no, there are times when they love it! They even dream about going back! That had to be the ending, because that was the point for so many of the miners I interviewed—you can't paint this story as all doom and gloom, that's not accurate to their lives!

It's a story about relationships, and about how your rescue team is the person working right beside you (an ambulance doesn't drive down there to dig you out' your fellow workers do. They're the ones who know how to do that). And it's a story of survival. So that moment of ultimate survival—when he makes it out of the mines—that was the climax for the story.

This is how you locate conflict in your story—conflict is what drives a story. Often, people tell stories once the "real" conflict is resolved. It's important, while you're telling a story, to be in the moment of each scene, because for those characters, they don't know what's going to happen! Donzel, in that story, doesn't know if he's going to make it out; his friends don't know if that second rock fall crushed him or if he was saved.

I could have told that story as if everything were a foregone conclusion. That would sound like this: "So we got boards, and we covered him over with boards, and I hollered, 'We're not leaving you Donzel, hold on,' and then there was another huge boom and that whole thing collapsed back on top of him. And we went back in, we took off those boards, and we saw that had saved him from that second fall."

Now that's telling as if the characters already know what's going to happen. It sucks all the life out of that story! It diffuses all the tensiveness that you worked so hard to identify, and establish. Living and telling in the moment, as if you don't know how it's going to turn out, that will help draw your audience closer to the characters. They'll empathize with the characters more because they're right there with you, following your lead, not knowing what's going to happen next either. It makes your audience more curious to hear more.

Look at one of your stories. Try to identify one tensive pull between the places in your story. Is one place darker and more threatening than another place? What about the colors in these places—is one place more vibrant or full of life than another? Again, it's not juxtaposition that you're looking for; it's not just labeling these opposites. You're looking for how these places relate to one another.

When you take your audience from one place to the next, you're not just switching scenes; you're taking your audience from one point (one side of that rubber band), and then the story, it propels you into another location—

and your audience still has that awareness of where we've left. Maybe we even come back to it in the end (as with the hero's journey). But even in that next place there's an awareness for the audience of what we've left behind.

What about the characters? Try to identify one tensive pull between two different characters in your story. Is there a tensive pull between the times that your story takes you, or a tensive pull between the times of life that your story takes us to? What about emotions?

Now, along with these tensive pulls, stand back from your story pieces and try to identify any repeated images or themes. A repeated image may be a pattern of light or dark in the places that you go to. Or a particular feature that keeps coming up in these different places and in these different people. See if you can locate one or two images that come up, or some key themes that keep arising from characters, or among the places.

As I said with the mining story, the reason why it's useful to step back from these pieces in your story, and to identify the tensive pulls between characters, and places, and times, and emotions, and to try and see the common themes or images, is to help you locate what's really going on in your story—what *your* purpose and meaning are in telling the story.

You, as a storyteller, will have your own unique voice, your own understanding of what a story holds. The real dynamism of a story is in how each of the pieces (the characters, the places), how all of these relate to each other. And in seeing these relations from the beginning, it can help you as you decide how to shape your story, because there can be a whole story in the friction between two of your characters (that may be where you want to focus your story), or there could be the makings of a nice short anecdote hidden in the relationship between one place of your story and another.

Remember, we started out by saying that storytellers' work does not begin with a beginning, and a middle, and an end, but the work starts by identifying the tensive potential—between characters, between places in the story, between the characters and the places. That's how it begins: identifying what's pulling at what in the story.

This idea of stepping back from your story, and seeing the pieces, and looking for the tensiveness and the relationships between those pieces—this is all a part of the cycle of story development. The process of developing a good story is just that—it's a process.

Stories, they live with us, and the more we get to know a story, the more we see in that story, and the more dimensions open up. The more we tell that story to audiences—either telling it formally or just sitting around telling it informally—the more you see how *others* see that story, and that opens up even more dimensions for you. And again, then, you step back once more, and you see relationships between the pieces.

A theatrical piece, that varies, too, according to the response of the audience, but the script that the actors follow, that script doesn't change. A book, too, that stays told exactly the same way. But it's not so with a story. For the professional storyteller, creating a story performance is an alchemical process, and that process usually involves an interconnected cycle of talking, writing, imaging, playing, and rehearsing.

Let's look at each of these parts of this cycle—and think of these as parts, not sequential stages. You could "start" at any part of this process of developing a story; you could start at any of these points. Of course, your rehearsal process for an office anecdote is going to be a lot less involved than the story you might prepare for a bigger event, such as toasting your brother at his wedding, or giving a talk for your club or a presentation at work.

So, talking—first, talking with yourself (because, as we've seen, you're always the first audience for your stories—the first person you tell the story to is yourself). And second, with your friends. Stories often come up as a part of conversation. Someone says something to you, and it sparks a memory that you then tell about in a brief conversation. That right there is an important part of the "rehearsal" process—talking with your friends. Telling a short, 30-second version of a story that you like, just to test it out.

It's a crucial part of developing a story, of keeping a story alive in shared conversation as you practice it, because if you start off by going in isolation, and crafting a story, and getting all the parts in order the way you want them,

163

and figuring out your wording just so, and then you take it out and you tell it, it might feel forced at one or many points in your telling of that story. Because the story is a living thing—like we said from the beginning, stories live as a part of that dynamic storytelling triangle, and your audiences will influence that story. You'll know if a part of your story is funny because someone else (as well as you, maybe) may laugh at that part.

Sometimes stories I didn't think were funny at all, I started telling other people, and they were laughing, and that taught me something about the story. That was the case with the story about me buying my child that book at the store, when I said, "Stop!" to the sales clerk. Your audience will teach you so much about what's there in the story.

Writing. That's another part of this cycle of story development. Jotting down ideas, those thoughts that you have in the car while you're waiting at the red light ("Oh yeah, this happened to me today—my child said something memorable or funny," or, "I got to work and this happened today"). Those memories come to you in quiet moments about things that happened to you long ago, those thoughts, too. You could take those thoughts that you wrote down in your hero's journey story—those ideas and images that you wrote, they're part and pieces of what could make a really good story.

Writing, and I don't mean scripting, I mean writing—journaling, sketching ideas, free association—we'll workshop several of these in the coming lectures. Writing works in tandem with telling your story aloud, to help you piece together the parts of your story.

Writing helps you remember, but it's important not to get tied to the wording you use in your journals and your sketches. It's not that precise wording isn't valuable—many storytellers highly value the precision of language, the ability to use words that shape images precisely for your audience. I'm not downplaying that precision. But I want you to veer away from, at the very beginning of your story-crafting, from sitting down from the outset to "write" a story, to script something out with the intention of memorizing that text.

When we write a story—and I mean sit down to write—we can fall into the trap of getting all heady about a topic, of going off in exposition that distances us from the action that makes up the story.

Telling the story is different. It's the opposite of that comfortable distance that a certain kind of writing can give us—distance both from the topic we're talking about and distance from the audience. When you're telling a story, you compose your thoughts and words from a position where you're immersing yourself in the full scene; you're really imagining that you're there in the midst of all these actions and places that you're describing as you tell that story. In storytelling, your wording flows out of immersing yourself into the scenes of your story and describing what's around you.

Imaging. When you're in the middle of telling a really good story—and see if you can think about the last time you told a story to someone when you really got into that story. When you get "into" doing something, especially storytelling, it means just that: You're immersing yourself, going "into" the story and seeing that story all around you. The places and the people of that story, they become real to you because they're there, and your audience believes your story and is drawn into your story because they can see you seeing these "real" people and places all around you.

Playing. This is one of the best parts of storytelling, playing with stories—exploring all the possibilities that your story can hold. When you "play" with a story, you're teasing out the characters and testing them out. How loud can the giant be? How frightening can the witch be? How ridiculous can your trickster be? You can also play with the story order. The order of the events can move, the order of the descriptions, the order of characters appearing. When I crafted that version of my "Little Red Riding Hood" story, it started out in my head at the little girl's house. And then as I played with it, I found that it was more interesting to start right there in the woods, especially if I'm telling to adults, and start right there at her encounter with the wolf. Then, in that conversation, she backtracks to her mission and why she's there.

You're testing the possible meanings. "I think this is a story about power, but it could also be maybe about love? I think this is a story about revenge, but maybe there's also forgiveness?" Playing with all manner of elements in your story—playing with the perspective of the narrator, with your own limits as a storyteller (you may feel comfortable walking in a certain way—could your characters walk differently? What would it take for you to play with different gestures, different than your own usual way of being?).

Usually, this playtime is just for you—when you're in front of the bathroom mirror, or when you're alone in your car. There's a good reason to play with stories as a part of a separate rehearsal time, because, for example, if you're telling a story to children, you don't want to just test out right there how gruesome a description of gore can really be, or how really terrifying a monster can sound. You don't want the first time you do that to be in front of a little child, because you might really, really scare her and do harm!

You also might feel inhibited to really "go there" and play with the limits of volume, of embodied delivery, or of content. So rehearsal can have its own place, and it can be a lot of fun.

Rehearsing. Really, all of these elements that we're talking about are a part of the larger rehearsal process, but here I specifically mean when you're learning the story. In Morocco, they don't use the word "rehearsal." They say "repetition." So to rehearse is to repeat, and to really get comfortable with a story, so that it lives inside of you, so that you know it by heart, it takes some repetition.

We all do this naturally, when we want to remember something. You hear words of advice that you want to remember, and you repeat them to yourself. Now, you may not say them to yourself aloud over and over, but you think of them from time to time. You might even say them aloud in the moment when you need to hear them, or you might say them to a friend who you think might need to hear those words. You want to remember them, so you repeat them in some way.

It's the same for stories. The stories that you learn are the stories that mean something to you. They're the stories that are worth repeating—to your audiences, and to yourself to even get to know them better.

In the coming lectures, we'll walk through several quick tips for how to maximize your retention of stories, and not just the words that you say, but the actual parts of the story (separate from the wording, which will vary from one audience to the next). These tips will not only help you deepen your memory, but they'll pinpoint which parts of the story you might be prone to forgetting (and hence, need to work at to remember a little bit more).

We've talked about identifying the elements of your story (characters, and place, and the like), and the tensiveness between those elements that will give your story energy. Now you have an idea now about the general cycle of story development. Each of these five elements (talking, writing, imaging, playing, rehearsing), they compose the major parts of the interconnected process of developing a story.

I say "interconnected" because you could start at any point in this cycle and jump to another, because stories come to us in different ways, and you will develop your own preferred way of working with a story, and it might change from story to story. I want to remind you again: This isn't beginning, middle, and end—this is a freer, more creative approach.

It's a repeating cycle, so it's not like you play once with a story, and that's it. As you develop a story and refine it, you'll go back to each of these parts of the process, and each time you're deepening your understanding of the story and reflecting on the different meanings your story can hold. So we can look at this loop as something that repeats. You're adding layers.

Each time you go through this loop, you tell a story to yourself first, you think about the images in that story, you may jot down a few ideas that you don't want to forget, you play some with the characters, and then you *tell* the story to a friend, and you see what they connected with. And then you go back to the loop again (you jot down a few more ideas; you play with the images some more, and it keeps looping).

With each audience, and each telling, your relationship with the story changes, and it adds another layer of meaning and experience. Sometimes this process of story development can be its own hero's journey, going deeper into the story until you emerge from the process with a version that you really feel comfortable with, and that you enjoy telling to audiences.

As you're preparing to tell a story, look at what you're heading into as a process. From the beginning it's a good idea to step back, and to take a look at all of these pieces that your story holds (or the pieces that it could hold), and sit with those pieces for awhile and kind of mull them over. You might make some important discoveries about where your story really wants to take you to.

You might feel yourself holding back from breaking your story apart. One of the big steps in preparing a story is really giving yourself permission to look at what all is there, and to tell *your* story, not just someone else's version of your story. And giving yourself permission to go through this process and claim your own voice as a teller. In the next lecture, you'll hear another story that I had to give myself permission to really play with in order to tell it. See you then.

Giving Yourself Permission to Tell
Lecture 9

A s you add layers of life onto a story and dig deeper into the meanings that the story may contain, you may also find a few layers of yourself and your own anxieties that you need to strip away in order to see what the story contains and what you, as the storyteller, can bring to your delivery. Part of preparing to tell a story is being able to let go of the things that might be holding you back. Sometimes, we worry about how well we can tell a story or how we might appear to other people when we tell. In this lecture, we learn about giving yourself permission to play with stories, make mistakes, and even "break up with" your stories.

Breaking a Story Apart
- In the last lecture, we looked at stories as a bunch of pieces that you can fit together to create a whole. It's important to see stories in this way from the beginning, because while a story is in pieces, you have creative freedom in putting it together.

- Think of a story like a mosaic. You've got pieces that you're fitting together to make a unified whole—a complete picture that has dimension, color, texture, and meaning.

- If you put the pieces together and they don't seem to fit, give yourself permission to break up what you've made and start over. See how the pieces could fit together differently.

Playing with Stories
- One of the most fun parts of storytelling is getting to experiment on your own with the dimensions of a story. You have to stretch yourself as a storyteller in order to see where the story could go. Rehearsals are an excellent way to play with possibilities; after you rehearse, you can trim your story and tame it down to what you actually will do when you tell the story for an audience.

- Choose the meanest character from a story you know; it could be the wolf, your boss, or your ex-spouse. Now, say out loud one line from that story as if you were that mean character. Exaggerate your delivery beyond what you would use for a public audience.

- Next, think of another character's reaction to what that mean character just said; again, this could be one of the three little pigs or yourself responding to something your boss has said. If this character didn't say anything, think of a line that describes what he or she did—sulked away or slammed the door. Out loud, say that character's response.

- If you're unable to try these exercises, ask yourself: What is holding me back from experimenting? Why can't I give myself permission to play? Remember, what you do in rehearsal is not the same thing you have to do in telling the story. Rehearsal is "you" time; it's time set aside for you to play with the story.

- As we've said, every storyteller has a unique style of telling, and every storyteller can improve his or her range of telling by experimenting. The stretching exercises in these lectures are aimed at helping you discover and become even more at home with your own style of telling.

- You play in order to become more familiar with a story, to see the story's depth, and to visit your own possibilities as a teller. Stretching yourself is a good thing—it's like stretching any other muscle in your body. When you limber up, you're all the more ready to perform well.

Making Mistakes
- Especially in the beginning phases of the rehearsal process and when you're playing with stories, give yourself permission to make mistakes.

- When you're playing with stories—seeing what might work, what doesn't fit, how big a character could sound, how small a voice could be—you will discover some things that you decide not to include in a public telling of the story. When you tell the story to some audiences, you will discover some things that don't work with a particular audience. But telling is a part of the story development process, and in that process, you will make mistakes.

- Allow yourself to take some risks in telling stories to friends, especially when you're working on developing a particular story to tell. These audiences are forgiving and less apt to focus on things that don't work in the story.

Going to the Dark Places

- Some stories appear to be relatively mild on the surface, but layered within them may be other possible themes. As you're developing a story, give yourself permission to go to the dark places.

- The story "Mama's Wings" began as a memory about playing with my dog and making something. But then I gave myself permission to see all that could be explored in that memory. The real meaning for me came through in the darker side.

- When I looked at the places and characters in the story—not only the main characters but the characters in the background—I could see that the tensive pulls were between the innocent and "light" things that happened up front and a dark background.

- Remember what we said in the last lecture about not being too quick to put a story into a structure. You need to allow other sorts of thoughts and ideas to come into your thinking.
  - Pull from your memories, write them down, hold onto them, and see how they might fit into a story.

  - A story about a little girl with her dog seems almost routine, but by giving myself permission to think about everything going on at that time—the sadness, too—I was able to find the tensive pulls, the drama, that made this collection of memories into a real story.

The story-sharing that takes place among small groups increases student retention at colleges and universities.

Digressing

- We often hear people discouraging digression, but in storytelling, digression gives flesh to the bones. Many business professionals are learning that the "digression" of storytelling and story-sharing during work hours can actually increase productivity, and many universities are now clustering freshmen together in small groups because the interaction that occurs in these groups measurably increases retention.

- Sometimes the most direct route to your final story comes from probing around the edges of that story. Give yourself permission to make digressions as you think about what to include in your story. Often, such digressions add a delightful slice of humor. Note, too, that you can jump to short digressions without completely losing the thread of the story.

- Discoveries about digressions may come while you're telling a story; they're a part of being in the environment with an audience. If your listeners laugh at something or you think of a tangent they might enjoy, give yourself permission to leave the story for a moment to make that further connection. When you return to the story, your audience may be all the more with you.

Editing and Breaking Up with Stories

- Of course, you can go overboard with digressions and lose both the thread of the story and your audience, so you also have to give yourself permission to edit the story. This may sound simple, but it's sometimes difficult to say only what needs to be said, especially with family stories or stories from your own experiences.

- This tendency also reflects the additive quality of story-making. As you develop your story, you'll find connections with other topics, other points in your life, and other stories.

- With an abundance of possible details to include, ask yourself: What story do I want to craft now, knowing that I may craft other versions of this story later? Give yourself permission to choose one of a number of possible stories you could tell—and might, at a later time.

- It's also important to give yourself permission to tell only what you're comfortable with telling. You may find that you are not able to tell everything about a particular story when you are first developing it. You might be too close to the events or too emotionally caught up in them to be able to bring your audience safely to a conclusion. Give yourself permission to wait until you're ready to tell the full story.

- As you are developing a story, you may also decide that you really don't like it. Some stories just aren't meant to be told. In those cases, give yourself permission to break up with a story or put the relationship off until a better time.

Getting into Stories

- Finally, give yourself permission to really get into your story—to really imagine that you're experiencing the events.

- In our next lecture, we'll start getting into the real "how to" of storytelling, and one of the first things you'll want to do as a teller is to visualize all the pieces of your story—the people, characters, and events going on around you. If these people and events are real to you, then they will be real and believable to your audience.

Suggested Reading

Bogart, *A Director Prepares*.

Ellis and Neimi, *Inviting the Wolf In*.

Questions to Consider

1. What might inhibit you from playing with your stories? Why?

2. How is it "risky" to tell some stories? When do the benefits outweigh the risks for you?

Giving Yourself Permission to Tell
Lecture 9—Transcript

Professor Harvey: As you add layers of life onto a story and dig deeper into the meanings that that story can contain, there also may be a few layers of yourself and your own anxieties that you need to strip away in order to really see what that story contains and what you as a storyteller can bring to the delivery of that story for your audience.

Part of preparing to tell a story is being able to let go of the things that might be holding you back from telling that story. Sometimes we worry about how well we think we can tell a story, or about how we might appear to other people when we tell—or worse, how we might appear just in the mirror when we're rehearsing in private, just with yourself! During the first stages of story preparation, it's necessary to be ready to give yourself permission to do several things.

Give yourself permission to break your story apart. When we ended the last lecture, I asked you to look at your story as a bunch of pieces that will fit together to create "the story." This is important to see from the beginning, because while it's in pieces, you have a lot of creative freedom for how you put that story together.

It's like a mosaic. You've got these pieces that you're fitting together to make a unified whole—a complete picture that has dimension, and color, and texture, and meaning. But sometimes, you'll put the pieces together, and it just doesn't fit. Give yourself permission to break what you've made apart and start over. See how the pieces could fit together differently.

Give yourself permission to play with your story. This is the most fun part of storytelling, getting to experiment on your own with the different dimensions of your story. You have to stretch yourself as a storyteller in order to see where the story *could* go, and rehearsals are an excellent way to play with the possibilities of what your story *could* do. And then you can trim it back and tame it down to what you actually *will* do when you tell that story for an audience.

We do this kind of rehearsal all the time in our heads—when you get out of the office and you just explode in the car about what an awful day you've had: "I can't believe that frickety-frick told me off in front of a client!" Then when you get home, you tone down your retelling of that story, when you're telling it to your family: "It was a tough day."

Let's try this right now. Take the meanest character from a story that you know of. It could be the big bad wolf, it could be your boss, it could be your ex-spouse—any mean character. Choose one thing that that person says in the story. Now take that thing that that person says, and say that line as if you were that mean person. Try it now.

Now that wasn't nearly mean enough. I want you to exaggerate the way that you say that line—make it the biggest, the loudest, the meanest delivery. I want you to say this line in a way that you would never, ever say in front of a public audience. Get your whole body into it. Try saying that line again.

Now, think of another character's reaction to what that mean character just said (in your story, it may be one of the three little pigs who reacts, or it might be you reacting to your boss, or it might be you responding to what your ex just said). Think of that line that that character says in response, and if they don't say anything, think of a line that describes what that character did in response (she sulked away, or she shook her fist, or he slammed the door).

Now, say that line in response, but bigger. If the response is you shrinking away, then make that voice as tiny and bitty as you can: "He shraaaank away!" Or if you tell that mean person to just to back off, then make it as big as you can: "Just back off!" At the count of three, that character's response, say it. One, two, three!

If for some reason, you didn't just right then give a big, out loud line delivery, ask yourself: What just held me back from experimenting? Why did I not give myself permission to really play just then? Are you afraid that what you do in rehearsal is something that you *have* to do when you actually tell the story to other people? No! Rehearsal, this time, it's you-time; it's time just for you to play with your story—and *you* get to choose what comes out of that rehearsal room and what doesn't. What happens in rehearsal, stays in rehearsal, if you want it to stay there.

Ask yourself: Am I afraid of how silly I'll sound? To whom—who is listening now—your family in the next room? Your friends in the room with you? The people in the car beside you (if you're listening to this on audio)?

Go ahead, tell them you're working on a story that you know they'll want to hear, and you'll share it with them as soon as you're done with this lecture. "Now don't worry that I'm making funny noises over here; that's just my rehearsal!" They'll thank you for it later, when you make them laugh with your funny characters.

Ask yourself: Am I afraid this will change who I am? Every storyteller has their own style of telling, and every storyteller can improve their range of telling by experimenting with how to tell their stories. The stretching exercises in these lectures—this one and others—they're aimed at helping you discover and become even better and more at home with your own style of telling. You're not going to become a different person, or a different style of teller, by being playful with your stories in rehearsal.

Remember: You play in order to become more familiar with a story, to see that story's depth, and to visit your own possibilities as a teller. Stretching yourself is a good thing; it's like stretching any other muscle of your body. When you limber up, you're all the more ready to perform well, whether you're running, or you're dancing, or you're playing sports. When you stretch your muscles before a game, you don't think, "But this is changing who I am!"

Playing with your stories stretches you; it makes you limber. It makes you ready to tell. So if you didn't really let loose just then and play with that line, consider that you may not be giving yourself full permission to really stretch yourself as a storyteller.

Along with being playful, give yourself permission to make mistakes. This is especially true at the beginning phases of the rehearsal process, and when you're playing with your stories. There's this wonderful spirit in comedy groups, "that nothing is not allowed." Improv comedy is so funny, because the practitioners feel so free to use whatever it is that comes out on stage. You take what's given to you by your teammates, and you go with it; you use it.

When you're playing with your stories—seeing what might work, what might fit, how big a character could sound, how small a voice could be—you're going to discover some things that you decide not to put in that public telling of the story.

Then, when you tell the story to some audiences, you're going to discover things that don't work with a particular audience. It's OK. Remember, telling the story to other people is part of that process of story development—it's a *process*, and you are going to make mistakes. I make mistakes; you are going to make mistakes.

When you're telling a short, impromptu story with friends, the stakes can be a lot lower. There are other cases (either for larger audiences, or for that one person who you really want to make the right impression on), there are some cases when the stakes are much higher.

Let yourself take some risks in telling those stories to friends, especially when you're working on developing a particular story to tell. These audiences are very forgiving, and like improv comedy, if something doesn't work or go according to plan, just go with it.

Give yourself permission to go to the "darkest" places in a story as you develop it. I mean this in a different way than the exercise that we just did about picking your "meanest" character and overplaying how that person speaks. Some stories may appear to be about something very mild, and they may be, on the surface. But layered in with that story are other themes and other possibilities.

Let's look at an example. This is one of my stories. It's mainly a story that I tell for adult- and high school-age audiences. In this story, I had to give myself permission to see not only what was going on in the foreground of that story, but also to see what was going on in the background. There are several tensive pulls in this story. See if you can locate some of them. There are also some unifying images and themes. See if you can locate some of those.

[Video start.]

Professor Harvey: I grew up on a small farm in northeastern Tennessee. We only had about three acres—it was a very small farm—but our neighbors, the Wagners, they had acres and acres. They owned a dairy farm, and they raised cattle. When I was growing up I was an only child, so it was me and my dog, Duffy, [panting], she was always ready for an adventure. It was me and my dog, Duffy, the neighbors' cows, their chickens. At one time the neighbors, they had these beautiful peacocks, blue peacocks. Have any of you ever seen a peacock in person before? Beautiful. That's my favorite color, that peacock blue shimmering. In the morning, when those peacocks would wake up, the sun was just coming up and they would stretch those feathers out in the early morning sun, kind of shake them around a little bit.

Right about that time my dog, Duffy, she would wake up and she would start to chase those peacocks all the way around the property. Eventually she ate all of those peacocks, but that's another story. So growing up, it was me and Duffy, and the cows, the chickens, at one time the peacocks. We grew up having lots of adventures.

One day, when I was in elementary school, my teacher told me that we had to read a biography. I chose the biography of Amelia Earhart. Finest woman pilot and brave and she was a cute little thing too. She had that curly, short hair and one of those scarves that wrapped around her and trailed off behind, just like Snoopy the Red Baron. She was taking off in her propeller plane to take on the world. I was particularly inspired by this story, because on the other side of the Wagners' property was the Tri-Cities Regional Airport.

I grew up listening to the roar of those engines as those planes, they passed overhead. I read that book and I could be Amelia Earhart. I was gonna fly, only I was gonna be better than Miss Earhart because

I was gonna build my own plane. I set about to do it; I went out to the front yard where we had these two huge maple trees that were 90 years old. They were as old as our house was. You could barely fit your arms around the trunk, they were so huge.

There had been a storm the night beforehand and a lot of the limbs and branches, they had fallen down to the ground. So I went out and I picked out a pretty good limb and I took that limb back over to my workshop. That was what I called my workshop; it was this place that underneath my tree house. I set that limb down and I set about to work making myself a pair of wings.

I took that limb and I tore off some of the little branches, but I left a few of them on there for rudders because I knew a little bit about aerodynamics. I left a few on there and I took this fabric that I'd gotten from the Wal-Mart. (I come from east Tennessee, and just a little vernacular: When you come from east Tennessee, you call it "*the* Wal-Mart.") So I took this fabric that I got from the Wal-Mart. I wrapped one end of that branch with it; I wrapped the other end of that limb, and I had myself a pretty good set of wings.

As I was building it, that airport that was nearby, I remembered, as I was building, I remembered the time when I had gotten to visit that airport. At one time I got to climb inside the cockpit of a helicopter. As I was building I remembered having been in that helicopter and seeing all those metal dials and switches in the cockpit. It looked like something out of *Star Wars*.

As I was building it I knew that I didn't quite have the technical know-how to be able to build something like that, but I had myself a pretty good set of wings, so maybe for now I could just glide along—if only I could get up enough wind under the wings to get it going. I put those on and I started running. I ran and I ran and I ran and I didn't get anywhere.

Then I saw my tree house, and I thought well maybe if I could just get these up in my tree house then I could jump off, only I couldn't get those limbs out of the way to get the wings up into the tree house. And then I saw it. I remembered. The Wagners.

Out on the Wagners' property, there was a deep ravine. It was created from where water had collected on the tarmac of that airport, and that water had run off onto the Wagners' property and it had worn a deep rut into the ground. It was about 20 feet wide and about 13 feet high. I thought that was just about right for gliding. I picked up those wings. "Come on Duffy." [Panting.] She was always ready for an adventure. We hopped over that fence and I got the edge of that ravine, and I gave myself a count: One, two—

I got a little bit scared, so I backed up just a little bit. I thought well maybe if I could get a running jump, maybe that would help. I tried it again: One, two, three, and I ran and I jumped. In that first split second, I knew I was flying. "Duffy, Duffy look, we're flying!" I could hear her behind me, [panting]. She was so encouraging.

I thought, "Won't Mama be so proud of me?" because I hadn't told my mother I was jumping off a cliff that day, because I thought that she might not approve. I knew even at that tender age that it is so much easier to ask forgiveness than permission. I thought about all of that in that first split second of flight before I realized that I wasn't going up, and out, as I thought I was going to do, but I was actually plummeting down.

I wasn't really scared because I didn't have time to be scared. I just thought, "What do I do? My elementary school hasn't prepared me for this. Do I stop, drop, and roll? No, that's if you're on fire," and before I knew it I was down on the ground. My face, my hands, elbows, knees, they were all planted into that dirt and my mouth, it was full of that red clay dirt. I could feel something wet on the side of my face as Duffy, [panting], she was looking for signs of life. I peeled myself up off the ground and disentangled my arms. My hands were starting to turn red and they had little bits of gravel embedded into them; they started to sting, kind of.

I looked up at that 13-foot drop where I'd come from. I looked down at my sad, little broken wings, and I thought, well heck, I can do better than that. "Come on, Duffy," [panting.] She was glad to know I was still alive. We picked up the piece of those wings and we took them back to my workshop, and I tried working on them a little bit more that day. After a little while I got cleaned up, went inside, and I told my mama all that I'd done. I said, "Mama, Mama, I flew, I flew," and she got this look on her face, like she hadn't expected her daughter to bring her this information that day.

She said, "That's good honey, that's good, now don't ever do that again without asking my permission first."

I said, "OK Mama." I spent most of the rest of that summer building those wings again and trying to make them stronger. All the time that I was working I thought, "Someday, someday I'm going to fly Mama to Italy. I'm gonna take her on that trip she's always wanted to go on, that trip that we could never afford. I'm going to fly her away from this house full of screaming. I'm going to take her away from those nights when Dad comes home smelling of alcohol, and perfume. I'm going to take her away from those nights when he doesn't come home at all. I'm gonna fly her to Italy, just her and me."

I never quite achieved full flight with those wings over that summer, but I did learn a few valuable lessons. One of those lessons was you should never jump off a cliff without asking your mama if it's a good idea first. I also learned that no matter how little you are, or how little you have, you can always build yourself some wings to take you places. Over the next few years, my mama, she took those big, strong wings that she had always had—those wings that she had wrapped around me and protected me with for so many years in that house full of screaming. She stretched those wings out; she tucked me underneath one of them, and she flew us away from that house. She took us to a better home. A safer home. Just her and me. Those were my mama's strong wings. I learned over those years that no matter how little you may feel, it's good to know you always have the choice to build yourself some wings, and take flight.

Mama's wings.

[Video end.]

Professor Harvey: When I started developing that story, it was just a memory about playing with my dog and making something. But then I sat down with that memory, and I gave myself permission to see what all was there to be explored. And I had to give myself permission to see that darker side of the story—because that was where the real meaning of that memory was for me.

When I really looked at the places and the characters—not only those main characters, but the characters in the background—the real tensive pulls were between the innocent and light things that happened up front, and what was really a very dark background. But in order to get to that dark place, I had to give myself permission to go there.

I had to be looking for the tensive potential of this story. Remember what we said in the last lecture about not being too quick to put a story into a structure. But allow other sorts of thoughts and ideas to come into your thinking. You want to pull from all of the memories that come in, write them, hold onto them and see how they might all fit. A story about a little girl with her dog, it seems so easy and familiar, and this could have been a very routine tale. But by giving myself permission to think about everything that was going on at that time—the sadness, as well as the good things—I was able to find that tensiveness, that drama that made this collection of memories into a real story.

Now, some of the humor of this story at the beginning comes from a little digression from the main story—when the dog ate my neighbor's peacocks. It's related to the story, but as I sat down with the story pieces in the beginning, all those things in my memory, I had to give myself permission to make digressions.

This is worth noting, because often you hear people discouraging digressions! It's rather a cultural thing, isn't it? Some regions of the country might permit digression more (in the American southeast, where I'm from, many people traditionally begin business conversations and business meetings with stories about each others' lives—"How're you doing? How's your family?"). In many parts of the US, we don't allow digressions because time is money.

But digressions give flesh to the bones, and many business professionals are learning that the "digression" of storytelling and story sharing during work hours, it can actually increase productivity, because you're allowed to pair meaning to the work you're doing, and your interactions with coworkers.

For instance, many universities are starting to cluster freshmen together into smaller groups who take their core classes together, because that interaction of story sharing that happens among the peers in their groups, that interaction measurably increases the retention among those students. They feel connected, and they want to stay at the university. It's the same with any other business—what seems like circumnavigating a topic by telling stories around it, or what might seem like "wasted time" with digressions, that can actually have the most direct effect on retaining employees, and mitigating workplace conflict.

The same principle applies with crafting your stories—sometimes the most direct route into your final story is to probe around the edges of that story. Give yourself permission to make digressions as you think about what to include in your story. That's what this process is for—it's to find out what might be a delightful little slice of humor to add into your story.

And as you saw, you can jump to short digressions without completely losing the thread of the story. That whole moment where I pause mid-fall to tell the audience what I was thinking, "What should I do? Should I stop, drop and roll? No, that's if you're on fire. And before I knew it, I was down on the ground!"—that's a digression, it interrupts the story that's going on, but it adds to the story at the same time.

Sometimes discoveries about digressions, they come when you're telling a story. They're part of the environment of being in the environment of the story with your audience, and your audience laughs at something, and it makes you think of something else. So give yourself permission to leave the story for a moment to make that further connection with your audience through brief digressions. When you return to the story, your audience may be all the more with you as a result. (You can, of course, go overboard with digressions and you can lose the thread as well as losing your audience—we'll talk more about that more in a lecture on story structure.)

And to that point, in this story, there are many different things that I could have included—and that I really wanted to include. But along the way, I had to give myself permission to edit the story down.

Now this may sound very easy, but sometimes it's hard to shut yourself up as a teller, and just say what needs to be said. Especially with family stories, or stories about your own experiences because you know all of the connections, and you know they're interesting to you, and you want to tell all of it!

This tendency also reflects the additive quality of story making. Remember in the very first lecture, one of the qualities of oral thought is that it's additive—"This happened, and then this happened, and then oh, yeah, then this happened!" You develop your story, and as it develops, you'll find connections with other topics and other points in your life, and other stories, and maybe even other cultural connections.

With this overabundance of possible details to include in your story, ask yourself: What story do I want to craft now, knowing that I may craft other versions of this story later? Give yourself permission to choose one of a number of possible stories you could, and may later, tell.

This story that I told is somewhat of a risky story for me. When I really saw what all this story held, and what all this story could point to, there were parts that I not only didn't want to tell, but that at the time that I first crafted this story, I really wasn't ready to tell them. You may discover that you're not ready to tell the "full" story. Give yourself permission to tell what you're ready and comfortable with telling. Give yourself permission not to tell everything.

You may not be ready to tell a story at all, once you get into the details of that story. You might be too close to the events (if it's a difficult event that just happened), or you might be too emotionally caught up in what happened to be able to bring your audience safely to a conclusion. But from the beginning, give yourself permission to wait to tell a story until you are ready to tell it.

Then, you may get into a story, and you decide you really just don't *like* that story. Some stories aren't for us to tell. There's kind of this notion of that you "date" a story before you marry it in performance. Give yourself permission to "date" a story for awhile, and give yourself permission to "break up" with that story or to put off the relationship for a better time if it's just not working out. Unlike human relationships, the story won't get its feelings hurt.

However, a word of warning: If it's a story that really needs to be told, and really needs to be told by you, you might hear that story nagging you from time to time, and nudging you to come back and to tell it later, when you're ready.

Lastly, give yourself permission to really get into your story—to really imagine that you're there. In our next lecture, we're going to start talking about the real "how to" of storytelling, and one of the first things that you'll want to do as a teller is to visualize all these pieces of the story—the people, and the characters, and the events that are going on around you. If these people and events, if they're real to you as a teller, then they will be real and believable to your audience.

As you'll see, visualization is one of the keys to remembering a story—it's not about figuring out how to word things; it's about letting your words and descriptions flow out of the story you're seeing all around you.

Visualization and Memory
Lecture 10

A s a storyteller, you are the audience's guide to a foreign place—the location of your story. In order for your listeners to immerse themselves in your story, for them to believe that they are present in the story, you have to believe that you are in the story. This sounds a lot easier than it is because we're trained to constantly think of the next thing—not to be present in the moment right now. In this lecture, we'll focus on what it means to truly visualize the places, people, and events of your story—to believe that you are in the midst of the action you're describing.

Visualizing Story Scenes

- When you're first learning a story, before you write the story down, sit back, close your eyes, and imagine the different places and people that the story takes you to.

- Experiment with visualization right now. Get seated in a comfortable position and picture the place one of your stories begins. Are you inside or outdoors? If you're inside, what do the walls and windows look like? If you're outside, what is the weather like?

- Next, imagine the characters that appear in the beginning part of the story. What are they wearing? Where are they standing? What is their relationship to one another?

- As you move to each different location or point of action in the story, imagine where you are and whether the mood has shifted. What happened to make this change in the story? Why did you move to a new place? What time is it in the story? What characters are present?

- Again, in the final scene, think about where you are and what has happened in the story. What is the last thing that someone says at the end of the story, and to whom are they speaking?

- Once you've given yourself time to look at each scene and listen to the characters, you will be well on your way to being able to visualize those places when you get up and tell your story.

- Try to end this exercise by telling the story to someone immediately. As you speak, try to see each of the places you are describing to your audience. The more details you can see in front of you, the more clearly your audience will see them. You don't even have to narrate all the details in words; if you visualize the places and people in your story, your audience will get a sense of those details by watching you see them.

The Purpose of Visualization

- When you visualize scenes around you, the audience sees you experiencing the story in real time. The audience takes its cues from you; if you plant yourself in a scene of the story and see it around you—experience it—the audience will experience the story, too, as opposed to merely understanding the story on an intellectual level.

- The more you visualize, the more your listeners will see, and the more they see, the clearer the identity of the people and places will be.

- Visualization helps you "visit" each scene in your story so that you really know each of those places and people. Many people worry about memorization or learning stories, but memorization has nothing to do with storytelling. The more you visualize as you begin to craft your story, the easier it will be to remember your story.
  - Storytellers move from image to image, not word to word. Unlike many other forms of performance, storytelling doesn't necessarily follow a set script. You don't ask, "What's my next line?" but "What storyline am I following?"

  - There's no need to worry about memorizing a script or knowing exact wording. You follow the images and simply describe what's happening in front of you.

o   Remember, if you memorize the words of a story, you're conveying words. If you visualize places, people, and actions, you're conveying an experience. Don't cheat yourself out of a dynamic story delivery by relying too heavily on the written word.

o   Storytellers learn scenes "by heart," meaning that the story is in the body—it moves the body—and the audience sees the story moving the teller as it is told. That's where the storyteller's gestures and movements come from—from seeing the scene.

Visualization in Action
- You can start using visualization right now to bring your stories more alive for your listeners. In fact, most of us already use visualization when we're talking from personal experience. We shift between being with the audience to being in the place and with the people that we're describing.

- One of the first things to do when you start to tell a story is to pause and try to see the first scene around you—not just in your head but around you. It takes only a few seconds to get the place in front of you so that you can give it to your listeners.

- If you rehearse with visualization, the story will present itself to you whether or not you lose track of the way you want to word your descriptions.

A Visualization Exercise
- Think of one main feature of the setting from one of your stories; it could be mountains off in the distance or a house that's right in front of you. Visualize that feature in color and in three dimensions.

- Think about your relationship to this feature of the setting. Does it relax you? Does it put you on edge? Does it have some special meaning in your story? Let your body react to that relationship with the space around you.

If you're telling a story about a huge storm, give yourself time to sense the smell of the air and the quality of the light around you.

- Do you want to move closer to that part of the scenery or farther away? While still visualizing, actually walk closer to or farther from the scenery. Is the feature close enough to touch? Reach your hand out and see if you can feel the texture of that place around you.

- With the knight in the George Buchannan story we heard earlier, I'm seeing something farther away from me that comes closer. When I look at that knight, I'm visualizing him, and I'm putting him in a specific place in space. The place where I've assigned that knight is called a "focal point."
  - A focal point is an imaginary point in space that you use to stand for some element of your performance. Focal points aid in clear communication and visualization for your audience; they help you show your audience what you want them to see.

- A focal point provides clarity to a painting, and it does the same thing for you as a storyteller. When you focus your attention on one point of the story and you see it—all your lines of focus are pointing to it—your listeners will focus their attention to that part of the story, as well.

- Try choosing another object in a scene of your story—something that you can reach out and pick up. Pick up that imaginary object and look at it. Now compare that object to a feature of the scene that's far away from you. Take note of the difference between looking at an object that's close to you and one that's far away.

- Next, imagine a large, hairy creature far off in the distance, but it's coming closer to you. From your perspective, this creature is getting larger. Now it's right in front of you! What did you just do with your focus? How did your focus change as that creature came closer?

- Note that you don't have to show the difference with exaggerated gestures or actions. Because you are immersing yourself in seeing what you are saying and believing that what you are saying is real, the moment becomes real for those who are listening.

Remembering Stories

- Think again of the very beginning of your story. Stand up and imagine that a friend is sitting in front of you (or try this exercise with a friend). Turn slightly to the left so that you are a bit turned away from your audience. As you visualize the beginning scene, it won't spill out directly in front of your friend but slightly off to the left. Assign focal points to the important characters at the beginning of the story.

- Next, turn to fully face your audience. Skip ahead to an important scene in the middle of the story, and again, look around and assign focal points to the people in that scene.

- Finally, move to the end of your story. Turn to the right, and visualize the end scene of your story.

- Now, face to the left and quickly visualize the starting scene; face forward and visualize the middle scene; face to the right and see the ending. Repeat the progression again.

- After the lecture, tell a short version of your story, keeping yourself as much as possible in those three scenes. Try to keep your visualizations "on" and really see what's in front of you. For now, don't worry about making eye contact with your audience; just move from beginning, to middle, to end and give yourself time to see the scene before you talk about it.

- Once you've told the short version of your story, step back and evaluate what you just did. Then, try telling the story once again, but this time, face forward the entire time and move only your head (rather than your whole body) in those three directions. The images will still stay to the left, center, and right, but you will face forward, toward your audience.

- This exercise is a great way to help you learn a story quickly. You can also use this technique when you're asked to give a presentation and you don't have much time to prepare. Locate the beginning, middle, and end; visualize what's in the "story"; and use focal points to place specific ideas or characters in space. This method helps you remember what's in the story, what comes next, and where you're going in the end.

Inviting the Audience into the Scene
- As a storyteller, you can't just look out into the scenery and not acknowledge the audience in front of you. You have to look your listeners directly in the eyes and invite them into the scene.

- This requires a shift in focus on your part. You're moving from the scene you've shaped in your imagination to the listeners in front of you, whom you're asking to come into the scene with you. You're shifting between "open focus"—looking directly into the listeners' eyes—and "closed focus"—visualizing the scene in front of you but closed off from the audience.

- This can be a subtle shift, but it gets to the heart of what a storyteller does, that is, jumping from the "here and now" to the "there and then." Your eye contact with your listeners in the here and now invites them in to see the world of there and then—it brings that other world into the present.

Suggested Reading

Collins and Cooper, *The Power of Story*.

Lipman, *Improving Your Storytelling*.

Questions to Consider

1. What surprised you about the visualization exercises? Did you begin to "see" new things in your story? What?

2. Think of a place that you have been before—try to visualize that place while you describe it aloud to another person. Keep your focus on "seeing" that place as it was then, with an awareness that you are explaining it to someone now. Ask your listener: What part of the story description was most vivid as you listened?

Visualization and Memory
Lecture 10—Transcript

Professor Harvey: As a storyteller, you are our guide to a foreign place, the location of your story. In order for your audience to immerse themselves into your story, for them to really *believe* that they're there in the story, *you* have to believe that you're there. This sounds a lot easier than it really is, because we're constantly trained to constantly think of the next thing, and not to be in the present right now. That's your challenge in storytelling—to be fully present with your story in the moment as you're telling it.

In this lecture, we're going to focus on what it means to really visualize the places, and the people, and the events in your story—to believe that you're there in the midst of all the action that you're describing. Visualization is one of the key ways to remember your stories, too. I'll be doing a lot of exercises and workshops that get my students, usually on their feet, experimenting with "seeing" the story out in front of them. These exercises, they're fun and you may want to try them, too; if so, you'll want to wear comfortable clothes!

First of all, what is visualization? Well, when you're first learning a story, before you write the story down into words, sit back, and close your eyes, and imagine the different places and people that that story takes you to.

I'd like for you to experiment with this right now. Think of a story that you're familiar with. It can be a family story, or a story that you heard that happened to a friend yesterday, or something that happened to you this morning. Think of that story.

Now, get in a comfortable seated position, and relax. Picture the place that that story begins—where are you? Are you inside or are you outdoors? What's at your feet? If you're inside, what do the walls look like in this place? Are there windows, and where are they? If you're outside, what kind of day is it? Are there clouds?

Now, *who* is in that beginning part of the story? Is there more than one person? What is their relationship to each other? Where are they standing? What are they wearing? Try to picture them in color.

Now, something happens in the story—you move to a different place or a different point of action. Where are you now? Has your location changed, or has the mood shifted? Where are the people standing now? What happened to make this change in the story—why did you move from where you were to this new place?

Something else happens in your story, and you move to a third location, and the story may be nearing an ending. What propelled you into this new place? What time is it here? Who is in the story now? Where are they in relation to each other?

You move to the final scene of your story—what happened? Where are you now? Look at what's under your feet—where are you standing? What is the last thing that someone says at the end of this story, and who do they say that to?

Once you've located these different scenes, and really sat there in each place, giving yourself time to look and to listen to the characters in each scene, then you're well on your way to being able to visualize those places when you get up and tell your story.

When you get up to tell the story—and I'd encourage you to just jump out of this exercise and try to tell the story to someone—really try to see each of the places you're describing to your audience. The more you can actively see and visualize in front of you— for example, where a mountain ridge lies on the horizon, or where your friend stands in relation to the trees that are off in the distance, and the house that's just behind both of you, that house with the open door. The more details *you* can see, the more clearly your audience will see them. You don't even have to narrate all those details in words. If you stand there in your performance and you see these places and these people; if you do that your audience will get a sense of those details just by seeing you see them.

For example, there's a ghost story that I tell—and, as my grandmother told me this story, she swore it was a true story from my family, about when my grandmother's mother came back after death, for a visit.

In this story, I describe the people that are gathered in the parlor of my great-grandmother's house when my great-grandmother came back as a ghost, and they hear her walking on the floor above them. As I'm telling that story I'm seeing that ceiling, and where the couch sits, and where my Nana and my aunt Evelyn were sitting, and what their faces looked like when they saw and heard what they saw and heard. I don't verbalize any of those details, but as I see them, and the presence of those people and that place, they become palpable as a part of the story.

Visualization, it does several things, for you and for your audience. When you visualize those scenes around you, the audience sees you experiencing the story in real time. The audience, they take their cues from you—so if you plant yourself in that scene of the story, and you see it all around you, and you experience it, then the audience will experience the story, too. This is opposed to just an intellectual understanding of the story, your audience engaging on an intellectual level only. The more you visualize, the more your audience will see. The more they see, the clearer the *identity* of those people and places will be to your audience. Or, if you're telling a story about your business or your organization, the clearer the identity of that group will become.

Visualization helps you "visit" each of the scenes in your story, so that you really *know* each of these places and people. Many people worry about memorization or learning the story. "How did you remember all those lines?" Actually, memorization has nothing to do with it. The more you visualize as you begin to craft your story, the easier it will be for you to remember your story.

This is a unique feature of story performance—storytellers move from image to image, not word to word. Unlike many other performance mediums, storytelling doesn't necessarily follow a set script, so you're not asking, "What's my next line?" But you're asking, "What's the storyline that I'm following?"

There's an Irish storyteller named Eddie Lenihan—he's wonderful, check him out. He told me once that he tries to visually fully each part of the story that he wants to tell. In that way, he has been to each of those places, and he has met all the people in the story. He said, "Once I've been to a place, you can't convince me that I haven't been there."

There's really no need to worry about memorizing a script or knowing the exact wording that you want to say when you're telling a story. You just follow the images, and you're simply describing what you see right there in front of you, and it's all happening right there before you. The words that you say don't come from a script—the words are flowing out of that scene that's unfolding in front of you.

It's not that I'm against writing your stories down—we'll be doing lots of exercises, writing exercises to help you remember and experiment with shaping your story. It's not that I'm against you thinking through the wording. You should experiment with the precision of language to think about the right words to describe the different levels of your story.

But there's a very bad trap that you can fall into when you just sit down from the get-go to write out a story. You come up with these words, and for many people the wording on that page becomes the focus. You start to think about the wording, that script, more than the images in your story.

If all you have are the words that you've memorized, you're conveying words. But if you've visualized the places and the people and the actions, you're conveying an experience.

I'm not just saying, "Oh, don't worry about memorizing a script," I'm warning you: Don't just mechanically memorize a script. For most people, that kind of memorization, it encourages you to develop a monotone voice—where-everything-you-say-is-the-same-tenor-and-the-same-tone-and-you're-searching-in-your-head-for-the-next-word-on-the-page. And the page is what you're visualizing, and you're trying to remember that page. Don't do that to yourself! Later on, we'll certainly move to using writing as a part of the story-development process, but don't start there. Don't cheat yourself out of a dynamic story delivery by jumping straight to the written word. It may be tempting for you, but don't do it!

Instead of memorizing a script, storytellers learn from images, and they learn these scenes by heart, meaning that the story is in your body—it moves from your body, and we see the story moving you as you tell it. That's where your gestures and your movements come from—from seeing all of these scenes around you.

So I'm not going to tell you that you should work on your gestures for interacting with the scene around you—when you interact with that scene, if you see it, you'll interact with it. You'll see it as a real world around you. When you're interacting with your real world, you don't have to worry about, "Do my gestures look real, or does this look normal? Is this really how I would touch a door?" No, it's just how you interact with the world around you! You touch the door!

It's the same with the world of your story. When you visualize it, you'll find your body—your arms, your head, your hands—your body will gesture to the things around you that you see just as naturally as you would if they were really there, if you were really in front of that house in your story, or if you really were sitting at that dinner table! So, storytelling: No memorizing lines, no "learning" gestures. Just seeing that world of the story around you.

You can start using this right now, in the very next story that you tell to a friend. It doesn't require any high-tech special preparation. You can start using visualization to bring your own stories more alive for your audiences—and most of us do use visualization when we're talking from personal experience. We move in and out from being there with the audience, to being in that place with those people who we're describing.

Being aware of how you may already be using visualization—and being aware of using it more from the very beginning of your story, it can greatly enhance your craft as a storyteller. If you're telling a story that you've learned from other sources, using visualization can be a wonderful way to remember the story, and make that story become all the more real to you, and to your audience.

Now, direct application. One of the first things to do, when you start to tell a story, is to pause and try to see of the scenes of the action around you—not just in your head, but around you. It only takes a few seconds—just pause to get that place into your head and out there in front of you. You want to get it out there, so you can give that story to somebody else.

So, you're telling story about a huge storm that came up—take a moment. Give yourself time to sense: What did the air smell like? Look out: What was the light like? This visualization of your story is your "safe space"— it's all there, out there for you, just waiting for you to describe it. If you mess up on your wording, it's OK—the scene and the events are still there waiting for you. You can just pick up with different wording and keep going. If you rehearse, starting with visualization, the story will present itself to you whether or not you lose track of the way that you want to word your descriptions. You don't have to worry about losing your words; just come home to that image in front of you, and all around you, and just describe what you see.

Let's see an example of what this looks like in a story—here's a moment from a story that you've heard before, and now we can start to look at it again to break it down.

In this one moment from the "George Buchannan" story, pay attention to how I'm looking at the scene around me and looking at the people who are there. Pay attention to where I place my focus when I talk about different characters and places, and how that focus changes.

If you're listening to the audio version of this lecture, you can still notice the nuances in visualization that are coming through in my voice. I change my visual focus, and when I do that, there's a corresponding change in my focus of my voice as well (we'll get to this more in the lecture on voice). So, here's an example of visualizing places and characters.

[Video start.]

> **Professor Harvey:** He walked down the lane, and there's a road that passed through that farm. As he walked through and crossed

that road he stood in the middle and he saw something, off in the distance. It was shimmering. He stood there in the road until that thing, it came closer, and as it came closer, he saw of it, it was a knight, on horseback. George, he had never seen a knight before. Being a clever man, he wanted to make a good impression, but he's George Buchannan; he often played the fool in public.

So as that knight came riding closer and closer George, he just stood there in the middle of the road staring straight up in the sky and he was taking up that middle of the road. That knight, he came riding closer.

[Video end.]

Professor Harvey: One of my favorite parts about telling that story to kids is when I see the knight, I usually get a few of the kids looking behind them to see the knight that I'm looking at—they believe that it's real! And they settle further into the story; it's great!

Now, there are several different things that I'm doing with my focus here. Let's break them apart, so that you can apply some of these tools in your storytelling.

To start with, in this part of the story, I'm not just seeing a flat scene in two dimensions. I'm seeing a dynamic, changing scene all around me. There are layers—some things are closer to me, some things are far away.

Think of one scene in your story. Now, think of one main feature of the setting of your story—it could be mountains that are off in the distance, or a house that's right there in front of you—any major feature of that scene. I'm going to do something with you; it's called "side-coaching." That means that as I give you directions, I want you to stay with looking at that feature of your scene.

Now, visualize that feature of the scene—see it in color, in three dimensions. Now think about your relationship to that thing in front of you—does it relax you? Does it put you on edge? Does it have some special meaning in your story? Let your body react to that relationship with the space around you.

Do you want to move closer to that part of the scenery, or farther away? Actually walk closer to it or further away from it while still visualizing. Is it close enough to touch? Reach out your hand (don't worry, you don't have to do this when you're actually telling the story to an audience; this is just for your rehearsal time with your story). Reach your hand out, and see if you can feel the texture of that place around you. The feature you chose may be so far away that you're reaching out and touching the air in front of you, and you can see those mountains way far behind you.

Now, with that knight, I'm seeing something farther away from me that comes closer. When I look at that knight, I'm visualizing him, and I'm also putting that knight out in a specific place in space. He's usually off to my left and slightly up from my line of vision, as the road rises up a hill and there are some trees off in the distance. I visualize that; I see it. The place where I've assigned that knight is called a "focal point."

A focal point is an imaginary point out in space that you can use to stand for some element of your performance. You use focal points to make the story clearer to your audience. Focal points aid in clear communication and in visualization for your audience—they help you show your audience what you want them to see. So I put all of my energy and my focus into seeing that knight in that place when he first arrives in that scene.

Now you may have heard of focal points in relation to visual arts, as in the focal point of a painting. So you look at Leonardo's painting of The Last Supper, and all of the lines in that drawing, the shading and colors, they're all focusing your attention on a single point—that figure in the center of the painting.

That focal point gives clarity and focus to the painting. It's the same thing for you as a storyteller. When you focus your attention on that one point in the story, you see it, and all of your lines of focus are pointing to it, and it causes the audience to focus their attention in their heads to that part of the story as well, and it adds clarity to your story.

Now, let's start to talk about what this is like for you, the storyteller. Go to that scene of your story, and look around. Again, I'm side-coaching. Choose another object in the scene—something that's close to you, something that you could reach out and pick up. Go ahead and pick that imaginary object up, that object from your story (maybe it's a pen on the table, or a plate of food). Pick that object up and hold it and look at it. It's close to you. You're looking at an object that's close to you.

Now take that object that's close to you away and look at another feature of the scene that's far away from you. See that feature far off in the distance. Now look back at the object in your hand. Take note of the difference between looking at an object that's close to you, and looking at one that's far away from you.

Now this may be adding to your story that you already have, but try this— see something far off in the distance. It can be a person, or an animal. Oh, let's say it's an animal. You see this creature off in the distance. (Again, I'm side-coaching; try not to look at me, and just focus on that creature that's way far off.)

It's way far off, it's a safe distance off, and you just see it there, and now you see it coming closer to you. Maybe you can tell it's big and it's hairy and it's coming closer and now it's about 100 yards from you and because of your perspective it's getting bigger all of the time. Now it's even closer to you and it's 10 feet from you and OK now it's right up on top of you!

OK, now think about what you just did with your focus. You saw something way far off—just a little pinpoint in the distance. You used focal points to assign that animal a specific place in space. As that animal came closer, it grew bigger, because it's coming closer to you, so you can start to see features, and more of its size coming into focus, and your focus widens out to take in its whole body, and maybe you're seeing different parts of its body. Then it's closer and it may be coming right up on top of you—and it's larger than you are—so you have to look up to it!

Here's the difference in using visualization and in not using visualization. Here's not using visualization: "So, I saw this thing coming off in the distance, and it got closer, and closer, and then it's right on top of me."

Now, with visualization: "I saw this thing coming off in the distance, and it got closer, and it got closer to me, and it got closer and then it was right on top of me!" You see it doesn't have to be this big, enacted thing to add to your story, because maybe that's not your style. It's immersing yourself into seeing what you're saying, and believing that what you're saying is really real, and that it's really there in front of you in the moment of your telling.

Now, let's put these aspects of visualization and focal points together, to help you remember a story that you want to tell. Let's go back to that first exercise, when I asked you to walk from one scene to the next in your story. I want you to stand up, and give yourself a good stretch right now. Imagine that a good friend is standing there in front of you. If you've actually got someone with you, so much the better—now friend, stand up, and you can face each other! If you're practicing right now without anyone, you can do this exercise now and then try it again later with a friend if you like.

So, from this standing position, turn slightly to your left (I'm going to mirror you). Turn to your left so that you're a bit turned away from your audience (don't worry—this is just an exercise—when you're actually telling a story, you can be facing them the whole time; this is just a memory trick that I'm teaching you).

Standing a quarter turn to the left, think of the very beginning of your story. Where are you? Try to paint that scene all around you, still turned a quarter turn away, so what you're visualizing doesn't spill out directly in front of that friend, but it's off to your left. Look at where you are, and imagine the people, and the objects, and the things around you. Are there one or two important characters at this beginning of the story? Where are they? Assign a focal point to each of them, and really look at their features. Are they tall, or are they short in comparison with one another? When you look up at one of them, do you have to look up to see their face? Does one person look down to the other one?

Now, turn to fully face your audience. Go to the middle of your story—you may be skipping through a few specific scenes, but think of a shorter version of your story—wherever the middle of the story is. Go to one important scene in the middle of your story. Where are you now? Who is there? Look around and assign the people in that scene specific focal points—he stands here, she stands there, and across from them, and I can look at one another.

Now, move to the end of your story. Turn a quarter turn to the right—again, you're facing partially away from that person in front of you. Visualize the end of your scene, of your story—who is there, what has changed? Where are these people? You may have stayed in the same place the entire time, but I'd say the mood has shifted in that room. How does that place feel differently than from the beginning? How is your relationship to the space different than before?

Now, go back to that beginning scene—see everything, quickly—see the places and the people. Face forward. See the people, and the places where one object is in that scene. Face to the right. See the ending—where are the people, and where are you now?

Try it again, quickly—face the left, the beginning—see it. Face the middle—see it, it's different. And face the right, the end—see it. When this lecture is finished, I'd like for you to tell a short version of that story—keeping yourself as much as possible in those three scenes, keeping your visualizations "on," and what you're really seeing in front of you, try to really visualize it. For now, don't worry about making eye contact with that audience member, just move from beginning, to middle, to end, and give yourself time to see that scene before you talk about it, before you describe what you're seeing. See it first.

Once you've told that short version of your story, step back and evaluate what you just did. You may have moved your body from left, to center, to right. Next, I'd like for you to try telling that story once again, but this time, face forward the whole time, and only move your head. Maybe you might move your torso also to those three locations—left, center, and right. But you keep facing forward towards your audience. Now, what we just did in the past, oh, 10 minutes, is a great way for you to help learn your story quickly. And you can use this when you're asked to give a presentation and you don't have much time to prepare, but you can locate the beginning, and the middle, and the end. By visualizing what's there in the story, by using focal points to place specific characters and the things in that story, to place them out in space, it will help you remember what's coming next in the story, and where you're going in the end.

Visualization also works to transform presentations into stories. Try to divide up your presentation up into a beginning, and a middle, and an end, and see if you can visualize what you're talking about. It's a great tool, and you'll look down at your notes a lot less, just try it.

As a storyteller, you're going to immerse yourself into these scenes, but you want to invite your audience into these scenes as well. You can't just look out at the scenery and not acknowledge the audience out in front of you. This is one of the distinguishing features that separates acting from storytelling. In storytelling, you look your audience directly in the eye. You invite them into that scene.

That takes a shift in focus on your part. You're moving from the scene that you shaped in your imagination, to this audience who's in front of you, and who you're asking to come into that scene with you.

You're shifting from "open focus"—looking directly into the audience's eyes—shifting from that to "closed focus," where you don't look at the audience, but instead you visualize the scene that's going on around you, off in front of the audience.

Let's look at a specific example of this from a story, this shift from looking at the audience, to looking at the scene that you're imagining out in front of you. Let's go back to that same scene from "George Buchannan," but this time pay attention to this shift in focus from the audience to being in that scene.

[Video start.]

> **Professor Harvey:** He walked down the lane, and there's a road that passed through that farm. As he walked through and crossed

that road he stood in the middle and he saw something, off in the distance. It was shimmering. He stood there in the road until that thing, it came closer, and as it came closer, he saw of it, it was a knight, on horseback. George, he had never seen a knight before. Being a clever man, he wanted to make a good impression, but he's George Buchannan, he often played the fool in public.

So as that knight came riding closer and closer George, he just stood there in the middle of the road staring straight up in the sky and he was taking up that middle of the road. That knight, he came riding closer.

[Video end.]

Professor Harvey: It's a subtle shift, but it stands for so much, because it gets to the heart of what a storyteller really does—jumping from the here-and-now (so here with your audience, at the water cooler, or in the boardroom, or in the living room with your friends). So you're here-and-now with your audience, but you're jumping to the then-and-there (to the time and the place of the story. You're remembering a past event from your grandfather's history, or if you're imagining a magical world full of knights and kings).

Your eye contact with the audience, here-and-now, it invites your audience to seeing this world, and it invites them into that place then-and-there. And it brings the "then-and-there" into the "here-and-now." So you're doing a lot of things with just a very simple shift in focus. The more you can visualize clearly the scenes around you, the more familiar you become with the story, and the more easily you can make these transitions.

That's the really fun part of storytelling—when you know your story well enough that you can see that story out in front of you. And you can see all of the characters—and you know it well enough to hear not only one voice (the voice of the narrator) but also the voices and the perspectives of the other characters.

Every character in your story brings the potential for a new perspective in the story. Try this: You've been looking around in this scene. Is there another person in that story? Are they in this scene? If there's another person in the scene, try to jump into that person's perspective—try to see the scene from their angle of view. Are they shorter than you? If so, do they look up on events, or do they look ahead, or do they look down on you? Are they taller than you?

What you're playing with here is "perspective," how you literally see the world of your story. Your perspective on the events of your story plays a huge role in shaping your story for an audience, and in you discovering your own voice as a teller. We'll talk about perspectives for the narrator, and perspectives for the characters, and for the audience in the next lecture.

Discovering Point of View
Lecture 11

Storytelling is a series of choices you make, and one of the most important of these is your choice of perspective. As we mentioned in the lecture on family stories, there is no such thing as an objectively told story. There is a power dynamic at play when you are the storyteller: You decide what gets left in the story and what gets left out, whose voices are privileged, whose experiences are worthy of mention, and who gets the last word. That's a huge responsibility! In this lecture, we'll reflect on how and why you make these choices, because your reflections on your own standpoint get to the heart of discovering your voice as a storyteller.

Point of View

- Let's begin by thinking about age. Our age affects the way we view life and our experiences; it influences the stories we're drawn to and how we tell those stories.

  o Think about an important event that occurred when you were a teenager, perhaps driving a car alone for the first time. How might you have retold the story of that experience when you were a teenager?

  o How might you tell that story now? You're still yourself and still narrating a story about yourself, but because you've had many more life experiences from that time to now, your vantage point on that event will have shifted.

  o You have probably had a wealth of experiences that put that event into a different perspective. Your conclusion to the story may change, or you might position the story within a larger context. As a parent, you may use the experience of your first time driving alone as a cautionary tale to your own teenager.

- Another critical part of your point of view is gender. Gender affects who we sympathize with in a story and how we think about stories.

o   Culture influences how we think of some stories as gendered. As a man, you might not think that you should tell a story about your mother's cooking, or as a woman, you might feel that you can't tell a story about your father's experiences in a war, but you can.

o   Such stories can be deeply meaningful to you and to selected audiences. Sometimes, one aspect of yourself might lead you to shy away from stories that you'd like to tell; thus, it's useful to evaluate not only what you're drawn to but what might be holding you back from stories.

- Your geographical location also affects your point of view. For example, we tend to root for the home team; in other words, we have a particular point of view based on a connection with "home."

- Not only where you're from but who you're from is another important factor in your point of view. If you were close to your mother or father, you may be drawn to stories that emphasize those kinds of close relationships, and you may be more inclined to see stories sympathetically from a mother's or father's point of view. If you have a strained relationship with family members, you may be drawn to stories that feature similar struggles.

- Connected with family background is your racial background and makeup.
  o   Race is both a social and a cultural marker. It can, to varying degrees, affect the peer groups we gravitate toward (our primary audiences), as well as the kinds of cultural stories we're exposed to as we grow up.

  o   Like gender and geographical background, race can be a factor that immediately connects you with an audience; it can be a neutral factor with your audience; or it can sometimes be a barrier to connecting with an audience.

- Your temperament also shapes your relationship to the world around you and your point of view. If you're a fast-paced person, you may be irritated by someone who moves slowly. If you enjoy short conversations rather than long ones, you will probably be drawn to stories that get to the point quickly.

- Class and economic background are additional factors in shaping your point of view on the world. They may influence who the hero is and who the villain is. You can extrapolate this to your position at work: Is management the hero or the villain in your stories? If you're telling stories to employees, how do you narrate those stories so that the characters help your audience relate to management and see things from the managers' point of view?

The Storyteller and the Narrator

- As a storyteller, you choose the perspective from which an audience hears a story—you narrate the story from that perspective. But the perspective you choose to adopt in narrating the story may be entirely different from your own actual perspective on the events.

- This adopted perspective is called a "persona," a word that comes from the Latin for "mask." The persona is like a mask that the

Your persona is like a mask you put on to tell a story; in fact, the idea of "persona" has given us the icon for drama, the masks of comedy and tragedy.

© iStockphoto/Thinkstock.

storyteller puts on to tell the story, and like a mask, the persona you adopt directs where you look and frames what you see.

- For example, the narrators in my stories are often either androgynous or masculine, even with personal stories. For me, imagining a masculine narrator frees me from using more feminine gestures.

- Your persona is influenced by your perspective on life and by the narrated perspective you choose to adopt in telling a story.

- As we've said, when you tell a story, all of the factors of your background weigh on how you tell that story—the point of view you take on narrating events. They also influence your particular voice as a storyteller. For example, if your temperament is one that finds humor in life, then many of your stories will probably emphasize humor; you will narrate stories from a vantage point that sees the ironies around you.

- Most of the time, when you're telling a story, you think you're telling *the* story. But the truth is that when you're telling a story—any story—you're piecing events together, making choices based on your perception of events and directing the audience's attention.

- Inside the story that you create—from your piecing together of events—is a narrator, who is both you and someone else. This narrator may sympathize with some of the characters in the story and not others. He or she may know everything that you know as the teller or may not have all the information you have.

- The narrator's perspective on events is what makes stories interesting; it's why a group of friends may choose one person to tell a particular story. That teller may have a unique perspective on the events of the story.

- Should a narrator always be objective? Remember: Stories reveal truths, and they do so by looking through subjective points of view.

In fact, stories often reveal powerful truths when the narrator asks us to look inside multiple points of view.

Choosing a Primary Perspective

- One of the first things you need to do when you're preparing to tell a story is to look at all the possible perspectives you could take on the story and choose one that you'd like to follow as you guide the audience through the story.

- Whoever your narrator follows most closely will become the main character of the story, even if that character was, in other versions of the same story, a minor character or someone with whom you wouldn't ordinarily sympathize.

- Storyteller Milbre Burch has a wonderfully thought-provoking version of "Snow White," told from the perspective of the "evil" stepmother. From this perspective, the stepmother is really trying to save Snow White from her father, whom the stepmother recognizes as a pedophile! She sends Snow White into the woods not to get rid of her but to save her.

- Classroom teachers sometimes use a similar role-switching exercise. They might ask students to stage the Lincoln-Douglas debate, then have them switch roles and debate the other side. Such exercises help students understand both sides of an issue and help them learn the material in a memorable way.

- In a corporate setting, an employee might be asked to explain the point of view of upper management to a small group, while a manager might adopt the perspective of employees. Such an exercise sets a foundation for meaningful cooperation in the future.

- In choosing your perspective for a story, consider those aspects of yourself that define your perspective on the world—age, gender, temperament, cultural background, and so on. Choose just one of those aspects and think about how it affects the stories you want to tell.

- As a challenge, try telling stories from a different perspective. If you're a woman, consider a story told by a male character. If you're comparatively wealthy, consider a story told from the perspective of someone who struggles. If you're healthy, consider a story from the perspective of someone who has a disability. All of these changes in perspective make for stories that are interesting to share with your audience and can be enlightening for yourself.

Suggested Reading

Burch, "What the Queen Saw."

Kling, *Alive.*

——, *The Dog Says How.*

——, www.kevinkling.com.

Lipman, *Improving Your Storytelling.*

Sacre, *A Mango in the Hand.*

——, *La Noche Buena.*

——, www.antoniosacre.com.

Questions to Consider

1. Your persona as a storyteller isn't a separate role that you play; it's you, but it's also your choice of how to see a story. Is there an experience you've had that you would like to narrate from a different perspective than your own? Why?

2. Even the most seemingly objective stories always originate with and are gated by narrators, each with his or her own values and perspectives. Whose perspectives do each of the following kinds of "stories" come from: magazine features, political rhetoric, news programs, scholarly articles, medical reports?

Discovering Point of View
Lecture 11—Transcript

Professor Harvey: Storytelling is a series of choices that you make, and one of the most important choices to be aware of is your choice of perspective, because your perspective on the story, it determines who has power in the story. It's not a small thing; perspective can completely reframe the meaning of a story. It has to do with power.

As we mentioned in the lecture on family stories, there is no such thing as an objectively-told story. There is a power dynamic at play when you're the storyteller—you decide what gets left in the story, and you decide what gets left out, whose voices are privileged, whose experiences matter enough to be worthy of mention to this particular audience, and how the story concludes— who gets the last word. That's a huge responsibility!

Your distinctive voice as a teller comes from your perspective on life, and how you make these choices about point of view in your story. We all do this in a more or less sophisticated way as parents, and grandparents, or colleagues; we all have a certain perspective from which we see life, and from which we then choose to talk about the events of life. In this lecture, I'm asking you to reflect on how and why you make these choices, because your reflections from your own standpoint get to the heart of discovering your voice as a storyteller. So, let's look at the impact that your perspective, and your narrator's perspective, have on telling your story.

I want to introduce you to a storyteller named Antonio Sacre—I want for you to listen to a portion of a story that he tells about "*La Llorona,*" the weeping woman. In this clip, he's just told the folktale of "*La Llorona*" to a group of middle schoolers, but watch what he does then with the story.

[Video start.]

> **Antonio Sacre:** Two years ago, I met a boy named Miguel Hernandez. Miguel went to a high school in Chicago. He had just come up from Mexico. He said, [Spanish] "Antonio, have you ever heard of '*La LLorona*?'"

I said, "Yes."

But he told me other stories about her, and he said, [Spanish phrase]. "Antonio, I know how you can see *La Llorona*."

I never heard that. I said, "How?"

He said, "It's easy. All you need to do is put a glass of water in your window. She'll come up from the river, and she'll drink the water."

I said, "Really?"

He said, "Yeah." He said, "Antonio last Friday night, I wanted to see her, and at midnight, [Spanish phrase]. Do you know what happened?"

I said, "What?"

He said, "Nothing."

"That's not scary."

He said, "I put a second glass of water in my window and at 12:30 at night do you know what happened?" I said, "What?" He said, "Nothing." He put three, four, five glasses of water and he said at one o'clock in the morning, [Spanish phrase]. Do you know what happened?"

I said, "What?" He said, "Nothing," and I started to laugh. He said but then he remembered an American legend, of Bloody Mary. Who's ever heard of this legend? He went into the bathroom, shut the door, shut off the light, looked into the mirror, and instead of saying Bloody Mary he called her name five times in Spanish: "*La Llorona, La Llorona, La Llorona, La Llorona, La Llorona.*" [Spanish phrase]—nothing happened in the bathroom. But when he went back to his bedroom, one of the glasses was missing from his ledge. He slid underneath his window, put his back to his wall, there were the four glasses right about him on the ledge, and he says he thought he heard somebody drinking the water and the glass hitting the ground.

Then he heard a sickening sound, like bone scraping against brick, worse than fingernails down old green slate chalkboard. He felt another glass getting pulled off that ledge, and he thought he heard someone drinking and the glass hitting the ground. Another glass got pulled off that ledge, and he slid out, and he stared at the two remaining glasses. Just as he saw a thin, gnarled, ghostly hand pulling the second-to-the-last glass down. There was one glass left, and Miguel thought, "I want to prove that she exists."

He stood up, got as close as he dared to that last glass, and when her hand reached around that glass, it lingered there. It didn't move. He thought, "Now's my chance." He took a deep breath. He reached up and she reached around and grabbed his hand. Grabbed him by the shoulders, pulled him out of the window, looked into his eyes, and she said, [Spanish phrase], which means, "I have to go to the bathroom."

With that, she disappeared, and I started to laugh, and I said, "Miguel, did that really happen?" and he said, "No."

[Video end.]

Professor Harvey: Antonio Sacre tells masterfully to kids and to adults; he connects with these audiences, but most of all, he's connected to the story and to himself. Antonio is a bilingual teller, and like all of us, his cultural heritage influences his perspective on the world.

Like we talked about in the lecture on your relationship with the story, there's a context that pushes you towards some stories, contexts that introduce you to stories—Antonio learned the folktale of "*La Llorona*" from the cultural context he grew up in.

But beyond that, because Antonio is bilingual, he had access to this little boy's story that bridged Latino and American cultures. Because Antonio speaks Spanish, the boy he was talking to felt comfortable enough with him to tell him the story, and he could tell it to him in Spanish, so the boy probably felt more confident in sharing the story.

Because Antonio has embraced that side of his cultural heritage, he saw that story as worth sharing to a group of middle schoolers, and because he's embraced his American roots as well, he was able to claim those roots in his introduction to the story. It made the story of "*La Llorona*" that much more accessible and that much more "cool" to his audience.

Your perspective gives you access to certain stories—and access to certain perspectives on stories—that other people don't. It's that perspective that people want to hear in your story.

Let's start with you—your point of view. There are some specific questions that I'd like for you to think about, and don't worry, this is just for you, so be honest with yourself, because the first question is your age. Your age affects the way that you see your life and the way that you see the experiences around you.

Your age impacts the stories that you're drawn to, and it affects how you tell those stories. Think about an important event that happened to you when you were younger, say, when you were a teenager. It could be a date that was important to you, or a date that went right or a date that went wrong, or a rite of passage ceremony (so a bar mitzvah or a bat mitzvah), or your first car, and the freedom of driving alone for the first time. Think of what that felt like at the time, and now think about who you might have re-told the story of those experiences to *when you were a teenager*.

When you were a teen, you probably told someone else about this experience. Think about how you told that story to your best friend when you were younger. Were you excited? Were you caught up in the details of the thrill of that experience, or the hormonal nightmare of your first date? Think about your point of view, then, on those events and experiences—your point of view then when you were younger and closer to the event. What was your vantage point? How did you tell that story then?

Now come out of that reflection, and think about the same story as you would tell it now—you're still yourself, narrating a story about yourself—but because of all your life experiences from that time until now, your vantage point on those events will have shifted. While you may sit and reminisce with that best friend about that first date, and the thrill that still may be there in the memory, there's also probably a wealth of experiences after that that put that event into a different perspective. Your conclusion to the story may change; you might position the story of that date within a larger context of marriage, and kids.

If you do have kids, you might use that story about your first car as a cautionary tale. In the moment, the thrill of driving fast, it was exhilarating, but now, as a parent, you're watching your babies take the wheel and it can be terrifying because you know how dangerous it is out there, and you know how stupid you were then!

You can empathize with your teen's situation, because you tell the story of how much you enjoyed the thrill of speeding, and the freedom, but you might position that thrill within a larger narrative of what's really out there on the road, and how much there is to be cautious of and look out for. You might even couple the thrill-ride story with a second story of a car wreck. So your age impacts not only your perspective on events, but the different kinds of audiences you have and your relationship with those audiences.

Age is a critical part of your point of view. What about your gender? Gender impacts perspective (who we sympathize with in the story, for example). Gender affects the kinds of stories that we're drawn to, and how we think about those stories. Bear in mind that "gender" is a different thing than "sex." Sex is the parts that you're born with. Gender deals with the varying degrees to which we are masculine or feminine—I know plenty of women who are drawn to more masculine stories, and I know plenty of men who appreciate a feminine hero in a story.

That said, you get a group of women together, and you just might hear some stories about fashion and food. You get a group of men together, and you might hear some stories about sports and beer. The reasons for this aren't as simple as, "Oh, that's just the kinds of stories we're naturally drawn to." In truth, we're heavily influenced by culture and what kinds of stories culture tells us that little girls should listen to and enjoy (stories about pretty unicorns and dollies), and the stories that boys should listen to and enjoy (about being tough in battle).

It's not that that's a bad thing, but culture impacts how we think of some stories as gendered. So as a man, you might not think that you "should" tell a story about how your mother cooked oysters; or as a woman, you might not feel that you "could" tell a story about your father's experiences in the war. But you can.

Those stories can be deeply meaningful to you, and they can be deeply meaningful to selected audiences. That's why it's good to evaluate these aspects of yourself and your point of view. Sometimes one aspect of your given self might lead you to shy away from stories that you'd really like to tell. It's useful sometimes to evaluate not only what you're drawn to, but what might be holding you back from stories. Gender affects what stories we even think that we *can* tell.

Age, gender. Where you're from, your geographical location, also impacts your point of view. For example, we tend to root for the home team (or the home way of life, or the home place)—we have a particular point of view based on that connection with home.

Where you're from, and who you're from. As we talked about in the lecture on family stories, your family background shapes your point of view. If you were close to your mother or your father, you might be drawn to stories that talk about those kinds of close relationships, and you may be more inclined to see stories sympathetically from a mother or father's point of view.

If you have a strained relationship with family members, you might be drawn to stories that feature similar struggles, or stories of reconciliation—and you may be more sympathetic to characters who have much to overcome.

Connected with family background is your racial background and makeup. Race is both a social and cultural marker. It can, in varying degrees, affect the peer groups we gravitate towards (who our primary audiences), as well as the cultural stories that we're exposed to as we grow up. Like gender, and like your accent, race can be a factor that immediately connects you with an audience, or it can be a neutral nonfactor with your audience, or, let's face it, race can sometimes be a barrier to connecting with your audience. Often that has to do with the same assumptions that people put on accents, the way you speak—some of your audiences for your stories, they may make certain assumptions about what they expect to hear, or how they expect to relate (or not) to your stories, based on the way they perceive your race, and what race they perceive you to be.

In addition to all of these parts of your given background, also your temperament shapes your relationship with the world around you, and it shapes your point of view on things. If you're a fast-paced person, you may be irritated by someone who moves more slowly than you do.

Or if you enjoy conversations that are short rather than long ones, you'll probably be drawn to stories that are to-the-point and less wordy than others. You may have taken the Myers-Briggs personality test that reveals your temperament—this test was actually developed based on Jungian psychology, which was also the foundation for our discussion on myth and the hero's journey.

Your class and economic standpoint shapes your point of view on the world—sometimes this shapes who the hero is and who the villain is. You can extrapolate this to your position at work—is management the hero or the villain in your stories? If you're telling stories to employees, how do you narrate those stories so that the characters are positioned in such a way that your audience relates to management and sees things from their point of view?

All of these factors of our background and personality, they impact how we see things. They shape what we *literally* see, our literal vantage point. When you were five, you saw things differently than you do now; you literally looked up on the world. When you have a certain job, you come into contact with these people, and not with these others. Also, they shape what we *want* to see. Our desires shape what we notice in the world around us, and what we don't notice or what we don't pay attention to.

Let's look more closely into this relationship between the storyteller and the narrator because these are two different things. You are the storyteller—you, Joe, sitting there in your car or your chair, you are the teller. And you choose the perspective from which we hear this story—you narrate the story from that perspective.

But—and this is the interesting part—the perspective you choose to adopt in order to narrate that story may be entirely different from your own actual perspective on the events. This adopted perspective is called the "persona"— it comes from the Latin for "mask." The persona is like a mask that the storyteller puts on in order to tell the story, and like a mask, the persona directs where you look and it frames what you see. Who we are—our personal background, our personal points of view—that impacts the kind of perspectives and stories that we're drawn to, but it's not the same exact thing as the adopted persona.

For example, when I'm telling stories, many times my narrators are either androgynous, or they're more masculine, even with the personal stories that I tell with women heroes in them. For me, imagining a more masculine narrator, it frees me up from taking on more feminine gestures when I'm narrating, so you'll notice that I often take a wide stance when I'm narrating. I'm squatting and scooping and doing and moving—that's something you can't very easily do in a skirt (which is one of those markers of femininity in our culture), so I never wear skirts when I tell. This costume, what I'm wearing right now, it suits a different kind of interaction and performance, yes? So there may be dimensions of yourself that give you perspective, but that doesn't limit the persona that you can take on in telling your stories.

This idea of "persona" is where we get the icon for drama, these two masks (comedy and tragedy), these different personas that an actor can adopt. In theatre, there's the tradition of *Commedia dell'Arte*, this Italian tradition of performance in masks. They're often leather masks, the original older ones. They're leather and they're shaped on the outside into these fabulous forms, but on the inside, for the actor who wears that mask, the inside of the mask, it starts to conform to the actor's own face. The leather, it conforms, so there, in the mask, you have this imprint of the actor on the inside, and the shape of the character on the outside.

If you look at this combination of the inside and the outside of the mask, that's the storytelling persona. There's the inside (you), and the outside (the narrator who your audience encounters). Your persona is influenced by your perspective on life, and by the narrated perspective that you choose to adopt in telling the story.

We've taken a good look at your own perspective on life—at that molded inside part of the mask, at you. Now let's look at what the audience sees, that outside part of the mask, the narrator of the story.

When you tell a story (you, the inside of the mask), all of these factors of your background are going to weigh on how you tell that story—the vantage point that you take on narrating the events of that story. They all impact your own particular voice as a storyteller because, for example, if your temperament is one that finds humor in life, then many of your stories are probably going to bring out the humor of situations. The way that you narrate your stories (the way you see things fitting together—those pieces of the puzzle of life fitting together around you, like Joseph Campbell described—the way you take those pieces of events around you and piece them together)—that way that you fit those events together, that's going to be from a particular vantage point that sees the ironies around you, and that takes events that someone else might narrate as tragedy, and you narrate as slapstick comedy.

Most of the time, when we're telling a story, we think it's just us telling *the* story—that's just what happened. But the truth is, when you're telling a story—any story, from your own life, a story that's a fairy tale or from a myth—when you tell a story, you're taking events and piecing them together. The way that you piece them together (who you foreground, who you place in the background; who's the hero and who's the villain from this narrator's point of view), these are all choices in how you perceive the events and then direct the audience's attention.

222

So, in your life, events happen. All these little bits of life, they happen. And that's the material that we have to work with, in the story. You, the teller, you take those events around you and you piece them together into a story that makes sense to you—a story that fits with your vantage point on life (that fits with your perspective). You're creating something—a story.

Inside that story, and at times maybe hovering somewhere over that story, is this narrator, who's this amalgamation of you (the inside of the mask) and it's something different (the outside of the mask). You take that narrator, and you stick him down in the midst of all these unfolding events, and that story's narrator, it walks through these unfolding events as the narrator sees them. The narrator, in a sense, takes the audience by the hand and guides them through this story. The audience follows that narrator and experiences the events as the narrator experiences them—seeing through that narrator's point of view.

This narrator may sympathize with some characters in your story, and not others. The narrator may take on the point of view of one particular character in the story (may even go inside that main character's head), or another character. The narrator may know everything that you, the teller, knows—and then again, the narrator may not have all the information.

The narrator you choose may not be completely reliable. Sometimes, you tell a story, and you tell it in such a way that everyone in your audience knows what's coming in the story, but the way you narrate it, it's as if the narrator doesn't know what's coming—and it can be delightful, or terrifying, in stories. It's dramatic irony.

The narrator's perspective on events is what makes stories so interesting—it's why, when you're with a group of friends, and something happened to all three of you, usually the group may turn the story over to one particular person to tell. And that person may not be the "best" storyteller in the group, but their perspective on the events (who they know, and how intimately they know those people who are featured in the story—which gets to the level of omniscience that they can narrate with—whose minds they can see inside, and what this person could see coming that no one else could)—that perspective makes them able to create a narrated account that slips you in and out of the events in a unique and delightful way.

But you might still be saying, "But wait! My narrator is always objective! If a story isn't objective, how can it be true?" Remember: Stories are there to reveal truths, and they do so very powerfully by looking through subjective points of view. Often, stories reveal powerful truths when the narrator asks us to look inside multiple points of view, to consider multiple sides of an encounter.

Ask yourself: Can you have a truly objective story? Even if we could achieve a truly objective story, would you really want to hear it? Would you be interested? You can choose the point of view that your narrator takes on the events that you lay out before that narrator. So one of the first things you need to do when you're preparing to tell a story is to look at all the possible perspectives that you could take on this story, and choose one perspective that you'd like to follow as you guide the audience through the story. You could choose to follow the main character of the story, and jump inside that character's mind from time to time, but mostly stick with that character's perspective on events.

Whoever your narrator follows most closely, that person will become the main character of the story, even if that character was, in other versions of the same story, even if that character was a minor character, or someone you wouldn't ordinarily sympathize with.

Storyteller Milbre Burch has a wonderfully thought-provoking version of the "Snow White" story. It's told from the perspective of the "evil" stepmother, who, from this perspective, is really trying to save Snow White from her father, who the stepmother recognizes is a pedophile! So she sends Snow White off into the woods not to get rid of her, but to save her.

A few years ago, I directed a group storytelling adaptation of *Beowulf* (we performed it in Scotland). We were most interested in this issue of perspective. Grendel is a marauding beast to Beowulf, but to himself, he's just taking care of his home. Beowulf, who the epic makes out to be the hero, he has monstrous flaws in himself as well—his pride, and his arrogance.

So, using masks, two storytellers took on the perspectives of Grendel and Beowulf, but they switched off those perspectives to one another throughout the performance—the person playing Grendel handed the Grendel mask off to the person playing Beowulf, and they went on telling the story. By having the storytellers switch perspectives, it tied those two characters together. The audience started to see the monster inside the hero, and the hero inside of the monster.

Schoolteachers do this in classroom exercises. You stage the Lincoln-Douglas debate with your students, and then you ask them to switch roles and debate the other side, with the educational benefit of really learning the perspective of those historical figures by dipping into their perspectives, and having to tell their story from their own perspective in a debate-style scenario, so you're really motivated to convince your audience that this story is worth believing.

Kids really remember that kind of teaching exercise years later (I do), because it gets them into the story (inside the historical figure's perspective), and in doing so it gets the story into them (they learn the material in a memorable way).

In a corporate setting, you may be in a situation where there's a divide between upper management and employees—where there's tension. If you can set aside a little time to sit down with them (if you're a small outfit, you meet in a small group, or in a larger company, by having project managers meet with their teams). And you listen to each others' stories—just stories, about how life at the company affects each other, stories from your life, and of their lives outside of work.

Then, still in small groups, ask an employee to tell the story of someone in upper management back to the group, and members of upper management tell the story of an employee (not as a generic group—the story of the employees—but the story of one person who you spoke with that day. One employee's story), and you tell that story to the group. This can be remarkably healing, because people on both sides watch and witness that other person, they not only heard them, but they listened to them, to the point of knowing their story, knowing it well enough to tell to someone else. They see their own story (and their frustration, and their anxieties), they see all of that getting out there into the wider discourse of management, and it sets a foundation for meaningful cooperation in the future.

I'd like to encourage you to try on some of these strategies for playing with perspective with your own stories. Let's reach back to where we began this lecture. I'd like for you to think about a couple of things.

What are some aspects of yourself that define your perspective on the world? We talked about several aspects: age; gender; where you're from; your family and your cultural background; race; also your temperament, and your economic situation. Choose just one of these aspects—how does that one aspect affect what sorts of stories you want to tell? What are some stories that seem to flow naturally from your own perspective? Think of something memorable that's happened to you—how does your perspective shape how you tell that story?

I want to challenge you to consider telling stories from a different perspective. For example, if you're a woman, consider telling a story that's told by a male character. If you're comparatively more wealthy, consider a story that's told from the perspective of someone who struggles. If you're relatively healthy, consider a story from the perspective of someone who has a disability. If you're quick-tempered, consider narrating the story of someone who is patient.

All of these changes in perspective make for stories that are interesting to share with your audience, and they can be very enlightening for yourself as well. These changes in perspective might mean that you need to talk with someone who has that perspective on the world—you're not just imagining what it's like to be disabled; you're asking a disabled person what it's like for them. You're not just imaging what it's like to have your spouse's perspective on an event; you're asking them what it *is* like for them.

Because what you *imagine* about that other perspective might be very different from what it's really like. What you *imagine* life is like for your employees may be very different from their actual experience. It's an intellectual and emotional challenge to change perspectives like this.

Once you've thought about your own perspective, and you decide on the perspective that you want your narrator to take, then you can start to use that narrator to guide the audience through the story. The narrator manipulates time, jumps us into the future or the past, and can make the audience feel like they're right there in the moment of events. We'll talk about how your narrator does this, in our next lecture.

The Artful Manipulation of Time and Focus
Lecture 12

The narrator is the audience's guide through a story. Once you've chosen the perspective from which you want to view a story, you can start to play with how your narrator guides the audience through the actions. For instance, the narrator may lengthen moments by expanding descriptions or speed up time by condensing or summarizing events. The narrator has the power to cede control of the story over to one character or another. He or she can direct the audience's attention to a single object or to a vast scene. These are some of the practical implications that grow out of the understanding of storytelling as an art, not an exercise in relating facts.

Degrees of Control

- You choose how much control your narrator has over a story. You can narrate your story in such a way—in conjunction with visualization—that your listeners have the sense that the narrator is creating the story before them. The narrator is in control of everything that happens and knows what's going to happen before it comes to life.

- This is different from a teller who narrates the scene as it unfolds; this second kind of narrator has less control over the events. We can see the difference in two versions of the same line from a story, one in which the narrator is fully in control of what's being painted in the scene and one in which the narrator has been plunked down in the scene and narrates what is happening in the moment.

- The difference is subtle, but each gives a different effect for the audience. You don't have to choose to tell a story using one or the other of these levels of control the entire time; you can give your narrator more control over events at some times and less control at others.

- We see an example in an excerpt from a story called "Sanntraigh." Here, the story starts with the narrator in control of the scene, looking out to the audience in epic mode (making direct eye contact). But the narrator quickly moves to take on the perspective of the woman in the story and becomes more uncertain about what's going to happen. The more the narrator gets inside the head of the woman, the less control she has over events.

- This loss of control is a great way to add suspense and interest to a story. And you can give that effect most successfully when you let yourself live inside the scene.

Manipulating Time

- Usually, a narrator has more control over scenes that are sped up; he or she may zoom the audience from one moment to another that takes place years later. This kind of narration is called "summary."

- Again, in the "Sanntraigh" story, we see an example of the narrator using summary to zoom through several weeks of time and transport the audience from one scene to the next. Note that the physical scene doesn't change, but the mood has changed, as have the relationships between the characters.
  - The first scene was tense; the characters stood at a distance from each other. In the next scene (after several days have passed), the narrator seems more at ease in describing the woman and the arrival of the fairy. The woman is still cautious, but she's no longer afraid of the fairy.

  - When the woman tells her husband "Say to the fairy as I have said," she's in control. There are also moments where the narrator is more in control; for example, in the narration of the woman going down to the dock and leaving for the mainland, there is little or no visualization.

- "Summary" is one of three ways that the narrator can manipulate time; it shortens the "story time" (the time it takes to tell that part of a story) in comparison to "actual time" (the time that would have actually passed in the story).

- The narrator also has the power to slow things down—to make us focus on a specific event or object. In other words, the narrator can freeze the actions going on in order to guide the audience to a new understanding. This is called "description," and here, story time is greater than actual time.
  - In the "Sanntraigh" story, we see description at work when our focus is drawn to the kettle.

  - The actual action of the story might take only four or five seconds, but the thoughts of the woman about the fairy and her kettle could be narrated for a half a minute or more!

- Most of the time in the "Sanntraigh" story, the narrator is moving at the same pace as the actual time it would take for the events to happen. This is called "scene time"—when story time is approximately equal to actual time.
  - The narrator can use scene descriptions in conjunction with visualization to guide the audience through a place that he or she is discovering right along with the characters.

  - For example, the time it takes for the narrator to lock the door against the fairy is about the same amount of time it would take to perform that action.

  - Scene time also takes place when characters are in dialogue, as we see in the exchange between the woman and her husband.

- A narrator can also manipulate time in order to give a comedic effect or to increase the energy or pacing of part of a story in dialogue.
  - In the dialogue between the husband and wife in the "Sanntraigh" story, notice that the narrator says "he said" and "she said" at the start of the dialogue, but as the pace of the conversation increases, the narrator's voice fades away, leaving just the two people talking.

o   Once you've established two characters are in dialogue and you've made a distinction between those characters (in attitude, through voice, or in other ways), your audience no longer needs the narrator.

Conveying Tense

- Most of the time, when you tell a story, you're talking about things that have already happened, and often, you use the past tense to talk about those events. But sometimes, you may bring those past events into the present by using the present tense, or you may tell stories about things you want to happen in the future: "When I go to Venice, I will take a gondola ride."

- All these tenses are appropriate for storytelling, but you'll want to decide which tense is most effective in telling your story. The one tense you should try to avoid is the present progressive: "He is traveling to the zoo, and he is seeing a herd of elephants." This tense tends to distance your audience from the action, giving the subconscious impression that your characters are acting rather than really doing the things you're talking about.

- In another excerpt from the "Sanntraigh" story, notice that even though the narration is in the past tense, you get the sense that things are happening in the present moment. You can make the "there and then" feel like the "here and now" by the commitment you have to discovering and reacting to the events you visualize going on around you. Remember: Your characters don't know what's going to happen!

- This is one of the keys to engaging storytelling: Your narrator has to care about what's happening. If your narrator cares about the characters, your audience will care; if the narrator doesn't care what's happening—or won't be affected by what's happening—then the audience won't care.

The Sanntraigh Story

There once was a woman who lived on the island of Sanntraigh, and that woman had a kettle. That kettle, it hung on a hook over the hearth by the fire.

One day, that woman, she was working in her kitchen, and she heard the door open behind her. She heard it open, and she wasn't expecting anyone, so she turned around to look, and there, standing in her doorway, was a woman of peace, a fairy. That fairy was silent. She glided through that room, and she went straight for that kettle, and she took out milky white fingers and she wrapped those fingers around the handle of that kettle, and the woman, she froze. Because here was a fairy, creeping out of her fairy knoll and coming down her fairy path and coming into her house through the town, disguised as she was, and through her door and through her kitchen and coming for her kettle.

As frightened as that woman was, she knew that was the only kettle the family had. They needed that kettle, so as that fairy, she laid those milky white fingers around the handle of that kettle, that woman, she plucked up her courage and she said some certain magic words. She said, "The due of the kettle is bones and to bring it safely home."

And that fairy, she turned and she nodded to the woman, and she picked up that kettle as if it were light as air and glided through that room, shut the door. The woman, well she worked all that day, and she thought about that kettle and she thought even more about that fairy. Soon enough, the evening came and she heard that door open. She turned and she saw, there was the fairy, and there was that kettle. It was heaped high full of flesh and bones and things that that woman thought would be delicious to put in a stew for that night. That fairy, she took that kettle light as air and glided over and hung up on that hook where it belonged, nodded to the woman, and went out the door.

- One of the ways to make the past tense feel present to you, the storyteller, is to allow yourself to commit to what you're saying as if it's the most important thing in the world right then.
  - In other words, you have to be present with the story in order for the story to feel present to your audience.

  - That doesn't mean overacting. It means you have to commit your attention and energy to seeing those events and caring about what happens to the people who are in the midst of them.

Guiding the Audience
- In making all of these choices—the degree of control your narrator has, how time is manipulated, and so on—you are guiding your audience's attention through the story. Your relationship with the audience is what sets storytelling apart from all other forms of communication or entertainment.

- You may, for example, sense that a particular audience needs to hear the story told in a certain way—to hear more about a particular aspect of the events or to pay attention to one feature of a character.

- Pick out a story that you like to tell and choose one feature of that story that is important—any feature that is worthy of drawing the attention of your audience. Then try to connect that feature to a specific physical part of the scene. For example, if the feature is something a character said, what did that character's face look like when he or she spoke?

- o Use summary to get your audience up to speed with the context of that feature in about 10 seconds. Now zoom in on the feature and take about 30 seconds to describe it in detail.

- o Here, you're making the same kind of artistic decision that film makers do when they zoom in on a specific feature of a scene. You can have the same effect and connection with your audience as zooming in for a close-up does by the way you manipulate time and use specific descriptions.

Suggested Reading

Lipman, Doug. *Improving Your Storytelling.*

Questions to Consider

1. Your narrator artfully controls where the audience looks and how the audience attends to certain features of your story. Identify one feature of a story that would be appropriate for the use of description to slow time down.

2. How might your preparation with visualization help you adapt in the moment if you sense that your audience needs more description or if you unexpectedly find that you have to summarize events to move quickly to another part of your story?

3. Choose a two-page selection from your favorite novel. Label all the passages on those two pages as scene, summary, or description. How does this author manipulate time and with what effects? How can you apply these ideas to your storytelling?

The Artful Manipulation of Time and Focus
Lecture 12—Transcript

Professor Harvey: The narrator is the audience's guide through the story; the audience follows the narrator. So once you've chosen the perspective you want to see this story from, you can really start to play with the way your narrator guides the audience through the actions. And there's an art to this.

For instance, the narrator plays with time—lengthening moments by expanding descriptions, or speeding up time by condensing and summarizing events. The narrator has the power to cede control of the story over to one character or another character. He can direct the audience's attention to a single object, or to a vast scene. These are some of the practical implications of understanding that storytelling isn't just a "just-the-facts-ma'am" enterprise; it's an art, and there's a craft to it.

Let's look at some of these ways that your narrator artfully guides your audience's experience of the story. We'll start by looking at the degrees of control that your narrator has over the events in the story, and then we'll look at how the narrator manipulates time, and how your narrator can use different tenses (past tense, present tense, future tense) to make the audience feel like they're in the present moment with the actions of the story. We'll look at one story in detail today, and from this slowed-down, detailed look at one story, we'll pull out some of the features and functions of narration that you can use in any story to connect better with your audience.

To start with, your narrator will have control over the story, but in degrees. You choose how much control your narrator has over the story. Here's what I mean by this: There's a way that you can narrate the story, in conjunction with visualization, where your audience has the sense that the narrator is creating this story before them (the narrator is in control of everything that happens, and knows what's going to happen before it comes to life in the world that you and the audience are visualizing).

This is different from a narrator who sees the scene in front of him, and then narrates this world of events that's happening around him—this second kind of narrator has less control over the events. Let's look at some examples of what this looks like—I'm going to tell the same part of a story twice. Here's the story phrase: "The old woman picked up her shawl, and said not a word, but headed out the door." The first time I tell it, I'm going to have the narrator fully in control of what's being painted in the scene around him, and to give this effect, I'm going say what's going on in the scene before I see what's going on. That's the first time I say it.

The second time I say it, it's reversed—the narrator has been plunked down in this scene, and he sees what's going on and then narrates what he sees happening in the moment.

"The old woman picked up her shawl, and said not a word, but headed out the door."

"The old woman picked up her shawl, and said not a word, but headed out the door."

So, it's subtle, but each of these gives a different effect for your audience. And, you don't have to choose to tell a story using one or the other of these degrees of control the entire time—you can give your narrator more control over some events at some times, and less control at others.

Let me give you an example of what this looks like. Here's the beginning of a story called "Sanntraigh." The primary source for this is a collection by Sir George Douglass but, as we discussed in the "Finding Stories" lecture, there are several other sources that contributed to this version of the story I tell.

In this story, I start with the narrator in control of the scene—the narrator looks out to the audience in epic mode (making direct eye contact), but the narrator quickly moves to take on the woman's perspective and we start to see things through her eyes, in her kitchen, washing dishes. The narrator loses a little bit of control over the events as she jumps inside this woman's perspective, and you can see that the narrator is more uncertain about what's going to happen. And then the narrator, seeing through the eyes of this woman's perspective, the narrator totally loses control of what's about to happen when someone comes through the door, so take a look, and see if you can discern the moments when the narrator loses control degree by degree.

[Video start.]

Professor Harvey: This fairy tale, it comes from Scotland, it comes from the northernmost part of Scotland, just off of that northern coast, on the island of Sanntraigh. There once was a woman who lived on the island of Sanntraigh, and that woman [grunt] had a kettle. That kettle, it hung on a hook over the hearth by the fire.

One day, that woman, she was working in her kitchen and she heard the door open behind her [squeak]. She heard it open and she wasn't expecting anyone so she turned around to look and there, standing in her doorway, was a woman of peace, a fairy. That fairy was silent. She glided through that room and she went straight for that kettle and she took out milky white fingers and she wrapped those fingers around the handle of that kettle and the woman, she froze. Because here was a fairy, creeping out of her fairy knoll and coming down her fairy path and coming into her house through the town disguised as she was and through her door and through her kitchen and coming for her kettle.

As frightened as that woman was, she knew that was the only kettle that family had. They needed that kettle, so as that fairy, she laid those milky-white fingers around the handle of that kettle, that woman, she plucked up her courage and she said some certain magic words. She said, "The due of a kettle is bones, and to bring it safely home." Can you say that part with me? I'll say it, and then you can say it.

Professor Harvey: The due of a kettle is bones.

Audience: The due of the kettle is bones.

Professor Harvey: And to bring it safely home.

Audience: And to bring it safely home.

Professor Harvey: So she said those words, say them with me.

237

All: The due of the kettle is bones, and to bring it safely home.

Professor Harvey: That fairy, she turned and she nodded to the woman, and she picked up that kettle as if it were light as air and glided through that room, [squeak], shut the door. The woman, well she worked all that day, and she thought about that kettle and she thought even more about that fairy. Soon enough, the evening came and she heard that door open: [squeak]. She turned and she saw, there was the fairy, and there was that kettle. It was heaped high full of flesh and bones and things that that woman thought would be delicious to put in a stew for that night. That fairy, she took that kettle light as air and glided over and hung it up on that hook where it belonged, nodded to the woman, and went out the door. [Squeak.]

[Video end.]

Professor Harvey: So we're breaking this story apart to look at what the narrator does and how the narrator does it—later, we'll look even further into characterization—but you can see the narrator shifts perspectives inside the head and eyes of that woman. The more the narrator gets inside her head, the less control the narrator has over the events and the more that narrator sees the things unfolding in the moment, just like the woman does, and with as little control over knowing what's next as you and I do in our everyday lives.

There's something delightful in a story when the narrator gives in to that scene, and doesn't really know what's going to happen next—even though, I know, you're telling a story, and of course you know how it's going to end—you're telling me the story, and you know what happens next. But when the narrator steps inside that scene, and either sympathizes with one character to the point where it's as if the narrator is standing right there beside that woman wondering what's going to happen next, or the narrator actually is inside her head looking at that fairy coming through the door.

In either case, it's such a great way to add suspense and interest to your story, when you don't know what's going to happen next. You can give that effect most successfully when you let yourself live inside that scene.

There's something else that I want for you to notice about what the narrator is doing here, and it has to do with how the narrator manipulates time. Usually, your narrator will have more control over scenes that are sped up—when you're passing through years of time, the narrator zooms us from one moment and another moment, we're years later. That transition narrative usually has the narrator in control of what's happening, because you're literally taking the driver's seat; you're taking the audience from this time and driving (speeding!) into that next other time. This kind of narration is called "summary"—when a narrator *summarizes* events that have happened into what's vital to the through-line of the story.

Let's pick up where we left off with the "Sanntraigh" story and see an example of this, when the narrator uses summary to zoom through several weeks of time and transport the audience from one scene to the next.

[Video start.]

> **Professor Harvey:** The woman thought she was in a good place because here was the fairy bringing her kettle and some food for her for dinner. And the next morning, it was the same thing. And the next morning, and the next, and the woman thought, "Well, this is pretty good." This went on for several weeks until one morning, the woman found that she had some business to do on the mainland. She got up early that morning and she told her husband; she said, "If you will say to the fairy as I have said, then I will go and do my business Castletown"—in [Scottish location], what's now known as Castletown—"if you will say to the fairy as I have said, I will go there."
>
> "Oh, I will say it, you just go on, I will say it." Assured, she was off. She grabbed her shawl, headed out the door, down to catch the ferry boat to the mainland. That man, he stayed in that house and he was spinning heather, that woody kind of flower that they have in Scotland, he was spinning heather into a rope to be cast over the house.

[Video end.]

Professor Harvey: Notice in that clip that the physical scene didn't change—they're still in that little hut and, they're still in that woman's kitchen. But the mood of that room has changed, and the relationship between the characters has changed.

In the first scene, things were tense—the characters stood at a distance from one another, that woman and the fairy. In the next scene (after several days had passed), as the narrator describes the woman, he's more at ease. So the fairy's coming in the door, that's normal, and the woman, she's still a little cautious but she's not really afraid anymore of the fairy. She feels more at home again in her own home.

Then, when she tells the husband to "say to the fairy as I have said," later in the story she's in control—and you see the narrator moving into these moments where the narrator is more in control of things—you hear the narration about the woman going down to the dock and leaving for the mainland, and there's little to no visualization with that summary.

We jump through time using summary—"The next day it was the same, and the next, and the next," and then we finally land in the next scene with the words, "until one day, when the woman found that she had business to do" on the mainland.

Summary is one of the three ways that the narrator can manipulate time, and as we said, summary speeds up the actual time that it would take for those events to happen. So if we look at the time that it takes to tell that part of the story (what we'll call "story time") and the actual time that it would have taken for those weeks to pass (what we call "actual time"), the summary makes the story time less than the actual time.

But the narrator also has the power to slow things down—to make us focus on a specific event or thing that, if we were looking at that object in real time, it would take us just a second to glance at it ("Oh, that's my ring"). But the narrator can freeze the actions that are going on, and draw that audience's attention to that one object, and to see it in detail, and to guide the audience into some new understanding about that thing.

This is called "description," when a narrator describes something that's going on, and the narrator slows time down so that the actual time that it would take to see what's going on is less than the time the story takes to narrate about it—so story time is greater than actual time.

This happened in the scene that you saw at the beginning—when the woman describes her kettle—if you recall, the fairy is gliding across that room, and the narrator goes inside that woman's head and describes what that kettle meant to the woman. "That was the only kettle that woman had, and she needed that kettle!" Let's look at that brief part again.

[Video start.]

> **Professor Harvey:** Standing in her doorway, was a woman of peace, a fairy. That fairy was silent. She glided through that room and she went straight for that kettle and she took out milky white fingers and she wrapped those fingers around the handle of that kettle and the woman, she froze. Because here was a fairy, creeping out of her fairy knoll and coming down her fairy path and coming into her house through the town disguised as she was and through her door and through her kitchen and coming for her kettle.

> As frightened as that woman was, she knew that was the only kettle that family had. They needed that kettle, so as that fairy, she laid those milky white fingers around the handle of that kettle, that woman, she plucked up her courage and she said some certain magic words.

[Video end.]

Professor Harvey: So the fairy enters that home and floats over to the kettle and wraps her fingers around the handle of that kettle, so, if I were to float across the room, [Professor Harvey walks], I float across the room and then I grab my fingers around—that only takes about four seconds in reality, maybe less.

But for that woman, time just froze, and she thinks about all these things: where the fairy lived, where she came from, and how she got into her house—and then she thinks about her kettle, and how much she needs that kettle, and then she plucks up her courage. All of that takes a while to describe—that part of the story, it lasts about 40 seconds!

Descriptions are when your narrator expands time—the story time (the time it takes to tell the story) takes longer than the actual time—so 40 seconds of description, which takes longer than the four seconds that it would actually take for that fairy to glide across the room. The narrator stretches out time in this description.

Most of the time in this story, though, the narrator is plugging right along at the same pace as the actual time that it would take for the events to happen—even though what he's describing, he's describing what's happening, he's describing them at the same pace that it would take those events to happen, and with visualization he's seeing the events as he's describing them. (And, remember from the last lecture on perspective—I call my narrator "he" because many times, my narrators are more masculine.)

This is called "scene time," when your descriptions in the story take approximately the same amount of time as it would for those events to actually happen, so story time is equal to actual time.

In this next part of the story, listen for how the narrator uses "scene" narration in conjunction with visualization to guide the audience through a place that the narrator is discovering right along with the characters.

[Video start.]

> **Professor Harvey:** This went on for several weeks until one morning, the woman found that she had some business to do on the mainland. She got up early that morning and she told her husband; she said, "If you will say to the fairy as I have said, then I will go and do my business Castletown"—in [Scottish location], what's now known as Castletown—"if you will say to the fairy as I have said, I will go there."

"Oh, I will say it, you just go on, I will say it." Assured, she was off. She grabbed her shawl, headed out the door, down to catch the ferry boat to the mainland. That man, he stayed in that house and he was spinning heather, that woody kind of flower that they have in Scotland, he was spinning heather into a rope to be cast over the house.

That man, he stayed in that house and he was spinning heather, that woody kind of flower that they have in Scotland, he was spinning heather into a rope to be cast over the house. He sat and he spun and he spun and he sat and after awhile he looked out the window, and he saw a woman coming towards the house. That woman, she had a shadow coming from her feet and he knew that that was the fairy.

He got scared. That fairy, that rope, it started to fall to pieces in his hands and he went over to that door and he [clap] locked it. He went back and sat down. He could sense that fairy coming over to the door. He waited. He could sense that that fairy had gone, so he crept over to that door. There was a kind of crack in that door. He peaked his eye through. There was no one there. And then he happened to look up, and what do you think he saw?

Audience: The fairy.

Professor Harvey: Two green eyes staring down at him. In that wall that came up, there was a hole in that wall where the wall connected with the ridge of the roof and that fairy was staring down at him. That man, he looked up and right then, he heard this noise behind him: Clink. Clink. He turned around and he saw that kettle, it was hopping up and down. On the third clink, it flew up into the air and he saw milky white fingers coming through that hole, those fingers, they wrapped around the handle of that kettle and [wsssht], they pulled that kettle out of the hole in the ceiling.

He went back to his spinning, and he sat there all day. The night came, and the kettle came not. That evening, way after sundown, that woman, she came back in, she [squeak] she opened the door, she was so tired. She set down her shawl; she looked all around, and she said, "Well where is my kettle?"

"To the devil with that kettle, I don't care where it's gone to. That fairy, she came for it. I did not open the door for her. And then she came in through a hole in the roof and took it away, and she did not come back."

"What have you done?"

"She'll come tomorrow with it."

"She will not come!"

[Video end.]

Professor Harvey: So in this part of the story, the man has this encounter with the fairy, and he watches the fairy coming to the door, and he goes over to the door and he locks it—and it takes about as much time to go over and lock a door as it does for me to give that narration about what I'm doing. I actually show you what I'm doing it as I tell you about it—it's one of those features of storytelling that distinguishes it from acting. If I were acting, I would just go and [clap] lock the door; I'd just show you. Storytellers show and tell you about what's happening.

The time it takes me to tell you about [clap] locking the door, is about the same amount of time it would take for me to [clap] actually do that—that's scene time in storytelling, when the story time is approximately the same as actual time. When the man and the fairy look at each other, that kettle, it hops up and down, that's all scene time as well.

Then we have some summary—"The night came, the kettle came not"—we skip over all this time until it's the evening, and the woman comes home, and then we jump into dialogue between those two characters. And we're back into scene time when the characters are in dialogue:

"Ah, she'll come tomorrow with it."

"She will not come!" So they're in dialogue. Dialogue is also scene time.

Scene is one of these three ways that your narrator can manipulate time—summary speeds time up; description slows time down. There's another way that your narrator can manipulate time in order to give a comedic effect or to increase the energy or pacing of part of a story, and it has to do with the moments when the characters in your story talk with one another.

You just saw an example of that in this clip, when the woman and man are talking with each other. The narrator begins by setting up the woman coming home, and there are a few "he saids" and "she saids." But then as the pace of their conversation increases, the narrator's voice fades away and it's just the two of them talking. Taking your narrator *out* of the conversation, taking out the "he saids" and "she saids," it can be a nice way of playing with the pacing and to increase the energy of your story.

We'll talk about characters and dialogue in the next lecture in detail, but here I want for you to take note that you don't always have to say the "he said" and the "she said" as the narrator. Once you've established that two characters are in dialogue with one another, and you've set those characters as distinct from each other (distinct in attitude, or in voice, or in other ways), then your audience doesn't need the narrator to butt in throughout the conversation. It's useful to think about what your narrator does, and what your narrator doesn't. When the narrator needs to enter into the conversation or comment on the events, and when the narrator can just fade away.

You'll also notice that I've been narrating this story in the past tense, even though I'm using scene narration that is supposed to mimic actual time in the here-and-now. Let's talk about the tenses that you use when you narrate, and the way that you convey those tenses with your speaking voice.

Most of the time, when we tell a story, we're talking about things that have already happened to us. Often we use the past tense to talk about these events ("He went here, she did that"), and sometimes we'll even bring those past events into the present by using the present tense. Sometimes, we even tell stories about what we want to happen in the future: "When I go to Venice, I will take a gondola ride through the town—it will be so romantic!"

Sometimes you follow up these stories later with past-tense versions of the story from a different perspective: "I went to Venice, and I went on a gondola ride, and what they don't tell you in the tour books is how sticky and dirty that water is, and how it sprays up on you when you go on a gondola ride!"

Present, past, and future tenses; these can all work well with storytelling. Most often, you'll use the past tense to describe events, but I'd like to call your attention to something in the next clip. Pay attention to how even though I'm narrating in the past tense, you get the sense that things are happening to the characters right now, that you're there with them in a "present" moment with them. See if you can get that sense of the way I'm using the past tense and what I'm doing with my voice to convey a "present" feeling for the audience.

[Video start.]

> **Professor Harvey:** She went out through the town, way out, long out into the fields, away from the town until she could see that fairy path, that green grass growing much greener than any of the other grass around it. (She was careful not to step on the path—they don't like it when you step on their path.) She walked beside it, and she walked and she followed it until she saw that fairy knoll.
>
> It was way late, what they call the "mouth of the night." She walked over, and that knoll, it was open, so she walked inside. She looked up to the right and to the left. She didn't see anyone. But she saw her kettle, and it was heaped high full of flesh and bones and good things that she thought would be good to eat, so she crept over to it and picked that kettle up. So heavy with all of that inside, but she backed away, she turned around, and she almost got out of that knoll when she heard a voice behind her.
>
> She looked up to the right and to the left. She didn't see anyone. But she saw her kettle, and it was heaped high full of flesh and bones and good things that she thought would be good to eat, so she crept over to it and picked that kettle up. So heavy with all of that inside,

but she backed away, she turned around, and she almost got out of that knoll when she heard a voice behind her.

It said, "Silent wife. Silent wife, who came on us from the Land of Chase. Now man on the surface of the brogue. Loose the black and slip the fears." And she heard the clink of the chain behind her and two dogs barking in the distance.

[Video end.]

Professor Harvey: When we get to this part of the story, the narrator is so invested in the story, and so invested in that woman's perspective, that the narrator makes the audience here-and-now feel like they're there with the woman back then in that fairy knoll, wondering what's going to happen next.

Your narrator can make the "then-and-there" feel like the "here-and-now" by the commitment your narrator has to discovering and reacting to those events that you visualize going on around you. Remember, your characters don't know what's going to happen!

This is one of the keys to really engaging storytelling—your narrator has to care about what's happening. If your narrator cares about the characters, your audience will care; if the narrator doesn't care about what's happening—or won't be affected by what's happening—then the audience probably won't care.

One of the ways to make the past tense feel present to you, the storyteller, is to allow yourself to fully commit to what you're saying as if it's the most important thing in the world to you right then. In other words, *you* have to be present with the story in order for that story to feel present for your audience. That doesn't mean over-acting. It means that you have to commit your attention and commit your energy into really seeing those events and caring about what happens to the people who are there (now) in the midst of those events going on.

Now in all of these choices (how much control your narrator has, how he manipulates time through various descriptions, making the past feel present for your audience), in all of this, you are guiding your audience's attention through the story. Your relationship with the audience is what sets apart storytelling from all other mediums of communication and all other mediums of entertainment. So you may sense that your audience needs to hear the story told in a certain way—to hear more about a particular aspect of events, or to pay attention to a feature of one character. Let's play with this for a second with one of your stories.

Pick out a story that you like to tell, and choose one feature of that story that is important—it could be the red dress that your mother wore to a dance, or the pivotal moment in a battle that you were in, or the way the toilet paper stuck to your friend's shoe as he walked across the boardroom and gave a big presentation—any feature of your story that's worth drawing your audience closer to! Choose that feature. Try to connect to a specific physical part of the scene. If the feature is something someone said, well what did their face look like, what did that look like when they said that?

I'd like for you to look at that scene around you. Use summary to get your audience up to speed with the context of what the feature is; that should take about 10 seconds. Now, once you've gotten the audience up to speed, zoom in on that feature of the story and take about 30 seconds to describe that feature in detail. What you're doing is the same artistic choice that filmographers make when they zoom in on a particular feature of a scene. For example, when you're telling a story through film, the camera directs your audience's attention. So right now, while I'm talking about how to tell a story, the camera could zoom in not on my whole body, but on my hands, and how I use my hands to tell the story.

It's reminiscent of that first story at the opening lecture, the story "Hands"—I used the same technique to make you focus in on my grandfather's hands, describing them in detail, and slowing time down to make you pay attention to that one feature of a person's body.

It's a lovely part of the art of storytelling and that technique of storytelling, and you can have that same effect and connection with your audience by the way that you manipulate time to slow down and use descriptions of very specific things, very specific things.

In this lecture, we've looked at how the narrator guides the audience through the scenes of your story, drawing your audience's attention to certain things using scene, and summary, and description, and making the past tense feel like the present, here-and-now, for your audience.

You also may have noticed that, at different points, the narrator has ceded control of the story over to the woman's perspective—we see things through her eyes mainly, and experience things with her reactions. We hear what she thinks as the narrator describes in the third person, but it's said with the intensity of a first-person account.

We'll talk about the narrator's connection with the characters and begin to talk about what it means to bring a character to life in your stories; we'll talk about that in the next lecture. We'll continue to look at these examples of how you can use "film editing" with your narrator, and you also might just get to hear the ending of that "Sanntraigh" story. See you then.

Narrator—Bridging Characters and Audience
Lecture 13

In any story, the narrator performs the job of shifting focus between the audience and the world of the story. In this lecture, we'll talk about the narrator's relationship with the characters, specifically, how the narrator can cede control of the story over to certain characters at different points in the story. We'll then start to discuss elements of characterization as they relate to how the characters interact with the narrator, the audience, and with one another.

Epic Mode

- As the narrator of a story, you will shift your focus from inside the world of the story, using "closed focus" (visualizing the scene, seeing the characters), to looking the audience directly in the eye— "open focus." The term that describes this shift between open and closed focus is "epic mode."

- Aristotle used the term "epic" in reference to narrative that is "not tied to time" versus tragedies, which he saw as time-specific. As the narrator speaking to an audience in epic mode, you're stepping outside the time of the story to jump into the present time with your audience. This movement brings the audience in the "here and now" into the scene happening "there and then" but also "now" in the present moment of the story.

- When you're telling a story about yourself, you may be one of the characters in the story, but that doesn't mean that you talk about yourself in the third person. The "you" in the story is in the "there and then"; this character isn't the same as the person telling the story. Unlike the "you" character in the story, your narrator has the power to stand outside of story time and to manipulate time.

Closed Focus and Visualization

- Let's play around with a story in closed focus. Pick one of your stories that has at least two characters and then choose one of those characters to focus on. What is your narrator's relationship with that character? Does the narrator like the character?

- If the character is you, your narrator may be thinking back on you when you were at a different point in life. What do you now think of the person you were? Do you like the old you? Do you laugh now at how this version of you handled the situation that your narrator sees the old you encountering?

- Think physically, in three dimensions: How tall is this character in comparison with the narrator? If the character is taller, you'll have to look up. The narrator has a relationship with the characters, and you can use visualization to show that relationship.

- Using visualization, try to see the character you have chosen in front of you. Out loud, describe what that person is wearing and his or her height. Assign a specific focal point for the character's eyes.

- Imagine that your character stays in the same place in the scene in front of you, but shift your focus from looking at the character in the eye to looking at your audience in the eye. Then shift back to the character and back to the audience once again.

- While looking at the character, pick out one striking feature that your audience should know. Maybe the character doesn't have much common sense or is wiser than he or she realizes. Or maybe your character is wearing something ridiculous! Shift your focus back to your listeners and tell them about that feature—while maintaining awareness that the character is still right in front of you.

- This technique gives your audience a compelling access point to your characters. It's not only a real world of actions and places, but it's a world of people with whom the narrator—and, by extension, the audience—can have a relationship.

The Sanntraigh Story

That woman, she picked up her shawl from where she had just laid it down and she was off, out the door. She went out through the town, way out, long out into the fields, away from the town, until she could see that fairy path, that green grass growing much greener than any of the other grass around it. (She was careful not to step on the path—they don't like it when you step on their path.) She walked beside it … and she followed it until she saw that fairy knoll.

It was way late, what they call the mouth of the night. She walked over, and that knoll, it was open, so she walked inside. She looked up and to the left. She didn't see anyone, but she saw her kettle. It was heaped high full of flesh and bones and good things that she thought would be good to eat, so she crept over to it and picked that kettle up. So heavy with all of that inside, but she backed away, she turned around, and she almost got out of that knoll, when she

heard a voice behind her ... and she heard the clink of the chain behind her and two dogs barking in the distance. Well, she didn't stick around; she didn't look around to see what was behind her and she didn't drop that kettle. She just started running: a-huff and a-huff and a-huff and a-huff and a-huff.

She didn't drop that kettle because she thought, well, if I get away with the kettle, so much the better. And if she didn't get away with it—if those dogs caught up with her—well, then, she could just reach in and throw some of that meat back and stop those dogs. And that was just what happened....

Those dogs, they caught up with that food, and they started digging into that meat and those bones. The woman kept running: a-huff and a-huff and a-huff. She could hear them again, so she reached in and grabbed a second handful, and she threw it back. [And that way], she got all the way to her gate. When she got to the gate, she took that entire kettle and she threw it out. All of it fell down onto the ground, and she ran inside her house and shut the door!

That was just in time because those dogs, they caught up with that gate, and they grabbed onto that meat and those bones, and they howled. They woke up all the rest of the dogs in the town and they howled long into the night.

From that day onwards, those fairy dogs never bothered that woman. From that day onwards, that fairy never came for that kettle. There's an old Gaelic proverb that goes: "Dlighidh coire cnáimh," or "Deserves cauldron bone." Where I'm from in Appalachia, there's a similar phrase: "A pot is entitled to a bone."

What that phrase means is that if you ever borrow anything, like a casserole dish or anything from a friend, you should always return that thing not only unharmed, but with a little present, as a way of saying thanks to the person who loaned it to you.

- The rapid switching of perspectives between the woman and the dogs is a technique known as a "crosscut" in film.

- How you use these techniques in storytelling will be unique to your own style and voice, and the more you play with these techniques, the more naturally they will come to you in the moment of telling an impromptu story.

- No two storytellers have the same style, and there's no right or wrong way to tell a story, but the more specific you can make your choices in visualization, focal points, and character perspectives and relationships, the more effectively you'll communicate your meanings to your listeners and the more fully your listeners will see your story unfold around them.

Dramatic Mode
- In an excerpt from a Japanese folktale told by Motoko Dworkin, notice how the teller switches back and forth between characters. As the pace of the story picks up, the outside narrator starts to fade away, and the characters carry the story. Motoko uses the tool of focus in a particular way to give the effect of distinct characters.

- In Motoko's story, when Tio and her mother-in-law are speaking to each other, the older woman looks up to the younger, and the younger woman looks down on the older one. Although Motoko is in closed focus (not looking at the audience) during these moments of character dialogue, she remains in "open posture," meaning that she's facing her body out to the audience the whole time.

- From this outward-facing position, the two characters speak to each other, but the teller fixes the focal points of each one throughout the conversation—lower for the old woman and higher for the younger one. Once the narrator has set up those focal points, she doesn't need to enter the conversation; the audience understands who is speaking.

- When two characters speak to each other in this way, the storyteller is using "dramatic mode," which is different from epic mode. In epic mode, you're breaking the fourth wall, looking out and making eye contact with the audience, but in dramatic mode, two characters are speaking in dialogue, and the teller doesn't make eye contact with the audience.

- You don't need much movement when you switch characters. In fact, too much movement is distracting; it interferes with the pace of the conversation, and it tends to obscure the teller's facial expressions.

- Try using dramatic mode with one of your stories. Begin with an open posture and assign focal points to two characters, either higher and lower or to the right and left. As the first character speaks, step into his or her perspective and look at the second character's focal point. Reply from the perspective of the second character, looking at the focal point of the first. Let each character's reaction to the conversation infuse how you deliver their lines.

- In our next lecture, we'll delve even deeper into characterization. Where you look to distinguish characters is one thing, but you can have even more fun as you play with bringing characters to life through gestures, voice, and facial expressions.

Suggested Reading

Dworkin, *Tales of Now and Zen.*

————, www.motoko.folktales.net.

Lipman, *Improving Your Storytelling.*

Questions to Consider

1. Watch your favorite film yet another time, paying attention to editing effects, such as crosscuts, panning (when the camera "looks" around a

room), and special effects. How might you apply these same techniques to how your narrator tells a story?

2. Take out your favorite novel and look for passages of dialogue. Are there points when the narrator's voice evaporates—the "he said" and "she said" descriptions go away, and the dialogue is just character quotes? Reread this passage. What is the effect for you as a reader in terms of pacing? Can you imagine using focal points to distinguish these characters, using dramatic mode?

Narrator—Bridging Characters and Audience
Lecture 13—Transcript

Professor Harvey: In any story, the narrator does a big job of shifting focus between the audience and the world of the story. In this lecture, we're going to begin talking about the narrator's relationship with the characters, and specifically how that narrator can cede control of the story over to different characters at different points in the story. We'll then start to talk about elements of characterization as they relate to how the characters interact with the narrator, and how the characters relate to the audience, and how the characters relate to one another.

We mentioned in a previous lecture that as the narrator, you will shift your focus from inside the world of the story (using what we called "closed focus," visualizing that scene, and seeing the characters), from closed focus to looking the audience directly in the eye using open focus. There's a term that describes this shift in focus, between open focus (on the audience) and closed focus (on the scene of the story)—it's called "epic mode." Epic mode is when a storyteller or a performer switches focus from direct audience address (looking the audience directly in the eye, being present in the here-and-now with the audience), and then moving focus to the time and place of the scene, and visualizing that scene all around them (that scene that happened not here-and-now with the audience, but in the then-and-there in the time of the story).

You might think of the works of Bertolt Brecht and his "Epic Theatre," and that startled audiences by directly implicating them in the actions that are going on onstage. He used various techniques, including narrative and direct eye contact with the audience.

Aristotle also used the term "epic." He used it in reference to narrative that is "not tied to time." He saw this as versus tragedies which he saw as tied to a specific time—so, as the narrator to your audience, you're stepping outside of the time of the story to jump into the present time with your audience—it's an interesting move!

This movement brings the audience in the here-and-now, into the scene happening "here-and-then but also "now" in the present moment of the story, through the method of speaking the past tense as if it were ongoing in the present. And your narrator who first introduces us to those characters in the story, that's the narrator's job.

Remember, when you're telling a story about yourself, "you" may be one of the characters in your story! I don't mean you start talking about yourself in the third person, "Hannah went here, Hannah did that"—no! But the "you" in the story isn't the same person as the "you" standing here-and-now telling the story—the "you" in the story is stuck back then-and-there. And unlike "you" the character in the story (who's stuck in a particular time and place, in the past), your narrator has the power to stand outside of that time and manipulate time—the narrator can jump outside of the whole situation, or can jump into the past and live there for a while in "scene time," and then jump back into the present with the audience.

Right now, I'd like for us to play around with a story in closed focus. Pick one of your stories that you like to tell. Try and pick a story with at least two characters in it. You're free to continue working with a story you've workshopped in a previous lecture. Try and get one in mind. OK, choose one of those characters to focus on right now—maybe it's the first character we meet in the story. Maybe that character is you!

What is your narrator's relationship with this character? Does the narrator like this character? If the character is you, your narrator may be thinking back on "you" when "you" were at a different point in life—what do you, now, think of this person who you were? Do you like the old you? Do you laugh now at how this version of you handled the situation that your narrator sees the "old you" encountering?

Think physically, in three dimensions: How tall is this character in comparison with the narrator? Is he taller than the narrator? Then you'll have to look up at him, right? Is he shorter than you? So, you'll be looking down at him. The narrator has a relationship with the characters around him, and you can use visualization to show that physical relationship between the narrator and the characters, and between one character and another.

Let's try this with that character you chose in your story. Using visualization, try to see that character in front of you. I'm going to side-coach you, so you just focus on visualizing that character, and just follow the prompts. I want you to describe, out loud, what you're seeing.

What is that person wearing? Out loud, tell me what you're seeing. How tall are they? Look them in the eye—do you have to look up or down? I want for you to assign a specific focal point for that person's eyes—not just some amorphous blob out there, but two eyes, you can pinpoint them—see them now.

Now, I'm still side-coaching you, and I want you to try something: Try to imagine that that character stays in the same place in the scene in front of you. Shift your focus from looking that character in the eye, to looking your audience in the eye (if no one is there with you, you can look at me, or you can look at some object in the room with you). Now shift back to looking that character in the eye—see them, their clothes, how tall they are—look that character in the eye. Look back to the audience. Now look back to that character.

Now, still looking at that character, pick out one thing that strikes you about that character—take a real appraising look at that character, and think: What's one thing your audience need to know about that character? Maybe they need to know that he doesn't have much common sense. Or, that she has more wisdom and strength than she realizes. Or, what he's wearing looks ridiculous! Shift your focus back to the audience, and tell them about that character, while keeping an awareness that that character is still there right in front of you. Go ahead, tell the audience about that character.

This technique gives your audience a compelling access point to your characters. It's not only a real world of actions and places, but it's a world of people who the narrator has a relationship with—and by extension, your audience can have a relationship with those characters.

You can use this technique in a story that you tell to friends at a party. So for example, "Now, I know we've all been young and dumb, but when I look at some of the things I did when I was younger, it's a wonder I am still alive!" So there, I'm speaking as the narrator, looking back and forth from the audience to a character, myself when I was younger, and though I don't describe that situation, I'm seeing in front of me a very particular situation, and I'm looking that young self, and I'm looking them in the eye and I'm thinking, "Girl, why did you do that?" My attitude as the narrator, and my use of visualization as I see that character, those (hopefully) make you see not only me, but to see yourself as that young person, through the metaphorical resonance that stories enable.

You'll notice that I put that younger character at eye level with my narrator; I look right over there—and that gives you the impression not only of the age of that younger self (if I'm on the same level, it might not be that long ago that I'm talking about this younger, dumber self)—but it also presents a certain attitude that my narrator has about that character. I'm on the same level—that's one kind of relationship your narrator can have with a character.

I could have chosen to put that character below the sightline of the narrator, and watch how the attitude changes: "Now, I know we've all been young and dumb [Professor Harvey looks down], but when I look at some of the things I did when I was younger, it's a wonder that I am still alive!" When I look at that character, she seems not only younger in age, but the narrator seems to have an attitude of superiority over her.

What happens if you make that younger self taller than the narrator? Watch how the relationship changes between the narrator and the character: "Now, I know we've all been young and dumb, [Professor Harvey looks up], but when I look at some of the things that I did when I was younger, it's a wonder that I am still alive!" When I narrate about that younger self, looking up at that character, it's difficult as a narrator to be superior to that person. I'm looking up, and for the audience it gives the sense that that in some way I kind of revere that younger self—and if I talk about that character in a disparaging way, I kind of have to do it behind her back, as if I'm telling a secret to the audience.

Try this with your character: Move the narrator above the character, so that you're looking down on that character. The focal point of their eyes will shift down. Now think back to one thing you wanted to tell the audience about that character. Say that same thing, but this time visualizing your narrator as being taller or above that character—say it now.

Now, move the focal point for that character's eyes up. You're looking up to that character. Say the same thing, but this time you're smaller or below that character—say it now.

You can use focal points to establish not only the physical relationship your narrator has with the characters, but you can also establish the emotional relationship your narrator has with those characters. This relationship can change over the course of a story—you may be telling people about someone who redeemed themselves in some way, so you begin by talking down about those characters in the story (literally placing them below your narrator), and by the end of the story, you're looking straight ahead, on the same level with them.

If your story is about a hero's journey, you might start out at eye level with the characters, but then as you descend into the abyss, everything else around them grows larger, and while you may still look the main hero in the eye (because you sympathize with that hero most), all of the other characters can seem huge and overwhelming in comparison, so you look up at these characters, or these personifications of your dragon. So, for example, "I went into that boardroom, and I had no idea what I was going to say" and I'm looking up at that dragon, which is my fear of not knowing what I'm going to say, now knowing what's going to happen, and it's huge." Like all of these storytelling techniques, you can use your placement of focal points in lesser or greater degrees in the stories you tell, to give added dimension and reality to the character relationships that you're bringing to life for your audience.

That's one way that your narrator establishes a relationship he or she has with the characters around him. So what happens when your narrator empathizes with these characters? Empathy is different from sympathy—sympathy is feeling *for* someone; empathy means feeling *with* that person. Empathy means that you dive into the head of another character. When your narrator empathizes with a character, the effect is that we start to hear the character herself starting to narrate—the narrator cedes control of the story over to that character.

In the last lecture, you heard part of the story of the island of Sanntraigh and the woman who lived there—we're going to pick back up where we left off, when that woman had just gotten inside that fairy knoll and went to fetch her kettle. You'll notice that at this point in the story, the narrator has ceded control of the story over to the woman's perspective—we start to see things through her eyes mainly, and we experience things with her reactions. We hear what she thinks as the narrator describes in third person, but it's said with the intensity of a first-person account—watch again, and pay attention to how the narrator jumps inside that woman's head and we begin to hear the story told from her perspective, through her eyes.

[Video start.]

> **Professor Harvey:** That woman, she picked up her shawl from where she had just laid it down and she was off [squeak] out the door. She went out through the town, way out, long out into the fields away from the town until she could see that fairy path, that green grass growing much greener than any of the other grass around it. (She was careful not to step on the path—they don't like it when you step on their path.) She walked beside it, and she walked and she followed it until she saw that fairy knoll.
>
> It was way late, what they call the "mouth of the night". She walked over, and that knoll, it was open, so she walked inside. She looked up to the right and to the left. She didn't see anyone. But she saw her kettle, and it was heaped high full of flesh and bones and good things that she thought would be good to eat, so she crept over to it and picked that kettle up. So heavy with all of that inside, but she backed away, she turned around, and she almost got out of that knoll when she heard a voice behind her.

[Video end.]

Professor Harvey: By the time we get here to the fairy knoll, the narrator, he's so empathetic towards this character that we hear her perspective told through the narrator. This is another way to add dynamism to your narrator's journey through the story. When you dive into other characters' perspectives, and you care about those perspectives, your audience will grow all the more fond of the people and care about what happens to them. And you'll hold their attention because they care how the story ends for these folks.

When you hop inside that character's perspective, your focal points will adjust to that character's point of view—so in the story sample you just saw, we move from the narrator talking about this woman going down a path, and the narrator sees her going down the path, and then when she reaches inside the knoll, the narrator hops inside that woman's head, and there she is, hunching down to duck under that tiny opening in the hill, and looking around in that place, looking like the vulnerable intruder she is. So there are so many fun little things you can do with perspective and focal points to bring your audience inside the minds of your characters, and to help them see the story from an inside view.

As we go further in the story, we move to start to see directly from the point of view of the woman and the antagonist. It's a choice that I make as a teller to cut out the narrator in these final moments and to cede control over to the characters' perspectives.

It's that artistic choice that results in the pace of the story picking up. Let's pick up on the "Sanntraigh" story where we left off, and pay attention to how, as the pace picks up in the story, the narrator starts to fade away and it becomes all about the characters. You may notice how, just as the narrator can manipulate time in how he narrates the story, the characters themselves can affect the pacing of the story when the narrator fades away altogether.

[Video start.]

> **Professor Harvey:** She heard the clink of the chain behind her and two dogs barking in the distance. Well she didn't stick around, she didn't look around to see what was behind her and she didn't drop that kettle, she just started running. A-huff and a-huff and a-huff and a-huff and a-huff and a-huff and a-huff and a-huff and a-huff and a-huff.

She didn't drop that kettle because she thought, "Well, if I get away with the kettle, so much the better," and if she didn't get away with it—if those dogs caught up with her—well, then, she could just reach in and throw some of that meat back and stop those dogs and that was just what happened. That woman, she kept on running. A-huff and a-huff and a-huff and a-huff. She could hear those dogs behind her [growling] catching up with her, and so she took her hand, she reached it down into that kettle and [slurping] oh, picked up some of that flesh and those bones and she [grunt] threw it back and she kept on running. A-huff and a-huff and a-huff and a-huff.

Those dogs, they caught up with that food, and they [growling]. They started digging into that meat and those bones. The woman kept running, a-huff and a-huff and a-huff and a-huff. She could hear them again, huff and a-huff and a-huff and a, [growling], so she reached in and she grabbed a second handful and she [grunt] threw it back. A-huff and a-huff and a-huff, [growling], a-huff and a-huff and a-huff and a-huff, [growling], and she got all the way to her gate.

[Video end.]

Professor Harvey: So, we switch back and forth rapidly from the woman to the dogs. This story is always a test of how in shape I am, because I love how the story picks up pace here, and I want to be in good enough shape to be able to satisfy that part of the story without huffing and puffing!

In film, this effect is called a "crosscut"—it's when the action quickly cuts from one image to the next. Here's an example of the crosscut effect using our own studio cameras. I want you to watch this example of storytelling through film, and as you do, please pay attention to what this succession of images does to you as an audience member.

[Video start.]

       [Professor Harvey acts out a fight scene.]

[Video end.]

Professor Harvey: How you use these storytelling techniques, and the degree to which you use them, that will be unique to your own style and voice as a storyteller—and the more you play with these techniques, the more naturally they will come to you in the moment of telling an impromptu story. No two storytellers have the same style, and there's no right or wrong way to tell a story—but the more specific you can make your choices in visualization, and in focal points, and in character perspectives and relationships, well then the more effectively you'll communicate your meanings to your audience, and the more fully your audience will see the story start to unfold around them.

Now, you'll notice that even in these crosscut scenes, when we see things primarily from the point of view of one character and another, the words are still in third-person descriptions—"She kept running, the dogs snarled behind her, and she reached into the kettle and 'ugh' threw another handful of flesh and bones behind her," the third-person descriptions ("He did this, she did that").

But there are other times when you'll want your narrator to guide you to a conversation between two characters—to character dialogue. Here's an example of this from a Japanese folktale told; it's told by a storyteller named Motoko Dworkin. Watch how she as a storyteller switches back and forth between characters.

You'll notice we start off with an easy, relaxed pace, and then the story starts to gain steam. Watch how the outside narrator in this story starts to fade away and we see the characters start to carry the story. And watch what she's doing with her focus to distinguish those characters from one another. This is a clip of a longer story; this clip picks up when a young girl named Tio gets married.

[Video start.]

Motoko Dworkin: Tio and the young farmer were married the next day. As it turned out, her husband was kind and hardworking and her mother-in-law was gentle, cheerful, and generous. So Tio started to work hard, cooking meals; cleaning the house; sewing kimonos; feeding the chickens and the pigs and taking very good care of her elderly mother-in-law.

But as days and weeks passed, the mother-in-law began to notice that Tio often looked very weak and sickly. Many times she would ask, "My dear Tio, are you feeling all right? Is there anything wrong?"

Tio would say, "Oh my dear mother-in-law, I am fine. Please do not worry about me." Yet as weeks and months passed, Tio began to look more and more sickly and finally began to look pale.

Finally one day, the mother-in-law could not take it any longer. She said, "My dear Tio, you have been such a perfect daughter-in-law. I care about you as if you were my own daughter. Now if there's anything wrong, you must tell me."

"Oh my dear mother-in-law, I am so sorry to worry you like this. It's just, I could not possibly tell you. This would offend you too badly."

"Nothing would offend me. Now Tio, please tell me."

Tio's face turned beet red. She turned this way and that; she seemed to hesitate a great deal. Finally she said, "Well, it's just, sometimes I have this urge ... to ... pass wind. Oh I know this is so terrible. That is why I have been holding it in."

"What? You mean gas? Is that it, Tio?"

"Oh my dear mother-in-law, please forget what I said. I'll be just fine the way I am."

266

"No, Tio. This is silly. Come on, we are family. You can pass gas if you like. Go ahead and let it go."

"Are you sure? Well, with your kind permission then, I think I will." She stood up, lifted her kimono, and let it go. What followed was a tempest of biblical magnitude. The roof was gone. The walls crumbled. The furniture broke into bits. The screen, the lantern, the chickens and the pigs and the neighbors' children, they all swirled all over the village. When the young farmer came home, he was amazed at this colossal destruction. Then his neighbor brought his mother home—he had found her in a tree 10 miles down the road.

[Video end.]

Professor Harvey: Motoko comes alive as the story progresses and you can see her seeing the scene, and the scene just takes over! You see her narrator looking up at these objects flying overhead, and when her focus is up, you see the narrator. The narrator feels dwarfed in the presence of this explosion of wind!

The characters start to talk back and forth to one another, and we hear their conversations in real time, what we would call "scene," when the story time takes approximately the same amount of time as the actual time it would take for the event to happen. And Motoko uses the tool of focus in a particular way to give the effect of these distinct characters.

Let's look at how you can apply these same choices of focus in distinguishing your characters from one another and putting them in relation to one another in a conversation—and it's really a lot easier than you may think. In Motoko's story, when Tio and her mother-in-law are speaking back and forth with one another, we have an older woman who looks up to the younger daughter, and the younger daughter-in-law who looks down to this older woman. While they are in closed focus (not looking at the audience) during these moments of character dialogue, the storyteller remains in an open posture, meaning that she's facing her body out to the audience the whole time (so we see her face the whole time).

From this outward-facing position, the two characters speak to one another—the woman (who we interpret from Motoko's body language as being old and hunched), she looks up at the daughter. Motoko assigns a focal point for the daughter above the old woman's eye line so she has to look up to see her, making us believe that the woman is physically shorter than that daughter. The daughter looks down at her mother-in-law, which gives the impression that she is taller and more upright than that older woman.

These focal points remain constant throughout their conversation. Once the narrator has set these up in conversation, once they've been established that when the characters are in conversation the narrator looks at one place and another, then we don't need to enter that conversation with the "old woman said" and "the daughter-in-law said." We don't have to go back to "he said, she said." As the old woman and the girl go about speaking with one another, they can look up and down and the audience understands what's going on, and the audience gets into the rhythm of the conversation.

This is one feature that live storytelling gives you: Your audience is reading not only your words but the way you're performing the story— here, how you're using focal points—and the audience buys into this storytelling trick.

When two characters speak to one another in this way, they're using "dramatic mode." Dramatic is slightly different than epic mode; epic is when you're breaking that fourth wall, you're looking out, you're making eye contact with the audience, the narrator is speaking to the audience. In dramatic mode, two characters are speaking with one another in dialogue, and they don't make eye contact with the audience—they use closed focus.

You see this throughout Motoko's performance—she uses focal points to have characters speak in dialogue with one another. It's there in "Sanntraigh" also when the woman and her husband speak with one another.

[Video start.]

> **Professor Harvey:** "That fairy, she came for it. I did not open the door for her. And then she came in through a hole in the roof and took it away, and she did not come back."

> "What have you done?"

[Video end.]

Professor Harvey: You'll notice, also, I'm not turning profile completely when one person speaks to the other person. Profile would be speaking all the way over here, and then over here. [Professor Harvey turns back and forth.] That would be clunky; it would look goofy, and you don't need all of that movement when you're switching characters. It's distracting because one, it interferes with the pace of conversation, all that moving back and forth, it takes time. And two, we're only seeing your profile, and we only get that part of your face that you're facing us with, just half of your face, so we don't see you reacting in the moment to what the other person says and we miss seeing your facial expressions.

Let's try using dramatic mode with one of your stories. Think of a moment when two of your characters speak back and forth to each other—and for this exercise, don't worry about the narrator's setup—just think about what those two characters say to each other.

Begin with an open posture—facing out to the audience—and assign focal points for each of these characters. For the first character, where does he or she look to speak to the other person? Are they looking up, or down, or straight across? If you're eye level with someone, it's useful to use focal points to the right and to the left for each character, so that it's clear to your audience when you switch back and forth. For instance, Motoko, she placed her focal points up and down. In "Sanntraigh," the woman and the man, they speak more or less on the same level, but one is over here (to the left) and the other here (to the right). I'm mirroring.

Assign your focal points. Where does the first character look to talk to the second, and where does the second character look to talk to the first? Now, who says the first thing? Step into that character's perspective, and look at that other character's focal point, and say that line to them. Now, move to the second character, looking back at that different focal point for the first character. What does he say? Now move back to the first character's perspective—what's their visceral reaction to what that person just said? Let that infuse how you say the next thing to that character—go!

Depending on your style as a storyteller, you will use this tool in greater or lesser degrees. When you're sharing a story at a party, the performance dynamics are different than Motoko up on a stage, so your gestures can be smaller, your reactions less pronounced—but it is delightfully funny to watch her get consumed by the reeling characters in that scene of Motoko's story.

In this lecture we've looked at how your narrator bridges between the audience and the characters in specific ways. In epic mode, the narrator moves between closed focus (visualizing the scene and the characters) and open focus (making direct eye contact with the audience). While the narrator is in the world of the story, he can empathize with the characters to the point that we start to hear narration from those characters' points of view. In dramatic mode, the narrator sometimes fades away to let the characters take over in dialogue with one another using closed focus and focal points, and they establish these characters and their relationship to one another.

In our next lecture, we'll delve even deeper into characterization. Where you look to distinguish characters, that's one thing—but there's even more fun as you play with how to bring those characters to life with your gestures, and your voice, and your facial expressions.

Developing Complex Characters
Lecture 14

Your narrator is one bridge between your audience and the world of the story, but once your listeners are in that world, the characters are what make them want to stay in the story. In this lecture, we will get into the nitty gritty of developing characters into people your audience enjoys seeing in action. We'll talk about how to add depth and dimension to your characters, and we'll work with gestures and body postures. Remember, the best way to learn the art of storytelling is by doing, not just talking.

Character Contexts

- If you think back to our lecture on perspective, we talked about all of the contexts in your life that weigh on your point of view—your gender, age, and so on. We'll use a similar mode of analysis to understand the dimensions of the major characters in your stories.

- To begin, let's return to the same story with two characters that you worked on in the last lecture. Choose one of those characters to focus on now.

- What is the gender of that character, and is that character more masculine or feminine? Keep in mind that our culture deems certain behaviors and postures "masculine" or "feminine." For example, a male character might stand and move in a boxy style, with the hips squared off and the feet planted apart, while the movements of a female character might be more dainty or delicate.

- Of course, you can embody these postures and movements to varying degrees. If you're at a party and talking with one or two friends, you might give just a suggestion of a certain posture, but if you're on a stage, you might more fully embody the posture.

- If we're talking about giving dimension to characters, we can't simply stop at "men walk like this and women walk like this." Not

© iStockphoto/Thinkstock.

Caricatures are one-dimensional representations, while characters have dimension, depth, and the capacity for change.

only is that not true to any good cultural analysis of how human beings behave in the world, but it also flattens your characters into a single dimension. And people—the real characters around us and those we re-create for a storytelling audience—aren't one-dimensional.

- Sometimes, in children's stories, characters may be delightful because they're utterly flat—the "bad guy," for example, who is completely bad.

- But if you're telling a story to adults, especially a story from personal experience, you want to think about more than one dimension of the major characters. This is the difference between creating characters and caricatures.

- Age is another dimension for your characters. What is the specific age of the character you're focusing on now?

o Note that younger people might walk breezily, with easy movements, perhaps more centered in the upper part of the body.

o A character in his or her 50s might walk a little slower, with less showy movements, and with more weight centered in the lower part of the body. Someone who is 80 or older usually walks much more slowly, perhaps with a cane.

o Keep in mind, however, the tensive qualities in people. You might have a character who is 70 but feels 20 or a feminine woman who adopts a more masculine posture when she goes into a business meeting. In a story, you may want to reveal those types of differences.

- As we said, temperament is another facet of your character's perspective—his or her knee-jerk reactions. Is your particular character quick-tempered or unflappable? Such characteristics might be reflected in that character's rate of speech.

Centers of Energy

- Theater professor Doug Cummins developed a series of exercises for experimenting with the different ways that characters hold their centers of energy. There are five major centers for energy in a person's body: head, shoulders/chest, stomach, pelvis, and anus.

- A head-centered person tends to hold his or her head up high when walking and looks up and out. In looking down, this character moves just the eyes rather than the whole head. What are some of the connotations we might associate with this way of carrying oneself? Perhaps proud, or snobbish, or preoccupied.

- Of course, the chest-centered person leads with the chest when walking and tends to look straight ahead. We might decode this carriage as proud or confident and in control.

- With stomach-centered people, the center of energy moves down to the stomach, and the gestures are in the same plane as the stomach. Notice that the energy center also moves the spine, as well; the spine curves, and the plane of vision is lower. This way of walking might be decoded as relaxed and, perhaps, more masculine.

- With pelvic-centered people, the energy center is in the hips. This way of walking tends to be interpreted as highly feminine, perhaps even sexual. The plane of vision is pulled downward, which means that people with this body center have to look up at others, perhaps diminishing the character and giving the illusion of smallness.

- Finally, anus-centered people locate all their energy in their behinds. This is the nerdy Steve Erkel character from the 1990s sitcom *Family Matters*.

Experimenting with Body Centers
- Get up on your feet and experiment with each of these body centers. Start by walking around in your space as you normally would.

- Next, try walking around as if you were head-centered. Pay attention to how that changes your perspective and what it does to your gestures. If this center feels strange to you, it may be that it's different from your own energy center. Where are you looking as you walk with this center of energy? If you're looking up, try looking down. Does it feel more comfortable to look up or down from this body center?

- Now, move to chest-centered walking. If this feels more natural to you, ask yourself why you might have adopted this posture. Do you use this posture at work? Try out gestures and notice where you are looking.

- As you move to stomach-centered walking, you may immediately notice a change in your pace. Moving to this center tends to slow you down. Are you more relaxed in this body center? Do you notice a slump in your spine? Keeping your center in your stomach, try making gestures up above your shoulders. This may feel strange because your gestures usually follow along with your body center.

- Next, move to hip-centered walking. You may not feel that this center is your "gendered" way of being, but give yourself permission to try out this body posture. How does concentrating your energy in your hips make you want to move? Are you interacting with the space around you differently? Where are your gestures? How do you feel with this body center? For what sort of character might you use this body center?

- Move to anal-centered walking. Notice immediately that this body center tends to curve your spine. What does it feel like to have this body center? Where is your gaze? How would this body center affect the way you interact with the world?

- Finally, change to the way you normally walk and see if you can tell which body center you usually gravitate toward. You might even find that you're drawn to one body center in more relaxed situations and a different one in more formal or tense situations. The body center often changes based on the circumstances we find ourselves in.

- Stop walking but remain standing and think about the character in your story. What would be that person's body center? Consider the connotative values we discussed for each body center.
  o Begin to walk around in the space with that body center while you think about that character.

  o How does your character see the world with this center of the body? How does he or she interact with the world from this center? Where does your gaze fall? Where do your gestures tend to be? Is your character actively performing a gender through this body center?

- o After you've tried out walking with this character, stop and speak a line to your other character, using a focal point to look at the second character.

- Start moving again as the second character. Again, consider what body center that character might have. It may be the same as the first character, but if possible, try to pick a different body center.
  - o How does this second character interact with the world? Where does your gaze fall, and where are your gestures?

  - o Stop and speak the line that this second character says in response to the first, using a focal point to look at the first character.

- Stand in place and remember the body centers for each of your characters. Without walking, stand with the first character's body center, and really exaggerate it. Move the focal point for the second character in front of you and say the line again. Then, do the same thing with the second character, speaking the response.

- Whatever your style of storytelling, these exercises are useful in developing and distinguishing your characters. The degree to which you enact these characterizations through your body and gestures is a matter of personal style and depends on the style of the story itself.

Suggested Reading

Dworkin, *Tales of Now and Zen.*

———, www.motoko.folktales.net.

Lipman, *Improving Your Storytelling.*

Rocha, *Under African Skies with Antonio Rocha.*

———, www.storyinmotion.com.

1. What is your dominant center of the body? What different centers of the body do you find yourself performing throughout the day and in what contexts? Think about why these different situations "call" for different centers. What would be the impact of performing the "wrong" center of the body?

2. The degree to which you enact character differences through your body will depend on your personal style and the context of the telling. How would you adapt your characterizations to suit a business meeting, as opposed to an office party or a storytelling performance for children? How much of this adaptation is a consideration of the audience and the appropriateness of the context, and how much is your own inhibition?

Developing Complex Characters
Lecture 14—Transcript

Professor Harvey: Your narrator is one bridge between your audience and the world of the story, but once we're in that world, the characters are what really make your audience want to stay in that story. In this lecture we're going to get into the nitty-gritty of developing your characters into folks who your audience actually enjoys seeing in action. We'll talk about how to add dimension and depth to your characters. And if you want to try out some exercises with me, you'll be up on your feet working with gestures and with body postures. I'll be doing something again called "side-coaching," teaching a student while he or she is up in motion. Because you learn the art of storytelling best by doing it, not just talking about it. So in this lecture, let's get ready to play.

If you think back to our lecture on perspective, we talked about all of the contexts in your life that weigh on your point of view—your gender, your age, all of those. We're going to use a similar mode of analysis in understanding the dimensions of the major characters in your story.

Now of course, you won't do this in-depth analysis with every one of your characters, and you may only want to choose a few of these elements of character to play with for a given story. But it's useful to consider all these different dimensions of your characters, because even one of these dimensions can help you convey something interesting about that character, and make that figure more memorable for your audience.

I'm going to ask you several questions about the characters in your stories. For an impromptu story that you tell at an office party, you may only want to focus on conveying one of these things for a given character, but you might find two or three that help you add even more life to your characters. So for this exercise, go back to the same story you were working on in the last lecture—the one with two characters who interact with one another. Choose one of those characters to focus on right now.

What is the gender of that character—are they more masculine or more feminine? As with any other difference that we point out in these lectures, these differences are culturally defined and determined. And how we express sexuality and sexual difference is highly culturally loaded.

We have these different ways of walking that our culture deems masculine or feminine. So if I've got a male character in my story and he's a very masculine male character, I might have him stand and move in a more boxed-off style, because like any other cultural expression of our character, these gestures are loaded—and because of that, they are "code" for something, they stand for something in our culture. You see someone walking in this way, and it's code for masculine behavior.

You know this because you've seen women walk in this way, and stand in this way—I walk this way sometimes, usually not when I'm in heels. When I'm in heels, it makes me walk in a more feminine way—A heel literally forces a different kind of performance out of me, I'm more up on my toes—and that's code for dainty, and delicate, and feminine.

If I have a masculine character in my story, I might change my body posture to have him hold himself with his hips more squared off, and feet more apart, with my weight more in my heels than the in balls of my feet. And if I speak as that character, I might speak taking on that more masculine posture. Now you can do this in varying degrees, of course—when you're at a party talking with one or two friends, you might just give a suggestion of this posture. Or if you're on stage giving a presentation you might more fully embody that posture. (Or if your style is more over-the-top, like mine, you might fully embody that posture for the party audience!) So you can apply embodiment in degrees to suit whatever audience dynamic and context you're in.

Now, we're talking about giving dimension to your characters—so we're not going to just leave it at "Men walk like this, and women walk like this," because not only is that not really true to any good cultural analysis of how human beings really behave in the world, it also flattens your characters into a single dimension. *People*, real characters all around us, who live in the real world that we, in our stories, are trying to create for our audiences—these characters aren't just one thing. It's why no one likes to be stereotyped.

The word "stereotype" comes from the Greek *steros*, meaning "firm or solid," and *typos*, meaning "impression," and that word was first used to refer to an actual object that they used in printing, when they moved from individually setting letters in type to print a single page of text, to creating a solid metal plate to print the pages of books. It revolutionized printing because now you didn't have to individually set keys for each page over and over again; you made one cast plate for each page (and that plate was called a "stereotype"). It saved a lot of time in printing hundreds of copies of books at a time, and Firmin Didot (the inventor) made a heck of a lot of money in the 18th century.

The reason why we still know this word, "stereotype," today, in our technologized cyber-world that is rapidly doing away with printed texts, the reason why we use this word and know it is that no one wants to be seen as a cast copy of someone else's definition for how to be a "real" woman, or a "real" man. That's what a cultural stereotype does—it reduces a multidimensional person to one thing. And you know that you are more than one thing.

Sometimes, in your stories, especially with some children's stories, you'll have characters who are delightful because they are flat; they serve the function of being the bad guy who is utterly bad. But if you're telling a story to adults, and especially if it's a story from personal experience, but also for fairy tales, for myths, and other traditional stories, you'll want to think about how the major characters (and even the villains) are more than just one thing. It's the difference between creating *characters* (which have dimension and depth and the capacity for change) and *caricatures* (one-dimensional representations).

For instance, age is another dimension of your characters, so think now for a character, what is that character's specific age in the story? (And try to be specific, don't just say, "Oh, he's in his 20s"—well is he 21 or is he 28? Because there's really a world of difference in maturity between a person who's just turned 21 and someone who's about to turn 30—and *that* level of maturity is a world away from someone who's 43, or 65.) So there's your character's specific age. And there's a way to stereotypically play someone's age: A 21-year-old might carry themselves walking breezily with easy movements, and may be a more centered person in their upper part of their body, so swinging their arms, as opposed to someone who's 55 who might walk with a little bit slower and less showy movements, and maybe be centered more with their weight in their lower body. And all of that as opposed to someone who's 82, and who has to walk much more slowly.

But you've probably known people who are in their 70s, but inside they feel like they're 20. There's your given age, and then there's your "life rhythm," how old you feel. And for that person, you might choose to have them hold themselves with the aged body of someone who struggles with walking and who struggles with holding their balance, but in their eyes you can see that 20-year-old coming out.

It gets back to the tensive qualities in people—those pulls between contrary poles in a story that add dimension and interest. So you've got someone who's 70, but they feel 20. Or a woman who usually behaves in a very feminine way, but when she gets into the masculinized boardroom situation of a business meeting, that testosterone starts flowing! In a story, you might want for that old man to reveal a change in a moment of the story, so you might see this old man come alive. That old man might say, "I can't do it now, but if I could I'd just take that woman in my arms and dance with her like we used to!" Or, like Motoko—she has a very feminine way of presenting the daughter-in-law in her story, but as she lets that character go and the character becomes more masculine, it's hilarious!

Gender and age are facets of your characters, and then there's that person's temperament—their knee-jerk reactions to things. Is this character a quick-tempered person (do they rush to snap at people in their responses, or do they speak quickly)? Or maybe they're a very steady person—nothing seems to faze them, they're very calm.

The man who does my taxes has a remarkably calm demeanor in the midst of the storm. He's a family friend, and this year we were late getting our tax documents to him so he could compile all of our returns, and we went to see him the day before everything had to be mailed. It's his busiest day of the year, and he's just smiling, "How are you doing?" Even-tempered.

If I'm describing him in a story, like I just did with you there, when I talk about him I start to embody that temperament. So I slow down my rate of speech down to match his, when I say his lines (which in that story were, "How are you doing?"). I'm using a focal point for him to speak to us (that focal point is out and slightly down—I'm a short person and he, along with most everyone else in my world, is usually looking down at me).

And I'm giving you a suggestion of how he behaves—if I were to more fully enact his character, it would look like this: The man who does my taxes, he has a remarkable calm in the storm. He's a family friend, and we were late getting our tax documents to him so he could compile all our returns. When we went to see him the day before everything had to be mailed, his busiest day of the year, he's just smiling, "How are you doing?" Even-tempered, calm.

You'll notice both of those ways of performing that story are hopefully entertaining, but they reflect different styles of telling. And no one telling is better than another—there's your choice, and what choices of performance are most appropriate to your given audience and your story.

With all of these dimensions of character—gender, and age, and temperament—there's also the way your characters appear physically. How that character holds himself and walks around in the world, and how he uses his gestures. I'm talking about these characters as if they really "do" these things—they walk, they gesture—because I want for you to think of your own movements and gestures as coming out of a lived experience for your character, rather than thinking, "I need to give that character a gesture so that people know that that's him." It's the difference between putting gestures onto a character, rather than looking at how a person holds themself, their "center," and how gestures and ways of walking flow out of that center.

Here's what I mean by that: We all have different ways of holding ourselves. You go to any public place and you go people-watching (sit down with your coffee and just start to watch people pass by), and you can look at how we have these different ways of walking and holding our balance. It has to do with how we hold our "energy center."

There's wonderful acting professor, Dr. Doug Cummins, he developed a series of acting exercises for experimenting with the different ways that a character holds themselves. The way that some acting professionals have looked at this is what part of your body you "lead" with—so, people lead with their heads—but a better way of thinking about it is really how a person holds their center of energy. There are five major energy centers for the body: your head, your shoulders, or your heart, your stomach, your pelvis, and yes the anal-centered person.

A head-centered person, they walk around with all of their energy in their head. [Professor Harvey flounces around.] So you walk around as if you're head centered, your energy is all up here and you know people like this, you've seen people walk around like this. (I once dated a guy who was head-centered, it drove me crazy.) We have these cultural connotations about the way people walk as being masculine or feminine. There are connotations for the centers of the body as well.

Think about it; what are some connotations that you have for a person who walks like this? I'm asking you to decode this body language—there's a denotative description of this way of walking (so I could describe it: The head is up, you'll notice that my gestures follow this energy center, so if I'm a head-centered person, my gestures are usually more up). My plane of vision usually follows this energy center as well, so if I'm looking up and out, that kind of fits with this head-centeredness. If I look down, and I'm still holding my body posture up, I may just move my eyes down instead of moving my whole head down. When you're head centered, you usually don't look past the end of your nose at people; you're looking over your nose.

So what are some of the connotative values you associate with someone who walks this way? Someone who's proud? Or maybe off in their own head? Stuck-up maybe? (I'm thinking about that guy I dated!)

OK, so that's head centered. Let's move down to chest centered. Chest-centered people hold their energy in their chest. [Professor Harvey walks confidently back and forth.] So what are some connotations of a person who walks chest centered? What is this code for? Someone who's proud, maybe not stuck up in the way of a head-centered person, but you'll notice that shifting from head centered down into chest centered, it draws my energy down. It also draws my gestures down to my shoulders and to my chest. My plane of vision also comes down so I can look at you more directly in the eye, rather than head centered and down at you.

You might think of this person as confident, in control. Often in public speaking classes, you're taught that this is the "proper" way to stand, or your mother tells you to "Stand up straight and pull your shoulders back," because in our culture this is a sign of confidence, and even of independence (which are cultural values that are prized in our society).

You want to give that impression, so you code those values into a way of walking, and you express those values through this embodied performance; it's a way of holding yourself. It's remarkable how culture works, and it's so fun to decode culture in this way—to look at how we perform daily life! So, that's chest centered.

Then, from chest centered, there's stomach centered. People whose energy is more down in their stomach, and my gestures are more down towards where my stomach is and on the same plane as my stomach. You'll notice that the energy center also moves the spine as well. So from chest centered, everything gets pulled downwards a little bit, my spine curves down and my plane of vision starts to move down a little further. [Professor Harvey walks, leading with her stomach.] What are some connotations that you have of someone who walks in this coded way of being? Is this person more laid back, maybe? You may have started thinking about some gendered ways of considering this body center. We tend to associate stomach centered with a more masculine walk; it's a little more boxed off.

Hip centered is slightly different, moving from stomach centered to hip centered. [Professor Harvey flounces about.] Your energy center here is in your hips. Again, you may have gendered connotations with this center of the body. It's why, if you go to a drag show—and I don't mean racing!—if you go to drag performances, this is part of that feminine performance that the male competitors try to master. There's the feminine performance and then there's overdoing it, and then there's just a suggestion of the hips—and either way, it's a highly feminized way of walking. By "feminized "I mean, there's nothing about this way of walking that makes it inherently feminine; it's that our culture has determined this walk means "feminine." It's code for "feminine."

You think of Marilyn Monroe, and they used to actually take the heels of her shoes and cut them at an angle so that she walked with an emphasis on her hips; it literally changed the way she walked and the center of her body. So, hip centered—many cultural connotations with this center: sexual, lusty. My plane of vision again is pulled a little more downward, so I'm looking up at you with this body center, which is more of a diminutive way of looking at someone else; it diminishes my character. It makes me smaller—which, isn't that what Euro-American culture desires: "Women, be smaller"?

I was watching this teenage couple studying together at a local coffee shop a few days ago, and the guy, he's sitting like this, he's slouched, legs spread, he's stomach-centered. The girl, whose torso was actually longer than his from this seated position, she was sitting across from him, but she was sitting hunched down, and her legs were together at the knees. [Professor Harvey sits in a compact manner.] She was making herself smaller, and a hip-centered position pulls you up through the pelvis, so it actually does draw your legs closer together. From this hip-centered seated position, she would toss her gaze up at him, and she would bat her eyes *up* at him, and then she would look away—even though I know she was actually taller than him in this seated position.

Even when your characters are seated, you can tell these centers of the body, the difference between stomach centered, and more pelvis centered. It's fun to watch people using these culturally coded ways of being in the world in order to perform gender. It's fun to play with these centers of the body for your characters—and again, you don't have to make a big to-do out of this when you're telling your story, but an awareness of these two different people with two different centers, you can give a suggestion of these different centers, an awareness of that, just like I did when I was telling you that story about this girl and boy at the coffee shop. It can add dimension of your stories.

The last center of the body is one that you know you've seen. Don't try and pretend like you haven't seen it—it's anal centered. It's all tucked down in here. [Professor Harvey gestures to her bottom.] You have seen people, don't pretend like you haven't, you have seen people who walk like this—it's all down in here, and your spine is just kind of curved down towards this energy center. My plane of vision is pulled down, my gestures are pulled down. If any of you ever saw the old 1990s sitcom *Family Matters*, this is the Steve Urkel character. He's so nerdy, and dear, and all of his energy is just pulled down here. And if I take on this posture, my gestures are all down on the same plane as my bottom!

I've done these. I'd like for you to get up on your feet and experiment with each of these body centers—let's try them on together! And you may have to go back to that lecture on giving yourself permission because yes, I want you to get up out of your seat, and stand up and do this, because this isn't something you just get intellectually, by just thinking about it. You don't just think about telling stories; you do it. Let me show you how this can work!

This again is side-coaching, so I ask you to do things, as I ask you to do them don't pay attention just to me, pay attention to your own experiences of these centers. Don't worry about watching the screen. So right now, walk around in the space you've got—don't just walk in a circle (that's our tendency, is just to kind of walk in a circle), but walk all around in the space. Walk just walk as you normally do. Now, I want for you to walk around, start to walk around as if you were head centered—all of the energy is up in your head. With this center, start to pay attention to how that changes your perspective—where are you looking?

Try out gestures with this center of the body—are your gestures up? Does this center of the body maybe feel strange to you? It may be different than your own center of the body! Take note of that. Take note of the differences in this way of walking as opposed the way you normally walk. Pay attention to where your eyes want to look in this center of the body. Now look down. Does it feel comfortable to look down from this body center? Does that move feel comfortable? Just take note.

Now move to more chest centered—walk around with a chest-centered body. How do you feel? Confident? Is this more like your own way of walking? Does this feel more natural to you? Ask yourself why this body posture might be one that you've adopted, if this does feel natural to you. Do you use this posture at work? Try out your gestures with this—where do your gestures want to go? What about your gaze, your eyes—where do your eyes want to fall and look? Do you look at people more at eye level?

Move to stomach centered—walk around with all of your energy center in your stomach. You may immediately notice a change in the pace of your walking. Because you're moving the center of your body down here, things start to slow down a little bit. How does it feel to be in this body center? More relaxed? Do you maybe notice a slump in your spine at all?

Where do your gestures want to be? You might notice that your gestures feel more natural down towards your stomach. To test this, I want you to try still walking around with stomach centered, but I want you to try something for me. Try moving your gestures up above your head, like this. [Professor Harvey holds her hands above her head.] Kind of feels like a caveman doesn't it? It doesn't quite feel right because your gestures usually follow along with your body's center. It's as if there's an imaginary line drawn at that body center and your gestures, if the line is here at your stomach, your gestures usually follow along with that line; they stick at or below that line.

Give yourself permission—you may feel like this is not your gendered way of being, but give yourself permission to really try out this body posture. Your center of energy, now, is in your hips. [Professor Harvey flounces around.] How does this make you want to move? Are you interacting maybe with the space a little differently? Try out hip centered. Where are your gestures? How do you feel your gestures moving with this body center? Are there times when you might use this body center—and when? For what sort of character might you use this body center?

Finally—yes, we're going to do it—anal centered. Your center of energy is all tucked into your anus; it's all tucked down in there. Notice as you're walking around—you do it—you notice immediately as you're walking around with this body center, you'll notice a curvature in your spine. What does it feel like to have this body center? Where is your gaze? You probably find yourself looking downward, mostly. How would this body center affect the way that you interact with the world? What do you see around you?

Keep walking but come out of that anal center and go back to the way you normally walk. Check in with yourself; see if you can tell which center of the body that you gravitate more towards. You might find that at home, you're drawn to one body center (maybe you're relaxed at home, so you're more stomach centered here), but then if you pay attention to how you are at work, you might notice a change in your body center (maybe you're more chest centered there).

Your body center usually changes based on the given circumstances—the context shapes our daily performances of ourselves. A person who's on a first date might have one body center, but if you've been married to your spouse for several years, you might take on a different body center on a date with your spouse. So, the context and location of two characters interacting, that can influence how they hold themselves. Sometimes we choose the way we hold ourselves, and sometimes the situation presses into us; the context literally forces us into a different way of holding ourselves: "Sit up straight, you're at a meeting!"

Stop walking now, but stay standing. I'm still side-coaching you, so stick with your own thoughts. I want you to think about that character in your story—the one who you were thinking about when we discussed gender, and age, and temperament. Think about that person, and think about what body center that person might have.

You can think about these connotative values that we discussed for each body center, and you can think about how you felt when you were trying on each of those centers. Choose one center of the body for that character (if it doesn't feel right now, you can always change it later). Begin to walk around in the space with that center of the body, and think about that character.

How does that character see the world with this center of the body? How do they interact with the world around them with this center—where does your gaze fall; what do you see? Where do your gestures want to go? Is this person actively performing a gender through this body center?

Now, keep walking, but I want for you to think about what this character says to another character in the story. Think of one line, one thing that that character says—get that line in your head. And now on the count of three I would like for you to stand in place and say that line, imagining that you're looking at that other character through a focal point—get ready to say that line. One, two, three!

Now start moving again. Think of that second character. Knowing what you know about this second character, what kind of body center do you think that character might have? Again, just pick the one that seems best to you right now, you can always choose a different one later. Begin to walk around with that body center—it may be the same as the first character; it may be very different, but if at all possible, try to pick a different body posture for this exercise.

With this second character, how does it feel to walk around in this character's center of the body? How does this person interact with the world? Where do you want to look—where does your gaze fall with this center of the body? Where do your gestures want to go? Think of what that character says in response to what the first character just told them. Think of that line that they say in response. At the count of three, stand in place and say that line, speaking as that second character and using a focal point to look back at that first character. Ready? One, two, three!

Stop, stand in place, and remember those centers of the body for each of the characters. I want for you to stand—don't move around, just stand with that first character's center of the body. Really exaggerate that body center—play with it, have fun with it. Move that focal point out in front of you, and say at the count of three, say that line to that character. One, two, three! Now, standing in place, move to that second body center for that second character, and look back at the first character—react to what you just heard, and say your line on the count of three say in response. One, two, three!

OK, thank you. You can sit down. What you just did looks like this in performance—watch this small snippet from Motoko Dworkin's story.

[Video start.]

> **Motoko Dworkin:** "My dear Tio, you have been such a perfect daughter-in-law. I care about you as if you were my own daughter. Now if there's anything wrong, you must tell me."
>
> "Oh my dear mother-in-law, I am so sorry to worry you like this. It's just, I could not possibly tell you. This would offend you too badly."
>
> "Nothing would offend me. Now Tio, please tell me."

[Video end.]

Professor Harvey: So it could look like that, or it could be as understated as the way that I've told the little stories that have flowed out of our part of conversation in these lectures today. Whatever your style of storytelling, these exercises are really useful in developing and distinguishing your characters. The degree to which you enact these characterizations through your body and your gestures, well that's a matter of personal style, and it's also dependent upon the style of the story itself.

Now that you've really dived into the possibilities of perspectives, and scenes, and characters, it's time to put it all together into a story structure—and as we'll see in the next lecture, there are many different structures to choose from. It's up to you to determine which structure fits best for your story and which structure fits best with the characters, and with the message that your story contains. See you then.

Plot and Story Structures
Lecture 15

N ow that you've dived into the places in your story through visualization, thought about the different perspectives from which you could see these places, and gotten to know the narrator and the characters in that world, let's work on putting it all into an order that makes sense for you and your audience. In this lecture and the next, we'll talk about choices for structuring the pieces of your story. What you're looking for is a structure that works well with the meaning you want to convey and gets you and your listeners from where you are to where the story wants you to be.

What Happened and What Matters

- Begin by choosing a story that you have worked on earlier in these lectures. Think back to our last few lectures on narrators, characters, and perspective and consider the different perspectives you could take on for that story.

- Choose one of these perspectives that you want to align with for this version of the story. Keep in mind that you can always return to this lecture, choose a different point of view, and perform these exercises again.

- From this chosen perspective, think about these questions: What is the one major event or happening in the story? What is the action about? What matters about what happened? What is the most important thing about this story to you; what truth does it convey? It's helpful to put the meaning into words—a few phrases or a sentence. This is the point that your narrator is drawing us toward; it's what shapes the journey for the narrator.

- Next, list the main characters in the story; then, go back to the first question about the action of the story—the physical drama. Which of these characters does the main action happen to? Put a star by that character's name.

- You arrived at the meaning of the story by adopting a particular perspective, and remember that your narrator conveys and lives with this perspective. That's the narrator's role: to link the audience with the events and characters from this point of view.
  - Your narrator may sympathize with one character more than another and follow one character more closely than others.

  - Most of the time, the narrator sympathizes with the character who is the center of the action. However, you may also find that the person who really matters to your narrator is someone who is supposed to be a secondary character.

- With this exercise, we've gotten a start on separating out the "plot" (the sequencing of events in the story—what happens to whom) from the "emotional arc" (how listeners feel about the events in your story—what matters about what happened).
  - Most of the time, this emotional arc moves with the plot of the story; thus, when you reach the climax of the plotline, you also reach the emotional climax of the story.

  - But this may not be the case when the narrator sympathizes with someone other than the person who is the center of the action. On your list of characters, put a star by the name of the person who helps you arrive at the main point of the story.

Developing Story Structure

- The story structure is a kind of frame you put around the events of your story. You need to choose a frame that "fits" the story—not so narrow that it cuts off half the story, not so large that the main point

© iStockphoto/Thinkstock.

There are three audiences that will help you in developing stories: the teddy bear, the mirror, and the best friend.

gets lost, and not so garishly obvious that it's distracting from the story. In other words, the frame should serve the story, not the other way around.

- A good way to begin threading together the plotline of your story is to "storyboard" the main scenes of action. This is a very organic way of following your storyline, in the sense that there's not a rigid structure that you're trying to fit your story into.
    - o A storyboard is nothing more than a series of drawings that you make to sketch out who and what is in each of the major scenes in your story.

    - o Draw a few boxes in your storytelling journal; then begin sketching the scenery and the characters for each scene in the boxes.

    - o Those quick sketches represent a flow of action. You'll notice that there are reasons that one scene flows into the next: The characters are propelled into the next scene both by what has come before and by what's waiting for them.

    - o Look at two scenes on your storyboard and ask: What motivates the action to move from one scene to the next? Draw arrows that show the two-way connection between these scenes and write (in a few words) what is pushing and pulling the characters into the next scene.

    - o Storyboarding is a highly useful rehearsal technique as you develop the flow of action for your story. You'll see that the separate scenes are connected both by a logical chain of events and by lines of force. The story isn't just a series of events—it's full of urgency.

Aristotelian Story Structure
- We've already seen one classic story structure: the hero's journey, which uses separation, initiation, and return as a form of beginning, middle, and end. Another structure followed by many stories was

first laid out by Aristotle in 335 B.C.E. and later amended by German playwright Gustav Freytag in the 19th century.

- o This classic story structure starts with an introduction, where we learn just enough about the protagonist that we care about what happens to him or her.

- o The introduction leads to an inciting incident (something that gets the action going), and then rising action builds to a climax.

- o At the end is the dénouement, or falling action, and the conclusion.

- o The main character has almost always undergone a transformation between the introduction and the conclusion.

- Note that this frame leaves you in a different place than you began. The conclusion is physically charted as being on a higher plane than the introduction. This is an appropriate way of thinking about a story, because when you experience a story, you don't return to the exact same place you were before you heard it.

- When you are developing a story with this kind of frame, you can work through the Aristotelian plotline from several directions.
  - o For instance, you can follow linearly, starting at the beginning, moving to the middle, and then going to the end. Ask yourself: From the main character's perspective, what propels the story forward? From that inciting incident, other actions follow.

  - o You might also start from the ending. Ask yourself: In order for my audience to "get" this ending, where must I start this story? Then work backwards, with that ending always in mind.

  - o You might even begin in the middle, with the incident that stands out the most to you in the story—either the climax itself or a particular part of the rising action that captivated you. You then work outward and backward from that point.

- Choose one of these entry points for working through an Aristotelian story frame and quickly sketch out the action of your story according to this frame.

- This is the prototypical Western frame for stories, and it can work quite well when your story is told from one point of view in a chronological fashion.

Alternative Story Structures
- Of course, we all know that there is more than one side to any story. In your story, you might choose to play with multiple points of view. Some well-known films have multiple characters telling the "same" story.

- You should also consider whether your story has to happen chronologically. Remember, your narrator has the power to expand and contract time through descriptions and summaries, but the narrator can also hop back and forth in time, using foreshadowing and flashbacks.
  - Look at the scenes in your storyboard and experiment with switching their order. This is especially useful to do to a story that you think must be told in chronological order. Try putting one pivotal point at the end of your story first.

  - In the Dadaist movement, artists would paint a picture or write a poem and then tear it up and throw the pieces on the floor to see what new and interesting image or combination of words fluttered down when those pieces reshaped themselves.

- Another way to structure a story is to start with the main "things" you are drawn to in a story and let the structure flow from these things.
  - In this case, a "thing" could be something that one character says to another, or it could be a place, a specific event, or a feeling at a certain point in the story.

o   Identify three to five things in your story and pair each with a specific image. Then, structure your story in a way that ties those images together.

o   Storytelling coach Doug Lipman advises students to look for the "MIT" ("most important thing") in a story. From the MIT, you can arrange the smaller insights into themes or chronological clusters of events to link together the plotline.

The End—The Resolution of Your Story

- Your story will come to some sort of resolution at the end, but that doesn't mean it has to have a happy ending. Some stories don't have a neat and tidy conclusion. In fact, you may be doing an injustice to a story if you try to make it fit the Aristotelian model! This structure works because most audiences recognize it, but it's not necessarily the best structure for every audience or every story.

- In thinking about the end of the story, go back to the first question we asked in this lecture: What is the main point of the story for your narrator? What is that "nugget" that you don't want your audience to lose?

- That main point will be the MIT for your story, which serves as an umbrella for any story structure and determines how your narrator will glide through the plot. It shapes the economy of your performance, because it determines how much information you need to give and what you can leave out. It tells you how far the introduction needs to go back and where the story lands in the end.

- On your storyboard, where is this point in the plotline? Is it at the very end, or does it coincide with the climax? Draw a circle around this point—the emotional climax of the story—on your storyboard.

- In the next lecture, we'll talk about the even more important role of the emotional trajectory of your story and how this emotional through-line offers the primary points of connection between your story and your audience.

Suggested Reading

Lipman, *Improving Your Storytelling*.

Questions to Consider

1. Plot is based in the action of the story—physical places, doings, and people. Where does your story take us? Try to visualize each of your storyboard scenes and ask yourself: Where do you go? In which scene is the peak point of action in your story?

2. To what story structure are you most drawn? Why?

Plot and Story Structures
Lecture 15—Transcript

Professor Harvey: Now that you've dived into these places within your story through visualization, and you've thought about the different perspectives from which you could really see these places, and you've gotten to know the characters and the narrator in that world, let's work on putting these pieces all together into an order that makes sense for you and for your audience.

In this lecture and the next, we're going to talk about the different choices you have for how you can structure the pieces of your story. You're looking for a structure that will work well with the meaning that you want to convey, the meaning, what this story is really all about, and choosing a format that gets us from where we are, to where the story wants us to be.

That kind of crafting is what distinguishes stories from anecdotes. There are two storytellers, Elizabeth Ellis and Loren Neimi, Elizabeth you saw earlier in a story that she told. They say that an anecdote is raw, unprocessed. A story is *crafted* to reach a resolution. So we'll talk today about some possible structures, and the process of story development that goes along with each of these structures. As we'll see, the idea of beginning, middle, and end; well that's just the beginning.

For today, choose a story you want to work on. It can be any story—fairy tale, personal story, myth, a story about someone else's experience, though it would be helpful to choose one you've already worked on before, because we're going to be building on previous knowledge. So have you got a story in mind?

OK. We're going to be doing some writing (part of that cycle of story development that we talked about earlier). We're going to organize the pieces of this story that will fit into your chosen story structure. You might want to take out a storytelling journal, if you're finding that device helpful.

Let's think back to our last few lectures on narrators, and characters, and perspective. Consider the different perspectives that you could take on for this story. You don't have to do a full character analysis for every character, but just think for a moment about the different perspectives that are possible for this story.

Choose one of these perspectives that you want your narrator to sympathize with most—whose perspective do you want to align with in this version of the story? (You can always return to this lecture later and perform all these exercises over again, choosing a different point of view—for now, just pick one.)

What we're going to do right now is an exercise in determining what happened, and what matters about what happened. From that chosen perspective that you have on the story, I've got four questions. One: What happened? What is the one major event or happening in the story? What is the action all about?

Two: What matters about what happened? What is the most important thing about this story to you—what truth does it convey? I'm asking about the meaning of the story, for you—what does this story really mean? I suggest that you put that meaning into a few words, maybe a few phrases, or a sentence—what is the real point of this story? This is the point that your narrator is drawing us towards—it's what shapes the journey for the narrator.

Third question: After I've thought about what happens, and what matters to me about what happened, then I think about all the characters in the story. I list the names of the main characters—the major players. You may want to write their names down the page as a list. I go back to that first question about the main action of the story—the physical drama that's there. Which of these characters does the main action in the story happen to? When that main action happens, who does it happen to? I usually put a star by that character's name.

Fourth question: Now still with that list of characters in mind, or on the page in front of you, think about this: You arrived at the point of your story—what the story really means to you—you came to this point by adopting a particular perspective on this story.

We clarified before, this is a perspective that you choose; your narrator conveys and lives with this perspective—that's the narrator's role, to link the audience with the events and characters through this point of view.

Your narrator may sympathize with one character more than another, and follow one character more closely than any other—this person may or may not be the character who most of the action happens to. Most of the time, the narrator sympathizes with the character who all the action happens to. For example, in the plotline of "Little Red Riding Hood," Red is both the main character, and she's the character who the narrator sympathizes most with when we arrive at the narrator's main point of the story—clever girls can save themselves from wolves, with a little ingenuity.

But you may find that what really matters to your narrator—the person who your narrator is really interested in—is that person in the corner who's supposed to be a secondary character. For example, one of the most powerful versions I've ever heard of the Biblical story of the "Prodigal Son," it was told from the perspective of a narrator who sympathized most with the brother who was left behind—when the Prodigal Son, he went off and he squandered his inheritance, this other brother stayed behind to help with the family farm. When that Prodigal Son came home, well that brother was ticked off that the father just welcomed the prodigal back in!

So while the peak action of the story came when the Prodigal Son returned and the father welcomed him, the real point of the story for this narrator was what happened off to the side, in a small conversation between the father and this other brother.

What we've just done is to start to separate out the "plot" (which is the sequencing of events in your story—what happens to whom), the plot from the "emotional arc" (which is how we feel about the events in your story—what matters about what happened). Most of the time, this emotional arc moves with the plot sequencing of the story—so we get to the climax of the plotline, and when we do we also reach the emotional climax of the story.

But, sometimes it's different. When the narrator sympathizes with someone other than the person the main action happens to—I go back to that list of characters, and I keep a star by the name of that person who carries the physical action of the story. But I put another star by the person's name who helps us arrive at the main point of the story. I might circle that name as well.

In this lecture, we're going to focus on the structure of the story and sequencing—the *physical* journey that your story takes us on—and how this structure relates to the main point of your story. Next time, we're going to go deeper into this emotional arc of your story—the *emotional* journey that your audience goes on as they follow that primary character to the real point of the story. These two lectures are linked, because (of course) the emotional journey is going to influence the physical journey, and vice versa.

Let's focus on the main events in your story, and putting them together into an order that makes sense. This story structure is a kind of "frame" that you put around the events in a story. You can imagine it as a literal frame around a picture—so there's all the stuff inside the painting (the figures, and the colors, and the subject matter), and then there's the frame around that painting that designates it—the stuff inside the painting, and the stuff outside.

If you've ever framed a photo with one of those frames that you just buy at the store, you may have had this happen to you: The photo is one size, but the frame is a little bit smaller, or a little bit larger, than that photo. You have to line the photo up just right behind that mat in the frame that you bought to make that photo look right once you've framed it up. It's the same with your story—you're choosing a frame to put around the characters, and the events, and the perspective that that story holds.

You want to choose a frame that fits that story—not so narrow of a frame that it cuts off half the story; not so large and all-encompassing that your main point gets lost in the weeds, and not so garishly obvious that it's distracting from the story. (You can imagine a chunky, glittered, and bedazzled frame around a little antique photo of your grandmother.)

Like any other aspect of storytelling (this includes whether or not you use props and how you use them, costumes, lighting, all these different aspects that you could use), you want the frame to serve the story, not the other way around. How might this frame connect with certain audiences? How might it alienate? How does it edit the story? Let the "container" or structure for the story be determined by the story elements—don't try to make a story fit a predetermined mold.

There are lots of tools that are useful when you're developing the structure of your story. We'll try out a few here today, but as you move along with other stories you'll probably find that there are some of these that are more useful to you than others. Do what's useful and what works best with your own personality and with your own thought processes.

One of the best ways to work on your structure of your story is just to go ahead and tell that story to a live person. There are audiences that will really help you in your story growth. There are three audiences in particular: the teddy bear, the mirror, and the best friend.

Each of these audiences has their merits—I regularly each of these three audiences. But there's really no substitute to telling to a live person. This is probably the best possible start for trying out an order for your story: You'll remember points, you'll insert different other points, and you'll almost certainly wish that you'd told it a little bit differently when you're telling it the first time to a person—it's a wonderfully educational exercise!

One of the next-best ways to begin threading the story together and threading the plotline of your story is to storyboard the main scenes of action— storyboarding, it's a very organic way of following your storyline, in the sense that there's not a rigid structure that you're trying to fit your story into.

A storyboard is nothing more than a series of drawings that you make— drawings, not scripted words—and these drawings sketch out who and what is in the major scenes of action. Take a page of your journal right now, and you can either draw lines to make it resemble a kind of tic-tac-toe board—you're making boxes on the page—or you can actually draw out these separate boxes. Each of these blank boxes represents a scene of action in your story.

In the first box: Where do we begin in the story? What's the first scene, and who's there? I'd like for you to draw—yes, draw—draw those characters in that box, and sketch out the scenery that's there.

You've already visualized these places, so the drawing should just be a reference for you—and don't worry about the quality of your drawing! All of my students can tell you that I am a terrible visual artist. My storyboards look like they're full of stick figures! It doesn't really matter what your drawing looks like to any other person. What matters is that you can look at it and you can recognize the people and the specific locations that are there in that scene. That's where we begin.

Where does the next action move—what happens next? Draw the next scene in that next box, the second box. You're moving from beginning, to the middle, to the end of your story—and you're probably going to take up more than three boxes doing this!

Now, look at the drawings that you've made. (You can laugh at your artistry if you like—I always laugh at my own artistry!) But look at those drawings. These storyboards follow the action of the story, and they represent a flow of action. So, with the "Red Riding Hood" storyboard, you see this girl in the woods alone. (I decided to start the action of the story there, rather than back at home when she's with her mother before heading out into the woods.) Then her meeting with the wolf at this fork in the road, then in another box, him with the grandmother (and the intestine at the door latch).

One scene flows into the next for a reason. The characters are being propelled into the next scene by what's coming before, and they're also being pulled into the next frame because of what's waiting for them there.

So, in the scene leading from the fork in the road (where the wolf meets the girl), leading into this next scene, the girl is propelled into the scene by her own arousal (there's something about that man-wolf that makes her want him; she's drawn to him). She's also excited about this race—it pushes her into the next scene. At the same time, there are things that are pulling her into that next scene—the grandmother's hunger (she needs what the girl is bringing to her), and the wolf draws her into the next scene as well (his desire for her).

For the next two storyboards, the girl's conflicted sexual desire propels her into bed with the wolf, and at the same time she's being pulled into that scene by her own bodily maturity, and by the wolf's hunger for her. Look at two of your storyboard scenes right now, and choose one of them that really moves into the second one. Really think: What motivates the action to move from this one scene to the next?

I want you to draw two arrows connecting these boxes—one arrow points forward to the next box, and the other points from the second box back to the first. Ask yourself: What propels these characters into the next scene? Write that (in a few words) above that arrow moving forward. Then ask yourself, what pulls these characters into the next scene? Write that (in a few words) above the arrow moving from the second scene back to the first.

Storyboarding is a highly useful rehearsal technique as you develop the flow of action for your story. Because you can see these separate scenes as connected, not only by a logical chain of events, but by lines of force—they're propelled into the future, and then there's something there in that next scene that's pulling them into that next future at the same time.

You see the story isn't just this, and then this, and then this—it's full of urgency and lines of action and force. Because you're drawing it, it gets you thinking in terms of images, of 360-degree scenes, and of character placement and of the interrelationships between each of these scenes.

Your storyboards are one way to follow the action of your story—they take you from beginning to middle to end. There are other ways of organizing the actions according to a predetermined series of events. We've already talked about one way of structuring your events through looking at the hero's journey.

That hero's journey, of course, takes you from separation, to initiation, to return (it's a form of beginning, middle, and end). There are specific roles and characteristics that you're called to draw out of that story to make it into a hero's journey.

There are other structures. The general shape of most stories follows the structure for dramatic plots that was laid out by Aristotle in 335 B.C.E. It was later amended by Gustav Freytag in the 19th century. In this classic story structure, you'd give an introduction (this is the start of the story, where we

304

meet the protagonist and we learn a little bit about him or her—just enough so that we care about what happens to them).

That introduction, it leads to an inciting incident (something that gets the action going), and then that rising action, it leads to a climax (so all of the events that lead up to this pinnacle moment or the turning point in the story. You'll notice that on a drawing of this, the line of rising action isn't smooth. That's because there will be these little dips and valleys along the way towards that climax, but eventually in that action, it peaks). Then at the very end you have the *dénouement*, or the falling action (this is what happens to the characters after the climax), and after that, the conclusion (they lived happily ever after, the end).

What's interesting is the main character has almost always undergone a transformation between the introduction and the conclusion. You'll notice that this frame leaves you in a different place than you began—the conclusion is physically charted as being on a higher plane than the introduction. It's one of the things that I like most about this way of thinking about your story because when you experience a story, you don't return to the same exact place that you were before. You've changed a little bit. Sometimes you've changed a great bit.

Now, when you're developing a story with this kind of frame, you can work through the Aristotelian plotline from several different directions. For example, you can follow it linearly, starting from the beginning, moving to the middle, and then to the end. So, ask: From that main character's perspective, what propels the story forward from this perspective—what circumstances prompt this person to move forward? From that inciting incident, other actions follow.

Or, you could start with the ending. In order for this audience to get this ending, what must I start the story with? Then you work backwards, with that ending always in mind. Or, you could begin in the middle of your story and can work outward and backward from that point. So, go ahead. Choose one of these entry points for working through an Aristotelian story frame, and quickly sketch out your action of the story according to this frame. Go ahead and draw this chart in your journal, and label the major actions of your story in that chart.

This is the prototypical Western frame for stories, and it can work quite well when your story is told from one point of view, and in a chronological fashion. But we all know that there's more than one side to any story. You might choose to play with multiple points of view, in which case you will veer from this Aristotelian model. It's like the Japanese film *Rashomon*, which tells the same story from three different perspectives (if you take any course on film history, you'll probably study this film—it was a black-and-white forerunner to many of the modern films that play with story structure).

So with this story, you have three men telling the "same" story, and these three stories culminate in the total film-story. If I drew that structure, it would look like three Aristotelian charts all strung together. *Rashomon* led to modern-day films that play with story structure, such as the film *Memento* from the year 2000. The movie begins with the actual ending of the story. This is something important for you to consider: Does your story have to happen chronologically?

This gets back to the main point that your narrator wants to convey—your narrator has the power not only to expand and contract time through descriptions and through summaries, but the narrator can hop back and forth in time using foreshadowing and flashbacks. That's the purpose of writing out these journal exercises—to keep checking back on your original thoughts about the story as you keep track and add more dimensions to that story.

For example, one of my students crafted a very compelling version of the Greek myth of Icarus and Daedalus—where the son and father are cast into prison on an island, and the father, he crafts these two sets of wings made of feathers and wax, and he tells his son not to fly too close to the sun, but as they take off, the son is so thrilled at this moment of flight that he forgets that father's warning, and he flies so close to the sun that his wings begin to melt, and he crashes in to the sea.

That description that I just gave follows an Aristotelian model. But what this student first recognized was that the point of the story for him was about the father's love for the son, so the story's told with the narrator sympathizing most with that father.

At the very beginning of his story, we see the father; he's looking up into the sky, and he's silently screaming for Icarus. He's silently screaming, and he watches his son fall to his death—and then the father wakes up, and he's in prison on the island, and then he builds the wings. Where the "ending" should be, the father sees one tiny feather floating down and he catches that feather as it floats down from the sky, as it goes into his hand, and he [puff], blows that feather off.

It's heartbreaking. And that tender point at the very conclusion is all the more poignant because we know what's going to happen in the end. We've already seen it at the very beginning. We jump from their close embrace on the shore before they take flight, to this tiny feather in his hand.

Does your story have to be told in chronological order? Could it be told in a nonlinear way, where you could incorporate flash-forwards, or flashbacks? You can go back to your storyboards in your storytelling journal for help in making this choice. Look at the scenes that are there. Now, switch the order of one of these scenes—pull one scene forward or another scene back in your storyline. Be playful.

This is especially useful to do for a story that you think has to be told in chronological order. Think of one pivotal point in the end of your story, and try putting it first. Follow the Dadaists—in the Dadaist movement, the artists, they would paint something or write a poem, and then they would tear it up and they would throw it on the floor just to see what new and interesting combination of images or words fluttered down when those pieces reshaped themselves on the floor. Be willing to be playful with story structure.

Another way to structure a story is to start with the main "things" that you are drawn to, and let the structure flow from these "things." For example, I was helping some members of my church develop stories as a part of an Easter program—they were enacting The Last Supper. Most of these people had no performance experience whatsoever. Many of them were engineers working at our local chemical company. And there was a reverence that many of these guys had for what to them was the holy word of God. That's good; that's appropriate, but to get to the real meaning of these Bible stories for them, I asked them to let go of that distanced reverence, and to really see the relationships that this healer had with the folks around him, to understand how a deity wanted to love people on a human level.

I asked them to look at certain stories from the Bible, and to write down not the story, but three to five things that stuck out to them from the story. And I used this term "thing" intentionally—a "thing" could be something one character says to another person, it could be a place, it could be a specific event, or a feeling that they had at a certain point in the story. I asked them to write down a list of three to five "things," and then with each of these things, to think of a specific image—something concrete, that you can see—an image that pairs with that "thing."

The man who played Peter in the show, one "thing" that stuck out to him was about how Jesus called him the "Rock," and from his concrete image was a rock on a dusty road. Another "thing" was foot washing, and his concrete image was that bowl filled with water, and drops of that water.

We arranged these "things" into an order that told the story of how this holy figure was an approachable friend (that was the overarching point of his story—that big point that welled up from these little things. The foot washing, and the rock on the road).

This is a story that he crafted from "things" and images, and in the story you he visualized some of those images as he told the story. So, if we chart that story out in terms of structure, you've got these two lines of action—so there are two stories here, and they're linked with an awareness of the two working together toward one main point.

That most important thing (the approachable friend) is what drives all of these little strung-together bits. (This is what storytelling coach Doug Lipman calls the "MIT," the "Most Important Thing." If you forget your story, at any point, you just go back to that most important thing and you've got it—"He's fishing buddy, that's the point—I've got it!").

From that Most Important Thing, that umbrella that arches over the whole story, you can arrange these little things, the little insights into themed clusters, or chronological clusters of events.

The Most Important Thing helps us link together this plotline—the structure of the events in your story. It helps us link that with the emotional through-line—what makes us care about these events. The Most Important Thing helps you identify where and how you want the story to end.

Your story will come to some sort of resolution at the end. That doesn't mean that it has to come to a happy ending. Some stories don't have a neat and tidy conclusion—that's OK! You're actually doing a story injustice to the story if you try to make it fit the Aristotelian model. This structure works well, because most audiences recognize it. But that doesn't mean it's the best way for every audience or every story.

Go back to the first question that I asked you in this lecture: What is the main point of the story for your narrator? What is that nugget that you don't want your audience to lose?

That main point will be the Most Important Thing for your story—and that Most Important Thing overarches any story structure, and it determines how you want your narrator to glide through the plot—it shapes the "economy" of your performance. (Remember that phrase from our earlier lecture? You don't want to do a wasteful performance.) Because the point will determine how much information you need to give in the introduction, and what you can leave out.

The nugget will determine if you include digressions, and how many of them you can include before you start to economically detract from the main point that we're driving towards. The first question will tell you how far the introduction needs to go back, and more importantly, where does the story land in the end?

Look at that point of the story. Now look at one of those structures that you used to organize the plot of the story (the storyboard, the Aristotelian chart, the umbrella of "things," for example). Where do we get to the point in this plotline? Is it at the very end? Or does the point coincide with the climax of the plot? Is it something that the characters themselves never realize—something only the narrator knows and can reveal from years of age and experience beyond the events that are described in the story?

Try to put your finger on that spot when you arrive at the point—and if you're keeping a storytelling journal of these exercises, you can go ahead and draw a circle around that spot. That spot is the emotional climax of your story.

What's interesting about the "Red Riding Hood" story and how it developed for me, is that my initial storyboard followed the plotline. I started the story as it usually does, with the girl getting the basket of goodies from her mother and heading out into the woods. But the more that I looked at the emotional arc of the story and the more that I played with the storyline, the more that I realized that my version needed to start in the woods. The emotional arc changed how this plotline unfolded. It reframed the storyboards, and the story.

In the next lecture, we'll talk about the even-more-important role of the emotional trajectory of your story, and how this emotional through-line offers the primary points of connection between your story and your audience.

Emotional Arc and Empathy
Lecture 16

Your listeners don't believe your story just because you tell them the facts; they believe your story because you make the progression of facts and events understandable and emotionally true. This is what the emotional arc does for your story. The plot is what happens in the story; the emotional arc is how we feel about what happens—whether we believe and emotionally connect with what happens. In this lecture, we'll add more nuance to a story by developing the emotional arc and considering how your performance choices contribute to that arc. Then, we'll talk about how conscious decisions relating to the emotional arc help tie together the ending of your story into a good resolution.

Emotional Tones

- At different points, your story may take listeners on a journey from an emotionally neutral place, to happy, to tense, to nervous, to elated, back to happy, and then to terrified; all of these are emotional tones that we feel when we experience a story.

- Let's return to the storyboard exercise we did at the beginning of the last lecture on story structure. In the upper left-hand corner of each of the boxes you drew for each of the scenes in your story, write one word that describes the emotional tone of that scene.

- The emotional tone will depend on the point of view that you've chosen. An emotionally neutral scene to one character may be an emotionally charged scene for another character—the one with whom the narrator most identifies. Or the narrator, standing outside the characters, may realize the sadness of a scene, given what he or she knows is coming.

- When we talk about an emotional arc, we're talking about how you as the teller shape and arrange the flow of emotional tones as we progress through your story. The image of an arc mirrors the image of the Aristotelian frame for a story.

- o Just as the events of a story climax, the emotional arc of a story reaches a climax, as well.

- o Most of the time, the emotional arc parallels the sequence and climax of the plot, but sometimes, you may want the emotional arc to climax at a different point in the plot.

- o For the teller of the Jarius story, the peak emotional moment doesn't coincide with the peak moment of action—when Jesus heals the girl—but occurs in a small moment afterwards—when Jesus gives bread to the girl. Notice that the teller gives a protracted description of this moment, artfully manipulating time.

- The success of storytelling is far more than relating a string of events; it's much more nuanced than that. It's about making the conscious decision to distinguish between the events in the story and what really matters to you in the story.

Emotional Investment

- You can communicate emotional arcs without being overly expressive, but you need to remember that when you tell a story, you're committing yourself to being fully present in the moment with the story and the audience. That's the storytelling triangle.

- Being present with someone else means that you are seeking a kind of empathy with that person's situation. Remember, sympathy is feeling for someone else—feeling from a distance—but empathy is feeling with someone. This emotional empathy is one of the key tools for effective storytelling.

- Psychologically, our emotional connection to a story is our "entry point" into the story. We talk strategically about winning "hearts and minds" because, like it or not, we're not programmed to be purely Sherlock Holmes individuals: It's not just our enlightened, rational brains that drive our choices or our actions, but it's our hearts, our emotional connections.

- Emotions drive material decisions, and emotional resonance is key to effectively communicating with your audience. The intellect of your listeners may draw them to the plotline of a story, but it's the emotions that make the story memorable.

- Empathy provides an emotional entry point to your story; it's what gets your listeners in the door and keeps them there. With empathy comes vulnerability on the part of the storyteller, along with belief. These two things are crucial in effectively communicating the emotional arc of your story to an audience because they give the audience permission to emotionally engage with the story.

We collect objects not because of their material or useful value but because of their sentimental value; such objects are emotional entry points to the story of our lives.

- o Vulnerability means that you're living in the moment of a story while you're telling it. Your narrator may know what's going to happen, but there are selected times when the narrator dips into the minds of the characters—who don't know what's going to happen next. This action on the part of the narrator gives the audience permission to be in the moment and feel with the characters.

- o Belief means that, at every moment of the story, you believe that you are telling about something real. Even if you're telling a fairy tale, you need to do the character work to make the characters believable to yourself and to visualize the scenes around you. Your belief in what you're saying gives the audience permission to believe the story and to act on it.

Charting the Emotional Arc

- Emotionally, where does your story begin? What's the emotional tone at the beginning of the story? Neutral or energetic and full of action? You want to create an emotional entry point for your audience so that the audience can begin to connect with some aspect of the story.

- Now think about the middle of your story. How do you want your audience to feel here? And how do you want your audience to feel at the end, when the story resolves itself?

- Go back to the Aristotelian chart you made for your story's plotline and begin to draw a second line over that chart that maps the emotional arc for your story. You may have some peaks and valleys along the way; the arc may not be smooth, just as the plotline's rising action will probably have valleys and high points along the way to the climax.

- We call it an "arc" because somewhere along the line, there is a crest in the emotional drama of the story.
  - In poetry, this moment is called the "fulcrum," and you can imagine the fulcrum as the literal thing that it is, the tipping point of a lever, the point on which everything else in the mechanism hinges. This metaphor of the fulcrum is useful for thinking about and identifying the emotional climax of your story.

  - A tipping point means that, at a certain moment, gravity takes hold and pulls an object in another direction. Imagine a teeter-totter: At a certain point, you're tipping past the level plane and heading upward, and then you pass that edge of balance and you begin to fall down again.

- Throughout your story, you want the emotional tones to help propel the audience from one scene into the next. For example, at the inciting incident—when something happens that hurls us into a conflict—there may be an emotional turn that moves the audience from a neutral place to an anxious place.

- Then, the action rises toward a climactic point, when that conflict comes to a head. With the Inanna story, the gods of heaven throw all the help they can down to Inanna in hell, and she will either rise from the dead or stay in hell. The emotional climax of the story is the point of no return; something has to happen or change.

- If you're having trouble locating the emotional climax of your story, ask yourself: What's at stake for the character who brings us to the main point of the story? What are his or her risks? What's on the line? And when is the final moment, the point of no return? At what specific moment does the primary character face the biggest risk and resolve it?

- Also think about how you want your audience to feel right before the climax. Whatever your choice here, your narrator will have to feel the same emotion—and build to that point emotionally. You'll have to communicate that emotional commitment through your words, your body, and the emotional resonance of your voice.

Working toward the Emotional Tipping Point
- As we discussed in the last lecture, the "most important thing" can keep you from getting "lost in the weeds," both in structuring your story and in your emotional commitment to the story.

- The most important aspect of developing your emotional arc for a story starts with your overall empathetic investment: your belief in the things happening in the story and your vulnerability to live in the moment with those characters.

- In a clip from the "Sanntraigh" story, we can hear in the narrator's description that she empathizes with the old woman. The narrator's and the primary character's attitudes and emotional resonance are aligned. The result for the audience is an even deeper emotional tie to the primary character.

- What you're doing with empathetic narration and emotional arc is adding nuance to your story. Storytelling is something we do every day, but the art of storytelling is about making many small choices that add up to a compelling story.

Suggested Reading

Ellis and Neimi, *Inviting the Wolf In.*

Questions to Consider

1. Does your emotional arc follow the plotline and plot climax, or does the emotional arc peak elsewhere? How will this affect your story delivery?

2. Belief and full-focused commitment are essential to telling a good story. Does this kind of vulnerability make you think differently about storytelling? What other areas of your life could benefit from this kind of full-focused commitment?

Emotional Arc and Empathy
Lecture 16—Transcript

Professor Harvey: Consider this situation: You're a lawyer, in court, and your client is on trial for shooting an intruder who was walking into his house in the middle of the night. To complicate things, the client was walking downstairs when the intruder came into the house. The intruder turned to the side; he actually stumbled out of the house off the threshold and out into the lawn, and your client shot him in the side.

If the client were in immediate danger of bodily harm, this would be a clear case of self-defense; it's something called the "Castle Doctrine." But your client was coming downstairs at the time, and there was a lot of room in between them, and the intruder had left the threshold of the house. He'd actually gone out into the lawn, and your client shot the intruder in the side. Could that intruder have been running away? The police later found out that the intruder was unarmed. Could there have been no bodily danger to your client?

In order to convincingly tell your client's story, your audience has to understand what happened, but you have to make your client's actions justifiable to that jury, so that when you come to the point in the story when he shoots, the audience says, "Well of course he shot—that's what anyone would do!"

Your audience doesn't just believe your story just because you tell them the facts. They believe your story because you make that progression of facts and events understandable and emotionally true for your audience. This is what the emotional arc does for your story. The plot is what *happens* in the story; the emotional arc is how we *feel* about what happens—whether we believe and emotionally connect with what happens:

> John was sleeping when a noise woke him up. It was coming from downstairs. He looked over at the clock—it was 3:20 am, and his children and his wife were all at home asleep upstairs in the house. He sat up. He heard the sound of a metal scraping coming from the entryway downstairs—he told his wife to get in the closet with the

kids, and he grabbed his handgun; he loaded it, and he walked over to the top of the stairs.

When he got to the top, he saw the door open. The streetlight was on outside, and he could see the outline of a figure walking into the entryway of the house. He knew there had been two other break-ins that same month in their neighborhood, and one older man had been shot in his bed during one of those break-ins.

So, standing at the top of the stairs, he shouted to the intruder that he had a gun—and he saw that figure turn—and that figure moved his hands like he was reaching for his belt, or something on his belt, and he backed away from the house into the lawn. My client didn't wait to be another victim. He shot, and his family is alive today because of it.

That story presents not only a plot of events, but there's an emotional arc that guides the audience into the story as well. When we come to the climax of that story—when the client shoots—you have emotionally connected with his perspective, and you buy it; you buy that what he did was justifiable.

The other side is telling their story about the situation, and their emotional arc wants to convince you that that the shooting wasn't earned—that it was senseless, and needless, and that your client wasn't in any real bodily danger. The guy was on the lawn.

In order for your version of the story to land, your audience has to emotionally follow the story, so that when you come to the resolution of the story, your audience believes that that moment was earned. Have you ever read a story, and the conclusion just doesn't ring right or true with you? "I just didn't buy that story."

The success of a story is far more nuanced than just relating a string of events. It's that emotional ride that influences the real meat of the storytelling experience, more so even than plot sequencing. The emotional connection is what sweeps us up, and that emotional ride is essential in bringing your audience into a resolution to the story that rings true for your audience.

In this lecture, we're going to add more nuance to the story by developing the emotional arc, and by considering how your performance choices will contribute to that arc. Then we'll talk about how these conscious decisions in emotional arc help tie together the ending of your story into a good resolution.

In the story that I just told you, the emotional arc of that story followed along with the plotline—it supported the plot. So if we were going to chart the arc of the plot and the emotional arc, you would see the rising action moving along at the same intensity as the emotional arc, and the climax of the plot (he shoots!) happens at most intense emotional moment as well.

This emotional climax is a moment of terror for the client—there's an emotional tone to this moment, and to all the moments that precede it. At different points, your story may take us on a journey from an emotionally neutral place, to happy, to tense, to nervous, to elated, and back to happy, and then terrified. All of these are tones that we feel when we experience a story.

Let's go back to the storyboarding exercise that we did at the beginning of the lecture on story structure. In the upper-left-hand corner of each of those boxes that we drew for each of the scenes in your story, try to write one word that describes the emotional tone of that scene. For instance, where do you begin, emotionally, in that story? Are you in a neutral place, or are you excited? What about the scenes in the middle—how do you feel in those scenes?

Remember this will all depend on the point of view that you've chosen. An emotionally neutral scene to one character may be an emotionally charged scene for another character, the one with whom the narrator most identifies. Or the narrator, standing outside of the characters, may realize the sadness of this scene, given what he knows is already coming. (So you may have already foreshadowed at the beginning of the story some moment, if you're been playing with story structure and playing with linearity.)

When we talk about an emotional arc, we're talking about how you as the teller shape and arrange the flow of emotional tones as we progress through your story. This image of an arc mirrors the image of an Aristotelian frame for a story. So, just like the events of the story climax, the emotional arc of the story will climax as well. Most of the time the emotional arc parallels the plot sequence and the climax of the plot, as with the story about the lawyer defending his client.

But, sometimes, you may want the emotional arc to climax at a different point in the plot. I'll show you what this looks like. I'd like for you to watch an example of a short story where the emotional arc peaks at a different time than the given events in the story. This is a story by a nonprofessional teller—he's someone from my hometown. This clip is from a local church storytelling event. In this story, a man named Jarius has a daughter who dies, and Jesus brings her back to life.

But for this storyteller, the story doesn't emotionally peak with that moment of the healing, so listen to this story, told by a man named Ben Mallicote, and see if you can distinguish when the real emotional peak of the story comes.

[Video start.]

> **Ben Mallicote:** I mean, if you weren't paying really close and honest attention, it was easy to miss what Jesus was really doing, and just see what you wanted to see. I'll give you an example. We got called to the home of a man named Jairus, and Jairus had a daughter; she was just about your age. When we were called, she was sick, and when we got there, the girl had died.
>
> Jesus entered the house and all of Jairus's neighbors and family were there grieving with him. Jesus put his arm around Jairus and said, "Why do you mourn? The girl is not dead; she is only sleeping." He got this sort of stunned laugh of scorn and disbelief. Without saying anything, Jesus turned and walked to where the little girl was lying, and he reached down, and put his hand on her.
>
> The little girl raised her head and then sat up in bed and then turned and put her legs on the floor, and stood up. Jesus brought this girl back from death into life. But here's what I want you to hear about this story: While everyone else in the room was laughing and

hugging and celebrating, Jesus did something else that nobody else saw. He took the little girl by the hand, and he gave her some bread and some figs to eat. He knew that it had to have been a long time since she ate and she had to have been hungry.

You see, Jesus didn't just raise the girl just for the sake of doing a miracle. He didn't do it just to prove how great he was. Jesus raised this little girl from the dead because he loved her like a father, and like a father, he tended to her needs.

[Video end.]

Professor Harvey: For this storyteller, the thing that stuck out to him in the story wasn't the peak moment of action in the story (when Jesus heals the girl). The peak moment for him—the real meaning of what the story was about—it happened in a small moment, afterwards. It turns that story around. You think that the miracle is the story, but this story is not just about the notion of restoring life, but sustaining life—giving the daily bread of life.

Let's break apart what this teller did. The plotline of that story has its own arc. The action of the story has an inciting incident (Jesus hears that the girl needs him), and then the rising action (he goes to her), it leads to a peak moment in the action (he heals her), and then the dénouement has this mention of what happens afterwards: He gives her bread, and he goes along his way. Most people might read the story and just stop with the plotline climax—and they'd assume that's where the emotional climax was as well. It's a foregone conclusion. But this telling is much more nuanced, much more powerful, because he finds a different emotional arc.

The emotional intensity of the story is relatively low throughout the act of the healing. The emotional arc starts to rise just as the dénouement of the story starts to descend. Jesus, he does something that not many people noticed (the emotion starts to rise)—he goes over to the corner, and he gives her a piece of bread. There—that's the emotional peak moment, this small part of the plotline.

That's the point for this storyteller, and that's the point when we spend a protracted amount of time in description and in scene time. Your artful manipulation of time will be influenced by where this emotional peak of the story falls, and how you want your audience to reach that point.

You see this same distinction in the story of the Prodigal Son—the version that I mentioned in an earlier lecture. You see the climax of the story is when the Prodigal Son returns home (that's the peak moment of action). But the emotional arc of the story, that peaks when the brother of the Prodigal goes to his father and says, "Why did you welcome him home?" and the brother has to face his own forgiveness of his brother.

It turns that story around—you think the story is about getting over youthful selfishness and reckless abandon, but it's really about getting over pride and self-righteousness.

The success of storytelling is far more than relating a string of events—it's much more nuanced than that. It's about making that conscious decision to really distinguish between the events of the story and what really matters to you in the story.

You can communicate emotional arcs without being an overly expressive person. This particular storyteller, he's a lawyer, and while he does a fair amount of public speaking he's not really given to overly ostentatious displays of emotion. But he clearly is invested in this story—he cares about the characters. It matters to him.

Sometimes my students have said, "But I just want to tell the story." Well, OK, but that gets back to what we discussed about perspective and emotional investment in the story. When you tell a story, you're committing yourself—you're committing to being fully present in the moment with that story and with this audience. That's that storytelling triangle. Really being present with someone else means that you're seeking a kind of empathy with what's at hand; for instance, when a friend tells you a story about how they just lost their job. You don't just sit there when you're listening to them like, "Oh, OK." No! When a friend is hurting, you hurt with them.

That's the difference between sympathy and empathy. We mentioned this difference in a previous lecture. Sympathy is feeling for someone else—it's emotional, but it's from a distance: "Oh, I'm so sorry for you."

Empathy is feeling with someone. You feel that hurt with them, and when that friend tells you that they lost their job (this happened to me a few days ago, I was on the phone with a friend and she said she just got laid off), and it just hit in the pit of my stomach, and there's this visceral response, and in my head I was thinking, "What are they going to do? What would I do if that were us? How would we pay our bills—how long could we go on our savings?"

All of these questions came up as she's telling me this, and it wasn't this panic, it was just this, "Ugh! How awful, I'm so sad, with her." That's empathy—feeling not just for, but with someone else, in their joys (you share in happiness in a joyful story), and in their pain.

Emotional empathy is one of the key tools for effective storytelling. Psychologically, our emotional connection to a story is our entry point into the story—we talk strategically about winning "hearts and minds." We do this because, like it or not, we're not programmed to be purely Sherlock Holmes individuals. Now I love Sherlock Holmes but we're not all programmed that way. It's not just our enlightened, rational brains that drive our choices, or our memories, or our actions. It's our hearts, too, our emotional connections.

You don't always fall in love with the person who, on paper, is the right person—no, it's a host of other emotional connections. We collect objects not just because of their material use or their value, but their sentimental value. Look around your room right now and calculate how many things you've kept around just because of their emotional value to you. Those objects are emotional entry points into the story of your life. Those objects tell a part of your story, and they enable you to enter that part of your story.

Emotions drive material decisions, and emotional resonance is key in effectively communicating with your audience. Because, for your audience, their intellect may be drawn in to the plotline of a story, but it's the heart (the emotions) that make that story stick. When you remember a really good story, you may remember the plot, but most likely you're going to remember some other key aspect of that story—something that emotionally resonated with you.

As a storyteller, your empathetic, emotional connection with a story— how you shape the emotional textures of your performance—those are what really make that story stick with your audience. Empathy provides an emotional entry point to your story. It's what gets the audience in the door, and it's what keeps them there. The reason why I was able to feel so deeply with my friend who lost her job is because of two things. One, I felt called into an emotional connection to the story, because she made her own self vulnerable to feel the emotions of what she said while she was saying it.

Two, I believed the truth of what she was saying, because she believed it. With empathy, there's vulnerability on the part of the storyteller, and there's belief. These two things, empathy and belief, are crucial in effectively communicating the emotional arc of your story to your audience. Because these two aspects of empathy (vulnerability and belief), because of these, they give your audience permission to emotionally engage with the story.

Vulnerability means that you're living in the moment of the story while you're telling it—so your narrator may know what's going to happen next, but there are selected times when the narrator dips into the characters' minds, and they, (in the then-and-there), those characters, the characters don't know what's going to happen next. They don't see the wider chart of events; they're just there in the moment, and you are too, and it gives the audience permission to be in the moment and feel with those characters.

Belief means that, at every moment in the story, I believed that she was telling me something real. We talked in the fairy tale lecture about how important this is, especially for kids. Even if you're telling a fictional story about a fantasy world—if you don't believe it, they won't believe it.

It's why you need to do the character work to really make these characters (even the big bad wolf, a relatively static character), to make them really believable to yourself, to give them flesh and to visualize the scenes around you, so you really believe you're seeing them. Your belief in what you're saying (and seeing, and experiencing through visualization), your belief gives the audience permission to believe the story, and to act on it.

With all these kinds of stories—political stories, fantasy stories, ghost stories, family stories—with all kinds of stories, empathy is crucial in giving your audience permission to feel something, and in giving your audience an emotional entry point into the story.

This starts from the very beginning of your story. Let's focus on the start of your story itself, when you begin telling that story and you introduce us to the characters. (There's a very important other emotional and social entry point that you give even before the introduction of the story; it's called a "mindset," and it gets your audience into the groove of listening to the story. We'll cover that in a later lecture on keeping your audience's attention). Right now, let's start from the beginning, and begin to chart the emotional arc of your story.

Emotionally, where does your story begin? What's the emotional tone at the beginning of your story? Is it neutral? Or energetic, or full of action? You want to create an emotional entry point for your audience, so that the audience can begin to connect with some aspect of the story.

Disney does this very effectively in their animated musical films. Usually in the first five minutes of the film, the primary character will sing a song that invites the audience to see that character's dilemma and their point of view, and we begin to sympathize and even empathize with that character from the get-go.

As you continue to feel empathy with your story, your audience will continue to feel those invitations to enter the story more deeply. Go to the middle of your story. How do you want your audience to feel here? Anxious? Neutral? How do you want your audience to feel at the very end, when the story resolves itself?

Go back to the Aristotelian chart that you made for your story's plotline. Begin to draw a second line over that chart that maps the emotional arc for your story. You may have little dips or peaks along the way. It may not be a smooth arc, just as your plotline's rising action will probably have little valleys and high points along the way to the climax. We call it an "arc" because somewhere along the line, there's a crest in the emotional drama of the story.

In poetry, this climax moment is called the "fulcrum," and you can imagine the fulcrum as the literal thing that it is, the tipping point of a lever, the point on which everything else in the mechanism hinges. I refer to the poetry fulcrum here because it's a useful metaphor for thinking about how to identify the emotional climax of your story.

A tipping point means that, at a certain moment, gravity takes hold and pulls an object into another direction. You can imagine a teeter-totter: At a certain point, you're tipping past the level plane and you're heading upwards, and you pass that edge of balance when you begin to fall down again.

Throughout your story, you will want the emotional tones of your story to help propel the audience from one scene into the next. So, at the inciting incident—when something happens that hurls us into a conflict, it gets the action of the story going—there may be an emotional turn in that moment that moves the audience from a neutral place, to being anxious: "What's going to happen?"

Then we rise in action towards this climactic point, when the conflict has come to a head. With the "Inanna" story, from our lecture on myth the gods of heaven have thrown all the help they can down to Inanna in hell, and they drip water and food over her, and it's the point at which she either rises from the dead, or she stays in hell—and she rises!

That's when the emotional climax of the story, that's what it does for your audience—it's the point of no return, something has to happen or to change. It's the point in the story at which you are unable to remain upright and you fall into some other kind of emotional state. She either rises, or she stays in hell. I want you to locate the emotional climax of your story—it may line right up with the plot climax, but then again it might be different. And if you're having trouble with this, let me ask you a couple of questions.

What's at stake here for that character who brings us to the main point of the story? What are the risks? What's on the line?

When is the final moment, the point of no return? After this specific point, that big risk and those big stakes are no more—it's done. At what specific moment does that primary character face the big risk and resolve it?

It's interesting to look this from the "Inanna" story, from this perspective (that hero's journey story), because Inanna dies (she faces the gates of hell, and she dies)—but depending on your telling of the story and your point of view, that's not the climax of the action.

Because then her helper comes, and brings her back to life, and she flees out of hell. That moment when she's brought back to life, for me, is the climax of both the plotline and the emotional climax of the story—because her risk is death, and she faces it (literally, she turns to the judges of hell and they kill her with their stare—you know, if looks could kill!), but the risk is finally dealt with when she's reborn.

Now that's the emotional climax when I'm telling the story to a group of friends. But, when I told this story to my hairdresser, the plotline, it remained the same, but the emotional climax shifted. The peak moment emotionally was when Inanna chose her beautician over her husband, and kept the hairdresser with her while her husband went to hell! Your audience will impact where you place this emotional climax of your story as well, even though your plotline doesn't change a bit.

Consider, how do you want your audience to feel right before the climax? If you're coordinating this with the plot sequence, this is the last moment of the rising action. Do you want them to feel anxious or nervous? ("What's going to happen to them?") Or do you want them to feel exhausted? ("We've been battling so long!") As if all hope is gone? (That would be right before the *deus ex machina* swoops down to save everyone.)

If you want your audience to feel like any of those emotions, your narrator will have to feel that, and build to that point emotionally. You have to communicate that emotional commitment through your words, and your body, and the emotional resonance of your voice. Remember: The more specific your choices are in performance, the clearer the stakes of the drama will be to your audience, and the more completely your audience will be pulled into that arc of the narrative.

Much of this investment comes from spending time with your story—visualizing, thinking about the scenes and the characters, and thinking about the lines of force that are connecting and propelling these moments of the plot and propelling them along. (That's what we discussed in the last lecture on story structure.) If you know your story well enough, and you immerse yourself into the story while you're telling it, these choices will make themselves apparent.

How can your narrator work toward that emotional tipping point? As we talked about in the last lecture, the Most Important Thing (the MIT) can help you from getting lost in the weeds, both in structuring your story and your emotional commitment to the story.

The most important aspect of developing your emotional arc for your story starts with your overall "empathetic investment": your belief in the things that are happening in the story, and your vulnerability to live in the moment with those characters.

I want you to watch this clip from the "Sanntraigh" story, and watch how the narrator moves into such a sympathetic position with that primary character, the old woman, that the narrator is describing what that woman thinks and feels, and you can hear in the narrator's description how the narrator empathizes with that woman. You hear narration spoken with the attitude of that old woman. Listen for that sense of empathy in the following clip.

[Video start.]

> **Professor Harvey:** That fairy was silent. She glided through that room and she went straight for that kettle and she took out milky white fingers and she wrapped those fingers around the handle of that kettle and the woman, she froze. Because here was a fairy, creeping out of her fairy knoll and coming down her fairy path and

coming into her house through the town disguised as she was, in through her door and through her kitchen and coming for her kettle.

As frightened as that woman was, she knew that was the only kettle that family had. They needed that kettle, so as that fairy, she laid those milky white fingers around the handle of that kettle, that woman, she plucked up her courage and she said some certain magic words. She said, "The due of a kettle is bones, and to bring it safely home."

[Video end.]

Professor Harvey: This narrator cares about and sympathizes with the primary character, and as a result there are moments when the narrator will speak in epic mode, making eye contact with the audience, so you're still connected with the outside world in the here-and-now, but the narrator says those descriptions as if the woman herself were describing what's going on around her.

You're aligning the narrator and the primary character's attitudes and emotional resonance. And the result for the audience is an even deeper emotional tie to that primary character. That's what empathy does. It doesn't matter if you're telling a story to a couple of friends at a party, or to a large group at a club meeting; empathy is absolutely necessary in successfully developing the emotional entry points that lead to a satisfying emotional arc for your story.

What you're doing with this empathetic narration and emotional arc is adding nuance to your story. Storytelling, it's something we do every day. But the *art* of storytelling is all about making these little choices that add up to a compelling story. What also adds nuance is in the next lecture—now that we've talked about how the narrator empathetically voices narration, we're going to talk next time about switching narrative voice. How your narrator can empathize with more than one character throughout a story.

Varying the Narrator's Perspective
Lecture 17

In order for the resolution of a story to be satisfying, your audience must care enough about the primary character to want him or her to succeed and must care about seeing the other characters resolve their tensions with the primary character. One of the best ways to encourage your listeners to develop their own momentum with the emotional arc of your story is to give them just enough of a taste of the different character perspectives (including that of the villain!) that they start to see your story in three dimensions. You do this by having your narrator switch allegiance from one character to another and narrate events from a new perspective.

Shifting Perspective

- As we've said, most of the time, your narrator is empathetic toward the main character of your story, but sometimes, you may want your narrator to dip inside the head of another character and narrate from that perspective. We see this in an excerpt from "Red Riding Hood," when the narrator shifts perspective from the girl to the wolf.

- Allowing the narrator to dip inside the head of other characters— even the villain—can give a wonderful dynamism to your story. It helps highlight the tensiveness we spoke about in a previous lecture and gives the audience a delicious variety of perspectives to take in.

- Note, however, that changing your narrator's allegiance should happen as part of the flow of the story; it shouldn't call attention to itself. This shift in perspective provides a new angle on things while contributing to the overall meaning of the story.

- Sticking with one perspective can be an effective choice, but you open the story up to many more possibilities when you allow the narrator to switch perspectives. Again, in the older version of "Red Riding Hood," when the narrator gives us the perspective of the laundresses, the potential for humor is introduced into what would otherwise be a terrifying experience if the story was narrated only from the perspective of the little girl.

Empathizing with Multiple Characters

- For your audience to truly experience the emotional resonance of different perspectives, you as a storyteller must believe that you are seeing the scene from different characters' points of view. This gets us back to our exercises on empathy and belief.

- Although you may be using third-person narration ("he did this," "she did that"), you must speak as if you are providing a first-person account of the moment. In this way, your listeners will start to believe that this character is really experiencing this event. They will be drawn into your story, because they see you believing the character's perspective as if it were happening to you, the storyteller.

- This is one of the unique features of storytelling; if you were an actor, you'd be tied to dialogue and would never get to use narration. You'd also be tied to one character role, while a storyteller plays multiple roles. But you don't lose your narrator's strong association with the primary character in doing this; if anything, seeing the villain from the inside allows the audience to bond even more fully with the main character.

An Exercise in Shifting Allegiance

- Choose one of your stories and list all the main characters in your storytelling journal. For each character other than the primary one, think about what he or she wants in the story. What does the antagonist want most; what does the helper character want most? Put into words the motivating desire of one of these characters.

- Next, stand up and speak aloud that character's desire. If you were working with the miner's story we heard earlier, you might say, "I want to get Donzel out of the mine." Assign a focal point to someone your character might be speaking to and repeat the line, in dramatic mode, until you believe it.

- Still standing and maintaining the focal point, change the line from first person to third person. Now, repeat the line in epic mode to the audience. Say the line until you believe it.

- Come out of that character and think about a moment in your story when this character and the main character are a part of the same scene. Practice moving back and forth between character attitudes. For the purposes of this exercise, speak everything in third-person narration. Don't worry about character dialogue between these two figures; just focus on how you're saying the narration.
  - ○ Start narrating the scene from one character's perspective—either the main character or the secondary character—while looking out at the audience.

  - ○ As you adopt the secondary character's perspective, think about what's going on with that character. Carry his or her beliefs and attitudes as you share descriptions with the audience. Concentrate on believing what you're saying from that character's point of view.

- This exercise will help you develop a kind of storytelling muscle memory so that you can respond in the moment when a new story calls for narrational dimension.

Internal Conflict
- You can also use this technique of having the narrator dip into other character perspectives when the main character is experiencing internal conflict. Imagine two sides of your own self, for example, battling against each other; think of having a devil on one shoulder and an angel on the other.

- As mentioned earlier, the hero's journey is a kind of mirror for the internal conflicts that go on in our lives, and the external "dragons" in such stories are often metaphors for our own internal beasts that we try to overcome.

- When you're telling a story that deals with an internal dragon, you may want to personify the thing you're struggling with. Give that area of conflict an attitude and claim that attitude in moments of description. You can even separate the two perspectives with different focal points and body postures.

- Robert Breen, a scholar at what is now Northwestern University's Department of Performance Studies, referred to this kind of internally conflicted character as a "bifurcated narrator." It's as if the one person becomes two characters, and the narrator of your story can then dip inside the perspective of each of these characters.

- This technique returns us to the very reason that we tell stories: Stories give form to our deepest desires, fears, and hopes. By giving form and embodied attitude to a disembodied area of conflict— the addiction, or the debt, or the unrequited love—by finding the differences in "character" between the easy path and the right one, you *name* these struggles. And in naming them, you and your audience gain a kind of power over those forces that doesn't exist without the story.

Story Resolution
- Adding nuance by teasing out the plot from the emotional arc and allowing the narrator to cede control to other characters' attitudes and perspectives add richness to the resolution of a story.

- There are as many different resolutions for a story as there are different kinds of stories to tell, but a key question to ask is: What purpose does the resolution of a story serve? It must bring the audience to a safe place in the end. But note that a safe place isn't the same thing as an easy place; for some stories, the point may be to make your listeners uneasy in order to make them think about things in a new way.

- A safe place in storytelling is satisfying.
  - Sometimes, it's appropriate to have everything turn out all right in the end. This might be the case in telling to children or at a party. Your audience wants a satisfying dessert, not a full meal that requires digestion. At other times, a sugar-coated ending may be inappropriate.

  - The audience and the context of the telling determine what kind of ending will "satisfy." You may adapt some aspects of the ending of your story to satiate the appetites of the specific audience, while other aspects

Sometimes, a satisfying resolution in storytelling is like dessert—sweet and light!

    remain consistent from one telling to the next. This, again, is the difference between the emotional arc (adaptable) and the plotline (consistent).

- A safe place leads the audience out of the story.
  - Toward the end of a story, the audience should feel that everything has been accounted for. The events have been treated, the emotional points have been established, and the characters have had a chance to speak.

  - The emotional arc of your story doesn't take listeners up and then plummet them back to earth in a heap. It guides listeners from the place they were when the story started to a different place at the end.

  - One definition of "resolution" relates to arriving at a plan of future action. The resolution of a story, then, is the point at which the audience is sent out from the story with a plan of action. It's similar to a commencement ceremony for graduates; it marks an ending, but it is also a beginning, a "sending forth." The resolution sends listeners out from the story with a new outlook, a new course of action for their lives, and new questions to explore.

o   You might also think of "resolution" in the sense of the quality of a picture on TV or taken with a camera. This definition relates to how clearly we can see something in fine detail. Thus, the resolution of a story is how listeners are left to see everything in the end. It's not just a wrap-up of the plot but how the characters and the narrator think about how the events played out.

o   You don't want to hit your audience over the head at the end with the meaning of your story. Remember, your listeners are smart people! Instead, your job is to help them see their own situations more clearly through the metaphor of the story.

• Finally, a safe place does no harm to the audience.

o   This characteristic of a safe place has to do with ethics. For instance, some audiences may feel cheated if you tell a story from personal experience and it later turns out that the story was fiction.

o   Likewise, you need to take the audience into account when you determine how you want the story to resolve emotionally. Are your listeners mature enough to handle the themes you're presenting to them? And if they are, do you land the audience in a place where they are ready to assimilate what they've encountered in your story in a meaningful way in their lives?

o   Another aspect of ethics has to do with your own emotional preparedness. Are you ready to tell the story? Have you dealt with the issues you raise and resolved them for yourself to the extent that you can make this story a meaningful experience for listeners and not just therapy for yourself?

Ellis and Neimi, *Inviting the Wolf In*.

1.   Where is one point of dynamic tension in your story—between what two forces? How can you use the tensiveness between these lines of force to build the emotional arc of your story?

2.   Some stories are satisfying in the end like chocolate cake and others, like bitter coffee. What is one thing you need to consider in order to end your story in both a "satisfying" and a "safe" way for your audience?

Varying the Narrator's Perspective
Lecture 17—Transcript

Professor Harvey: The emotional arc, along with the plotline, will come to a resolution in the end. In order for that resolution to be satisfying, your audience has to be drawn into the emotional trajectory, and has to care enough not only about that primary character to want him or her to succeed, but also to care enough about seeing the other characters get out of the way—to want them to have their comeuppance in the end, or to see them resolve the tensions with the primary character!

One of the best ways to encourage your audience to develop their own momentum with the emotional arc of your story, is to give your audience just enough of a taste of the different character perspectives (including the villain) that they start to see your story in "3-D"—from different angles. You do that by having your narrator switch allegiance from one character to another—those moments in the story when the story's narrator cedes control of the story to another character's perspective for just a little while, and lets them narrate events from a new perspective.

Most of the time, your narrator is empathetic towards the main character, but sometimes, you may want for your narrator to dip inside the head of another character and narrate from that other character's perspective. Let's look at an example of this—watch this portion of the "Red Riding Hood" story, or "The Grandmother's Tale"—and, pay attention in my version to the attitude of the narrator when the wolf approaches the grandmother's house.

[Video start.]

> **Professor Harvey:** There, standing in the middle of that fork in the road, was a man. He was tall; he had that scraggly hair on his chin and on his arms. He asked her where she was going, and you know how it is when you see somebody you kind of like, and your heart starts going, and your breath starts kind of picking up a little bit? That was what happened with her and she just started saying the first things that came out of her mouth and into her mind.

She said where she was going, that she was going to that house that was in the clearing on down that path. That man, he asked her, "Well, those legs of yours look fast. Why don't we race there?" She thought that sounded good. He said, "Are you taking the path of the pins, or the path of the needles?" because he knew that both of those paths—the pins and the needles—led back to that clearing in the woods.

She looked up at him and she said, "Well, I'm taking the path of the pins," because she was a good girl, "I'm taking the path of the pins."

"Oh, well I'll take the path of the needles and we'll see who gets there first." She was off; she raced, and she had those young, long legs and she raced. But that man, he raced, and he got down on all fours and he went faster. Because he was *bzou*, he was werewolf, he was wolf-man. He ran and he got to that clearing in the glen and he saw that house that that girl had described, that house by the oak tree.

He went and he knocked up onto the door, he knocked and he heard a voice: "Open the latch, pull that latch and come on inside," and he pulled that latch; he came on inside; he saw that old woman over there on the bed. He ate her up. [Snarling.] He ate all of her flesh. [Snarling.] He ate some of her bones. [Choking.] She was very stringy; she was very old. [Snarling.] That meat, it was very tough, and then he had an idea.

[Video end.]

Professor Harvey: When they meet up in the woods, we hear the narration primarily as if we're siding with the little girl. But then, as we follow the wolf through the woods, the narrator starts to see that world around him from the wolf's perspective—and so by the time that we get to the grandmother's door, we begin to hear the narration from the wolf's perspective. The narrator is enjoying this meal—"He ate all of her skin, and some of her bones, and [slurping] because she was stringy." I'm smiling while I describe this! If I were still narrating as if I were empathetic with the little girl in this moment,

I could not enjoy this meal. But no, the narrator has stopped letting the little girl rule his sympathies, and now the narrator is ceding narrational control over to that wolf.

By providing times when your narrator also dips into the head of the other characters—even the villain—it can give a wonderful dynamism to your story. It highlights that dramatic tension and tensiveness that we spoke about in a previous lecture.

When the narrator moves from narrating from the little girl's perspective, to narrating from the werewolf's perspective, the audience gets to shudder—and maybe even sadistically laugh—at his enjoying this meal of the grandmother, and the blood dripping off of his paws as he puts on the nightcap and pulls the sheets up over himself.

Because we've not only seen what's waiting for the little girl in that house, but also we've seen how much the wolf has enjoyed doing what he just did—because of that, we're able to cringe all the more when she goes into the house, and pulls that [click] intestine latch, and walks over to the bed!

Having your narrator jump inside the attitudinal perspective of the other characters, if only momentarily, it gives your audience a delicious variety of perspectives to take in. The next time you watch a film, look at how often the camera angle changes in just one scene. Even in these lectures, we've been switching camera angles—it helps to break up the story and provide more dynamic action.

But if you haven't noticed those camera changes up until now, that's a good thing. It shouldn't be something that just jumps out at you; that would call attention to the device instead of the story. Changing your narrator's allegiance should happen as part of the flow of the story. It provides a new angle on things while contributing to the overall meaning of the story.

Let's look at another example of how the narrator can shift allegiance—this is from later in that same story—and this time, pay attention to how I'm fully empathizing with each of these characters as I narrate from their perspectives. Here again, from "The Grandmother's Tale."

[Video start.]

Professor Harvey: She ran off through those woods until she came to another clearing and there was a river coming through this clearing and there were laundresses, three laundresses, who were washing these white sheets in the river. They turned and they saw this girl, naked, running through the woods. They took one of those sheets and they wrapped it around her shoulders. They listened to her story and right about that time that wolf, he was sitting there in that bed, growing very impatient.

He hollered out to her, "Well are you watering the trees or are you feeding the grass?" After awhile his impatience grew to where he threw down the sheets—they were still kind of stuck to his fingers—but he threw down the sheets and he went out and he [sniffing], he followed that cord and he came to that plum tree. [Sniffing.] He started to sniff her out. He got down on all fours and he started to follow her scent through the woods. About that time, that girl had explained to those laundresses what had happened. The laundresses, they took that sheet, one of those sheets that they were washing, and they stretched it out over that river; they held it taut. That girl, she walked across that sheet bridge. She got to the other side and she turned around—that was just in time because she could see that wolf coming, raising up from all fours and walking through that glen.

The women, too, they were old, and they were wise. They looked and they saw something kind of comical: a wolf-man who had a blood-covered bonnet slightly askew. He was trying to walk towards them, and he said to them, he said, "You make that bridge for me so I can get across."

They said, "Very well." They took that sheet and they stretched it across that river and that wolf-man, he started to walk across that bridge but as it got to the center—

[Video end.]

340

Professor Harvey: In that part of the story, you heard narration from the little girl's point of view, then the laundresses as they see her coming, and then back to the wolf when he finds that [sniffing] thread around the tree, then back to the girl, then to the laundresses with the sheet, to the girl going across the sheet, and then the laundresses watching the wolf coming out of the woods at them. The woman, they're older and wiser—they have a different perspective than this girl watching the wolf. There are lots of switches in perspective!

It can be an effective choice to stick with one perspective, but you open up the story to so many different possibilities when you allow your narrator to switch perspectives. Because while the little girl seeing the wolf tearing through the woods—while all she would remember was something terrible, and that's what she's seeing—the laundresses have a totally different perspective. They're older women. They see this funny shaggy beast wearing a woman's nightcap. It's a strange sight, but they're more confident than the little girl in their ability to outsmart him.

If we can return to the lecture on fairy tales for a moment, these women are also more sexually mature than the little girl. To the older women, this wolf is just a lecherous man, and they're not drawn in by him; they're not turned on by him; they're not scared of him—they're wise to him. And because they can laugh at him, the audience can laugh at him. So if you allow your narrator to dip inside the laundresses' perspective, you open up the possibility of humor into what otherwise is a very terrifying experience if you kept on narrating from only one perspective.

I asked you not only to pay attention to when the narrator shifted allegiance from one character to another, but also to pay attention to how the narrator empathized with all of those characters while he was narrating from these different perspectives.

For your audience to really experience the emotional resonance of all these perspectives, you as a storyteller have to believe that you're seeing the scene from these different characters' points of view. It gets back to what we talked about with empathy and belief.

If you'll notice, all these lines are spoken in third-person narration. Remember—first-person narration is me talking about me ("I did this, I did that"). Second-person narration is me talking about you (so, "You go here, you do that"). And third-person narration is me talking about everyone from an outsider's point of view ("He did this, she did that"). In third person narration ("He did this, she did that"), you can have levels of omniscience. Sometimes, you see inside the thoughts and feelings of all the characters; sometimes you're only seeing inside the feelings and thoughts of one character. When you narrate with empathy from a character's perspective (any character—the main character, minor characters, the villain)—when you narrate with empathy from a character's perspective, the words coming out of your mouth, they may be in third-person language, but you say them with the conviction and belief as if they are a first-person account for you in that moment.

I'll show you an example. Here's a snippet of the story you just heard—listen to me say these lines as if I were the little girl, saying the lines in first person:

> As I was walking out with that cord tied to me I grabbed a parcel that I had left on that table and I ran out of that clearing, and that cord was trailing behind me and I ran over to a plum tree and I took parcel out and I took my sewing scissors out. I took those scissors and I cut that cord. I took that red thread and I tied it around a plum tree that was growing there in the glen and I ran off. I ran through the woods until I came to another clearing.

Now, listen to that same section again, this time in third person, but I'm saying these lines with the conviction of that first person account.

[Video start.]

> **Professor Harvey:** She was walking out with that cord tied onto her, she grabbed a parcel that she'd left on that table and she ran out into that clearing, that cord trailing behind her. She ran over to a plum tree and she took, out of that parcel, she took her sewing scissors, and she took those scissors and she cut that cord.

She took that red thread and she tied it around a plum tree that was growing there in the glen. She ran.

[Video end.]

Professor Harvey: When I say those lines, I'm immersing myself into that perspective of the girl so much, that even though I'm using the third-person word, "she," I may as well have been saying those lines in first person. And the effect for the audience is that they really start to believe that this character is really experiencing this event. They're drawn into the story, because they see you believing the little girl's perspective as if it were happening to *you*, the storyteller. ("I ran, and I ran, and I ran, and I ran.")

This is one of the unique features of storytelling—if you were an actor, you'd be stuck in dialogue (you'd never get to use narration). You'd also be stuck in one character role—you play only the girl, or only the wolf. The storyteller plays all of these roles, and you don't lose your narrator's strong association with the primary character in doing this. If anything, by seeing the villain from the inside, we're able to bond even more with the heroine.

Hearing these other narrational perspectives, it gives dimension to your story. It can give dramatic irony. You might even hear a kind of quarrel going on behind the way the other characters narrate events versus how the main character narrates those events. Another character might contradict the main character's narration. I want for you to try this with one of your stories— try allowing your narrator to shift allegiance to take on the attitude of other characters, and narrate from their perspective.

I'd like for you to think about the characters in your story. You might want to write them down in a list, maybe in your storytelling journal. Now, for each of the characters on your list, I want for you to think about what each of those characters really wants in that story. For the antagonist of your story, what does that figure most want at the beginning of that story? You may have a helper character, so what does that helper figure want most?

Choose one minor character, and whatever that character's motivating desire is, put it into a statement: "I want to get Donzel out of the mine," for the "Miner's Story" that I told earlier. Now, you'll want to stand up for this part, if you're able (remember that sitting down, it can pull your energy down in your body—standing up, it frees your body to move and respond to a character more freely). And say that sentence out loud. Now say it again, with belief. Look out in front of you and visualize the person whom this character might say that sentence to. Focus on that focal point in dramatic mode, and say the line again. Now say that line again, until you believe it.

Stay where you are, still with that focal point, but change that sentence from first person to third person. So instead of "I want to go home," you'd say, "She wanted to go home." Say this with the same sense of belief as if you were saying it in first person. Say the line. Now say it again. Say it until you believe it.

Now, change focal points and roles—you're going to look at the audience, still staying this line with that sense of the first person belief, but you're telling this to the audience now. Use epic mode; look at that audience in the eye. Now once again, say the line and say it until you're sure you believe it. When you're sure you believe it, the audience will believe it, too.

Come out of that character, and think about a moment in your story when this character and the main character are part of the same scene. I want you to practice moving back and forth between character attitudes. For the purpose of this exercise, I want you to speak everything in third-person narration. Don't worry about character dialogue between these two figures; just focus on how you're saying narration.

Think of a scene in your story that features both this character and the main character. Have you got a specific part of a story in mind? OK, now visualize that scene all around you. Really see it in color; see what's going on in that scene. I want for you to start narrating about that scene from one character's perspective. Depending on your chosen scene, it may make more sense to begin with a minor character, or maybe with the primary character's narration, but begin narrating from what you see from that perspective, and look out to the audience when you do this narration.

Move into that other character's perspective. Think: What's going on for that character—what are they doing? I want for you to narrate about what's going on with that character, and carry the belief and attitude of that second character as you share these descriptions with the audience. Different attitude, different narrator. Really see and believe what you're saying from that character's point of view.

When you're telling a story for your friends at a party, of course you're not going to go back and do all this background work—you're in the moment, you think of a story, and you tell it right then. But doing these exercises now will help you think on your feet about character attitudes.

Just like any other muscle memory (you shift gears in your car, and it becomes second nature—you don't have to think about it when you're driving down a new road; you just do it)—just like any muscle memory, you're developing your storytelling muscles so that you can respond in the moment when a new story calls for narrational dimension. You'll be surprised how easily you can use this technique in the moment—it just takes focus, moment-to-moment focus on your story.

What if your story is about a conflict that goes on inside of one person? You can also use this technique of having the narrator dip into other character perspectives, even when you don't have two characters in conflict, but you have two sides of yourself battling against one another. You can imagine that devil on one shoulder, and the angel on the other. "I was 16, and I saw that girl, and she was so pretty."

"But she was dating Troy Alberson who would beat me up if he knew what I was thinking." We talked about the hero's journey being a mirror for the internal conflicts that go on in our lives, and how the external "dragons" in the story are often metaphors for our own internal beasts that we try to overcome. It's like Macbeth's internal struggles. (Macbeth agonizes over the entire play: First, "Should I kill the king?" Then his guilt over killing the king and taking his throne, and then the struggle over murdering others to keep his throne). This was Freud's genius, to lay out these inner competing desires in us—but it goes back to St. Paul, too, in the book of Romans: "I do not understand my own actions. For I do not do what I want, but I do the very thing that I hate."

When you're telling that story, and you deal with that internal dragon, it helps in the telling to personify that thing that you're struggling with. Give that area of conflict an attitude, and claim that attitude in those moments of description. "I really wanted to ask that girl out."

"But Troy Alberson would beat me up if he knew what I was thinking," and there's a totally different attitude—and I've even separated these different attitudes out by adding different focal points and body postures.

Robert Breen was a scholar at what is now Northwestern University's Department of Performance Studies. He called this kind of internal conflict a "bifurcated narrator"—a narrator, a single person, who has a kind of split personality. It's as if one person becomes two characters, and the narrator of your story can dip inside the perspectives of each of these characters to describe the story from each perspective.

It adds so much nuance to your story. This actually gets back to the very reason why we tell stories—back to those very first lectures. Stories give form to our deepest fears, and desires, and hopes. By giving form and embodied attitude to that disembodied area of conflict—the addiction, or the debt, or the unrequited love—by finding the differences in "character" between the easy and the right paths, you *name* these struggles—and in naming them, it gives you a kind of authority and power over those forces that doesn't exist outside of the story.

Not all stories have a narrator who empathizes with the main character. Consider the connections between your narrator and the main character. Does the narrator care? Is the narrator doubtful? You may strategically choose to have a narrator that is unsympathetic towards the primary character, so that the audience emotionally identifies with that primary character as the underdog. The audience forms its own connection with that primary character in opposition to the narrator's position towards the characters, because we've seen her point of view and sympathized with it.

If I'm talking about that girl in the third person, "I saw that girl," I'm delivering those lines with the sense as if they are a first-person account—as if she herself is taking hold of the story to tell you about herself. It's as if this character has wrested control, narrational control of the story away from the unsympathetic narrator and has taken charge of these third-person lines for herself.

There are lots of ways that you can play with third person narration, and perspective, and character roles to build the dynamic tension of your story. The more you play with moving back and forth between these perspectives, the more dynamic tension you'll be able to add to your story as you build towards the climax.

If you're adding nuance by teasing out the plot from the emotional arc, and you're doing this interesting exploration of how the narrator cedes control to other characters' attitudes and perspectives—with all these nuances in your telling of the story, the resolution of your story becomes a far richer entity. There are as many different resolutions for a story as there are different kinds of stories to tell, so what I want to focus on here is what purpose the resolution of a story serves. When you get to your resolution after you've done this nuanced treatment, your resolution has to serve the purpose of bringing the audience to a "safe place" in the end.

This safe place isn't the same thing as an *easy* place—for some stories, the point may be to make your audience uneasy, in order to make them think about things in a new way. So, what does a safe place look like in storytelling? A safe place has certain characteristics. A safe place is satisfying. This, again, is a reminder that storytelling is an art form. I say "satisfying" because that word has so many culinary associations. There is a wide variety of meals that are deliciously satisfying, but in different ways—so at the right time, a steak is satisfying, and at the right time, a slice of dark chocolate cake (with ganache icing) is satisfying, and at the right time, a bitter cup of coffee is satisfying. But it depends on the context.

It's the same with your stories. Sometimes it's absolutely appropriate to have everything turn out all right in the end for everyone—on your child's birthday, or at a party, these are kinds of stories that are absolutely appropriate. It's time for dessert; the audience wants that—they don't want to hear a depressing ending, then.

But sometimes, a happy ending is absolutely inappropriate for your audience. When you've got a friend who's got cancer—and yes there's a great need for happy, silly stories then—but sometimes, in those conversations, that person has been through hell, and they don't need some syrupy-sweet, sugar-coated ending about how everything's going to be just fine.

The audience, and the context of the telling will determine what kind of ending will satisfy. There are aspects of the ending of your story that are adaptable to satiate the appetites of your specific audience—parts that can change and mold to fit the setting—and there are aspects of the story that will remain fairly consistent from telling to telling.

This, again, is the difference between emotional arc and the plotline. The plotline is that part that will remain fairly consistent (unless you change your narrator's perspective completely from one telling to the next, which could result in a different story altogether), but the plot will usually remain consistent. All your visualizations in that world of the actions and the plotline, well those will remain the same

But emotionally, where we wind up—how those characters feel about how the story ends, and the wording that the narrator gives us at the end of the story—whether we hear a punch line from the narrator that makes everything we've just heard laughable, or whether the narrator gives us some more serious thoughts to sit with as we exit the story. That's all tied to the emotional conclusion of the story, how you want your audience to feel about the plot they've just witnessed.

A safe place leads the audience out of the story. Towards the end, the audience feels that everything has been spoken for. The events have been treated, the emotional points established. The characters have had a chance to speak, and in the end you feel this fullness.

When you get to that end, the emotional arc doesn't just, end your story: "Bloomp!" And go down, and then leave you plummeting down to the ground from where you came from in a heap. Usually, the emotional arc takes you to someplace different than you were when you started out, and it guides you out of the story.

This "guiding out" is one of the definitions of "resolution"—it's one of my favorite ways of thinking about this word. One definition of "resolution" has to do with where you go from here. It's arriving at a plan of future action—resolution. The resolution of your story, then, is the point at which your audience is sent out from the story with a plan of action. It's like the commencement ceremony for graduates: It marks an ending, but it also means "beginning." It's a sending forth. Your resolution sends the audience out from the story with a new outlook, a new course of action for their lives, and new questions to explore.

You also might think of the resolution of your camera or your TV—how high a quality of picture your camera can take, its pixilation or its resolution. It has to do with how clearly we can see something in fine detail. The resolution of your story is how we are left to see everything in the end. It's not just how things wrap up in the plot, but how the characters and narrator think about how things end up—how clearly your narrator "gets" the real meaning of the story.

This is all part of that art of storytelling as well, because you don't want to conk your audience over the head at the end with the meaning of your story. Remember what we said in those opening lectures about your relationship with your audience. Trust them; they're smart people. You don't have to lay everything out for them. So, when I say you're helping your audience see things clearly, I'm not talking about stating things outright—unless you're telling a fable, and then that's the nature of that kind of story. I'm talking about how you help your audience see their own situation more clearly through the metaphor of the story. How your audience, who might have seen things dimly, or pixilated—unable to see a way around a problem, or around their current situation, or even a way out of their own mundane view of life—your story sharpens their focus, helps them see. In the end, you help them see, through your resolution, a clearer vision for their lives.

Lastly, a safe place does no harm to the audience. The last thing I must say about how you choose to end your story, it has to do with ethics. You, as a storyteller, have the potential to do harm to your audience. For instance, some audiences feel cheated if you tell a story from personal experience, and it turns out that the story really was a fiction. Likewise, you have to take the audience into account when you determine how you want the story to resolve emotionally: Is this audience mature enough to handle the themes that you're presenting to them? And if they are, do you land the audience in a place where they're ready to assimilate what they've encountered in your story in a meaningful way in their lives?

Another aspect of these ethics has to do with your emotional preparedness. Are you ready to tell that story? Have you dealt with the issues that you raise and resolved them for yourself enough to bring this story into the public and make it a meaningful experience for them—not just therapy for you?

These are some things to consider as you're bringing your audience to a safe place at the conclusion to your story. And from these examples, you've probably noticed that one of the primary tools a storyteller uses to help build suspense, and give a sense of these different character's perspectives as they travel along this emotional arc towards the resolution, is your voice. Next time we'll play with using pause, intonation, character voices, and a host of other vocal tools that can help you build this emotional arc and make your stories really fun to tell.

Vocal Intonation
Lecture 18

Our past four lectures have focused on bringing different characters to life, how those characters move along in the plot of the story, and how the narrator guides listeners through the plot in such a way that they develop an emotional relationship with the story and the characters. Through all these elements, there is a flow to the story; the arc guides the audience along in a rhythm. Some of the most dynamic storytellers make use of dynamic vocal intonation not only for individual character voices but in how they use pacing, pause, and rhythm over the entire arc of the story. In this lecture, we'll talk about one of the most important tools of a storyteller—your voice.

Vocal Warm-Up

- We all do some unconscious vocal warm-ups as part of our morning routine. Let's look at how effective some of these unconscious behaviors can be when you consciously use them in preparation for storytelling.

- Begin by sitting up straight, rolling your shoulders back, and yawning. As you reach the end of your yawn, put two fingers between your lips just inside your mouth to prevent your teeth from clamping down. Your fingers will stop you from biting down at the end of your yawn and tensing your muscles. Now try another yawn.

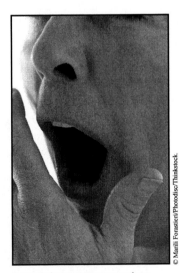

A yawn loosens up your jaw muscles so that you can move your jaw freely.

- Next, place the tip of your tongue behind the bottom front row of your teeth. With the middle part of your tongue, push up and out of your mouth. Try this only two or three times to avoid straining your tongue.
  - The average human tongue is about eight inches long, reaching all the way back to the voice box, or larynx, which also houses the vocal folds (or vocal cords).

  - In action, the folds look and act like a second set of lips. It's the vibration of these vocal folds that produces a vibration in the air coming from your lungs and forced out by your diaphragm.

  - All of the rich power of your voice starts in the diaphragm muscle, which pushes the air up and out of your lungs. That air travels up through the trachea, where the vocal folds vibrate. As they vibrate, they produce sound waves that travel up through your mouth. Your tongue further shapes those waves into speech.

  - You stretch your tongue to help limber up one of the many muscles that contribute to vocal dexterity and power.

- Another way to warm up the vocal system is to do some closed-mouthed humming.
  - Keep your mouth closed, take a deep breath (feel your diaphragm expand underneath your lungs in your ribcage), and maintain a continuous hum.

  - Bring up the volume on your hum and try to feel the force of air coming up from your diaphragm.

  - Try moving your lips around, as if there's a bee stuck in your mouth, and bringing the sound higher and lower in pitch. As you vary the pitch, pay attention to how that change feels in your trachea.

○ Finally, turn your close-lipped hum into an open-lipped "mee" and throw that sound to the back of the room that you're in: "mee-YO."

Articulation

- We tend to be very lazy with our mouths in everyday speech; we don't move them as much and articulate as clearly as we could. Most of us get by with our communication, but at times, a listener may have asked you to speak up or to repeat something that you have said. In order to tell a good story, though, your audience must be able to understand what you're saying.

- Tongue twisters make for excellent articulation exercises. The one below is from Gilbert and Sullivan's 1885 opera *The Mikado*. As you say this poem, project your voice, not with the force of air coming from your chest but from your diaphragm. Also make sure you enunciate the end consonants clearly.

> To sit in solemn silence in a dull, dark dock,
> In a pestilential prison with a life-long lock,
> Awaiting the sensation of a short, sharp shock,
> From a cheap and chippy chopper on a big, black block.

- Practicing tongue twisters doesn't mean that you should sound like an exaggerated model of proper elocution. You should sound like you, only more intelligible.

Rate, Pitch, and Tone

- You don't have to do much to change your voice to sound like different characters. You can change simply your rate of speech or your pitch—how high or low your voice is. The pitch of your voice affects your tone, that is, how the pitch is interpreted to mean something.

- For example, if you start your pitch low and end high, your tone seems quizzical, as if everything you are saying is an unanswered question. A character whose pitch descends at the end of each sentence may have a condescending tone.

- Using different pitches and rates to distinguish characters is especially useful if you don't want to use accents for your characters. In fact, unless you are well trained in using accents, it's probably best to avoid them so you don't risk offending members of your audience.

- You can use pitch to make a character sound more approachable or more menacing. For example, a moderate pitch and a slower rate of speaking can make a character seem more calculating but still approachable, while a lower pitch and a faster rate can seem darker and more forceful. In contrast, speaking slowly and deeply gives the impression of a big, slow character.

- Give yourself permission to be playful with your pitch and rate and experiment with character voices. This extends not only to the words someone says in dramatic lines but also when you choose to narrate from the perspective of a "little narrator," that is, when you allow a character to take over and narrate from his or her perspective.

- In one of your stories, choose two characters between whom you can identify tensive qualities. Make sure the characters are not too similar in manner or role; look for some clear distinction.
  - Think about the pitch of the first character and identify a specific point in the story when that character either speaks to another character in dramatic mode or becomes a "little narrator." Try speaking as that character, intentionally varying your pitch and adjusting your rate of speech to match the character.

  - Try the same exercise with the other character, choosing a different pitch or rate. Either of these qualities can distinguish your characters for your audience. Note the contrast that just these small conscious choices can yield.

- Other factors of rate include pacing and pause, which can be used to add dynamism and shape tension in your story.
  - Pace is the relative speed of your story. Usually in the introduction, you'll want to use an easy pace, but you will speed up the pace toward the climax.

  - Pause makes your audience wonder what's going to happen next. In conversation, we're often afraid to pause because we think we might lose our listeners' attention, but in storytelling, pausing gives the audience a needed moment to catch up and let the meaning of a story or a piece of the action sink in and resonate.

- In Connie Regan-Blake's ghost story, she intentionally lowers the volume of her voice at times so that her audience must listen carefully to hear her. When she does this, she's still projecting from the diaphragm, but she turns the volume down a notch to pull her audience in closer.

Sound Effects
- We naturally think of sound effects in conjunction with stories for children, such as the bear hunt story, but they can also be useful and fun in stories for adults.

- One of the best ways to easily insert sound effects is to add the effect to a particular word in the narration that describes the action. For example, if a door is creaking open, you could make the word "creak" itself into a sound: "The door creeeeaked open."

- Such effects add to the "sensorium" of the story—the full array of senses that a story can evoke.

Suggested Reading

Linklater, *Freeing the Natural Voice.*

Lipman, *Improving Your Storytelling.*

Lundberg, *Cords (Hear Us and Have Mercy)*.

Regan-Blake, *Chilling Ghost Stories*.

———, www.storywindow.com.

Stern, *Acting with an Accent*.

Questions to Consider

1. Check in with your body following the vocal-physical warm-ups in this lecture. Do you feel different following these stretches and warm-ups?

2. How small can a change in voice be to make a difference in characterization?

Lecture 18: Vocal Intonation

Vocal Intonation
Lecture 18—Transcript

Professor Harvey: Our past four lectures have focused on bringing different characters to life, and how those characters fit and move along with the plot of your story, and we've also focused on how the narrator guides the audience through this plot in such a way that we develop an emotional relationship with the these characters. We feel the characters' attitudes at moments of narration, and we hear them speak through character dialogue.

Through all of these elements, there's a flow to the story—the arc guides the audience along in a rhythm. Some of the most dynamic storytellers, they make use of dynamic vocal intonation, not only for character voices, but in how they consider their use of pacing, and of pause, and rhythm over the entire arc of the story.

In this lecture, we're going to talk about one of the most important tools a storyteller uses—your voice—and we'll be doing lots of vocal exercises to help you warm up your voice, and to explore the different aspects of vocal intonation available to you for your character development. Perhaps most importantly, we'll consider how your vocal rhythm impacts the overall flow of your story.

First, let's warm up your voice! Most of us sit at computers most of the day—we don't consciously warm up our voices to prepare to go to work, but you may do some *unconscious* vocal warm ups as a part of your morning routine. I want to highlight how really effective some of these unconscious behaviors can be when you *consciously* use them in preparing for your storytelling.

It's useful to incorporate some of these warm ups into your morning routine, both for the benefit of your everyday storytelling, and when you also have to give a presentation or just speak in front of a group of people. Because when you don't warm up your voice, you can hurt yourself (you can strain your vocal folds). If you aren't ready to project your voice, you could hurt yourself, and if you don't project your voice your audience can't hear you.

You aren't as prepared to be as playful with your voice while you're telling (it's just like stretching before a game—it's just more enjoyable when you've limbered up).

These are vocal-physical warm ups, because your voice (like your brain), it isn't some disembodied entity that exists outside of your body—no, it's here, it's in your throat, and it's in your mouth, and it's here in your diaphragm, which is the real power of where your voice comes from. It's not up here in your lungs; it's down here in your diaphragm—and we're going to warm up all of this system right now, starting with some things that you probably do every morning.

The first thing is, you woke up this morning; you may have yawned. Go ahead, sit up straight and comfortable, roll your shoulders back. Feel that strain, too—we'll work on warming up the rest of your body in a coming lecture, but right now, we're working here in your throat and in your diaphragm. Roll those shoulders back a couple of times and sit up straight, and give yourself a good yawn. Big yawn, really feel your cheeks and your jaw muscles stretch out. You can make yourself yawn any time, just start that yawn—if someone else is there with you, you might look at each other; yawns are very catching.

When you come to the end of your yawn, I want for you to do something. Take two fingers and put them between your lips just inside your mouth, so if you tried to close your mouth, with your fingers in there, your jaw would catch your fingers and you couldn't shut your mouth. [Professor Harvey gently bites her fingers.] Ahh.

While that looks incredibly silly, what these fingers do is they keep you from clamping down your teeth at the end of your yawn, which is something that many of us do as an unconscious stress gesture. We have this lovely stretching yawn in the morning, and we bite down on the end of that yawn and it just tenses all of these muscles right back up.

These fingers keep you from clamping down and straining those muscles that you just so nicely loosened—so when you finish your yawn, either place your fingers there, or just imagine those fingers are there and just end your yawn with your mouth open about an inch. Give yourself another yawn—it's very lovely, very relaxing.

This is another facial stretch that you might have seen your cat do. If you've ever seen a cat really stretch, you'll see them stretch out those front paws, and then those back legs, and then the cat just sticks out its tongue and it stretches its tongue out—the cat gets its whole body into the stretch! Even a cat realizes that a tongue is a muscle, just like any other muscle.

We're socially trained not to stick our tongues out (unless you're really mad at someone on the playground), but we're going to stretch your tongue. It's the same principle as a cat might use, but we do the stretch a little bit differently. I want you to take the tip of your tongue, and place it behind the bottom front row of your teeth. This is a Kristin Linklater stretch. (Linklater is a professional theater vocal coach; she trains actors to use their voices in a variety of styles, including classical Shakespearean.) With this stretch, in the middle part of your tongue, I want you to push up and out of your mouth, and it looks like this. Kind of silly, but it looks like this. [Professor Harvey stretches her tongue out.]

Now I don't want you to do this stretch too much—don't do this more than five times a day or five times at a time—because I actually did have a friend who sprained her tongue when she did this several times in a row. It was kind of painful for her! So, not too much.

But just about three times, keep that tip of your tongue on the lower row of your teeth, and stretch the middle part of your tongue out of your mouth. You should feel it stretching all the way back in the back of your throat, back here. The average human tongue is about four inches long, and you can feel the muscles connect and stretch when you do this stretch all the way down into your throat. This vocal tract is a lot longer than we give it credit for, and these muscles, they reach all the way back to what is commonly known as your "voice box," or the larynx. This is the part of your throat that controls the pitch and the volume of your voice. The larynx also houses the vocal folds (or what we commonly know as the "vocal cords").

In action, the folds, they look and act like a second set of lips. It's the vibration of these vocal folds that produces a vibration in the air coming from your lungs and forced out from your diaphragm (which is down here in your tummy, and underneath the lungs. These are the muscles that make you breathe). When you want to speak loudly enough to be heard, the diaphragm is what forces that air out faster and more powerfully so you can speak with authority, and you can speak at a loud enough volume to be heard.

All of that rich power of your voice, it starts down here in the diaphragm muscle, and it pushes that air up and out of your lungs, and that air travels up through the trachea where the vocal folds vibrate. When you sing, these folds can vibrate about 400 times a second! Those folds, which are muscles, they make little waves in the air, and those waves are sound waves, and they travel up through your mouth, where your tongue further shapes these waves into speech, and that is how your audience can hear you and understand you.

We do this tongue stretch to help limber up one of these many muscles that will contribute to your overall vocal dexterity and your vocal power. We loosen up the jaw muscle with a yawn so that your jaw is nice and loose and free to move in the way you want it to.

You can massage your jaw muscles—you can take your fingers and place them where your jaw connects with your skull, and on the sides of your face; just rub gently there. You can feel those muscles, and when they're tight (if this feels good, you're probably loosening up those tight muscles), when they're tight, you're not as free to move your mouth and to speak.

Another safe way to warm up this whole vocal-breath system is to do some closed-mouth humming—you can never hurt your voice by humming. So, keep your mouth closed, and take a deep breath (feel your diaphragm expand under your lungs in your ribcage) and keep a continuous hum going. [Humming.] Now make that hum a little louder, and bring the volume up. [Humming.]Try and feel that force of air coming not just from your chest, but from your diaphragm to force that air up. [Humming.]

Now move your lips around, as if there's a bee stuck in your mouth. [Humming.] Now bring the sound up in pitch—make it a little higher hum.

[Humming.] Bring it down lower. [Humming.] It's very silly but it's very fun. And as you vary the pitch, try to pay attention to how the change feels in your trachea—it's those vocal folds, those muscles moving in there that are changing that pitch. [Humming.] You can feel it here in your trachea.

Now we're going to work on projection, projecting your voice out into space, so that you can be heard. You're not shouting, "Aaahhh." You're projecting.

Take that humming, [humming], and I want you to turn that closed-lipped hum into an open-lipped "mee" and then throw that sound to the back of the room that you're in, like this: "Mee-YO!" Try that with me: "Mee-YO!" What you're trying to do is to feel that "YO!" down here punching out from your diaphragm—it's forcing that air out, pushing that forceful voice out. One more time, try it with me: "Mee-YO!"

OK, thank you. Those are a few exercises to help you warm up this whole system and to get you thinking about projecting your voice out to the back of the room. So that gets your voice up and out. Let's work on making that sound into something intelligible. Let's work on articulation.

Because we tend to be very lazy with our mouths in everyday speech. By that I mean we don't move our mouths and articulate as much as we could. Most of us, we get by with our communication, but have you ever had someone ask you to repeat yourself because they couldn't make out what you said? Or ask you to speak up?

In order to tell a good story, your audience has to understand what you're saying, and you have to articulate these sounds and control the sounds coming out of your mouth, so that these air vibrations do what you want them to do, to communicate clearly the words you choose to say.

Let's do some articulation exercises. Tongue twisters are great for this. You may have a favorite tongue twister or limerick that you can easily remember. In theatre circles, one of the favorites is to recite a portion of Gilbert and Sullivan's 1885 opera *The Mikado*. I'll say this poem one part of a time, and then we'll say it together.

As you say this poem, try to project your voice, not with the force of air coming from your chest (that results in breathy kind of voice and it will strain you; it'll wear you out if you try and force the air from your chest), but focus on that power of your voice coming from down here in your diaphragm, and try to enunciate these words:

To sit in solemn silence in a dull, dark dock

To sit in solemn silence in a dull, dark dock

In a pestilential prison with a life-long lock

In a pestilential prison with a life-long lock

Awaiting the sensation of a short, sharp shock

Awaiting the sensation of a short, sharp shock

From a cheap and chippy chopper on a big, black block

From a cheap and chippy chopper on a big, black block

Now, we're going to do it again, and this time really enunciate the consonant sounds at the end of each word—now again, we tend to be very vocally lazy throughout the day, so enunciate the end consonants— the end sound of each word. Here we go again, I'll say it and then I'll repeat it for you:

To sit in solemn silence in a dull, dark dock

To sit in solemn silence in a dull, dark dock

In a pestilential prison with a life-long lock

In a pestilential prison with a life-long lock

Awaiting the sensation of a short, sharp shock

Awaiting the sensation of a short, sharp shock

Awaiting the sensation of a short, sharp shock

From a cheap and chippy chopper on a big, black block

From a cheap and chippy chopper on a big, black block

Another one. I'll say it once through, and then we can take it in parts:

A box of biscuits

A box of mixed biscuits

And a biscuit mixer

Let's say it together:

A box of biscuits

A box of mixed biscuits

And a biscuit mixer

Now, all of this doesn't mean that I want you to wind up sounding like a model of proper elocution—no, you should sound like you, only more intelligible. But what I just did there, over-enunciating to the point of creating a kind of character voice, an elocution professor—someone who talks like this. You don't have to wind up sounding like that character in order to be understood properly! But that voice makes for a great character, because he has such a distinctive way of speaking and of holding himself—it's so over-done that it's comical. While you may not choose to have your narrator speak like this, you might use your voice to create character differences.

I really didn't do a whole lot to make that vocal change. To change my voice into sounding like this character, I might change the rate of my speech—how quickly or how slowly I speak—so this character might be a little more slow and a little more deliberate. That gives you a sense that he's a different character.

I also change my pitch—how high or low my voice is. His pitch changes as he says his words. He's lower in my vocal register, and there's also a predictable pattern to his pitch. He starts his sentences high and then ends them low. You might contrast this from other characters, maybe a character who starts their sentences low and then ends them high? As if they are always? Asking a question? Even if it's a declarative sentence?

The pitch of your voice affects the tone of your voice. Tone is how we interpret the pitch of someone else's voice to *mean* something. So when I'm speaking? As if everything? Is a question? You interpret certain meanings from that. It's said with a quizzical tone—as if everything this person says is an unanswered question, which is why we associate this speech with a person who doesn't have a clue of what's going on. For this elocution professor, his pitch *descends* at the end of each sentence—it's the descent of the con*descend*ing tone. We get the impression he's looking down on everyone from his condescending tone.

You can use pitch and rate to distinguish characters whether they're characters in real life or fictional characters (like the big bad wolf). And this is so useful, because you may be thinking, "I can't do accents for my characters!" Or, "I don't want to use accents for my characters!"

In fact, unless you're prepared to use a "foreign" accent in front of a group of people for whom that accent is their native tongue, it's usually best not to use an accent at all. You risk doing it wrong and offending that group of people. (For my stories, I use those accents that I've been trained to speak or that I've studied heavily with natives of that population.) There are inevitably times when I'll get it wrong but I have trained and I try. Now if you check your course materials, you'll see some suggestions for places you can look to get training in different accents, but it's important that you study with someone who's either a native or study from those suggested resources. You don't want to offend the population to whom you're speaking, or about whom you are speaking.

But you can use pitch to make a character sound more approachable, or more menacing. The wolf at some moments is at a more moderate pitch, but speaks at a slower rate, which makes him seem more calculating, but approachable. Then at other times, he speaks with a lower pitch and a faster rate, and the effect is that he seems darker and more forceful.

You can combine a low pitch with a slow rate, and you have someone who talks like this—and we get Snuffleupagus, that character on *Sesame Street* who looks like a wooly elephant. Speaking slowly and deeply gives the impression of a big, slow character. Give yourself permission to be playful with your pitch and your rate, and experiment with character voices. This extends not only to what someone says in dramatic lines (lines that a character says), but also when you choose to narrate from that character's perspective.

Listen to this audio clip; it's by a storyteller named Connie Regan-Blake. Listen to how she uses pitch and rate to distinguish between the hero, Mary, and the dead man who crawls up on her back in this story about Mary Culhane and the dead man.

[Audio start.]

> **Connie Regan-Blake:** She walked for a ways until she came to that side entrance of the graveyard, and then she started following that path along until she came to the new-dug grave. She saw her father's walking stick lying there in the loose dirt. She reached her hand out for it. A voice came from out of the grave, "Leave the blackthorn, Mary Culhane, and help me out of this hole."
>
> Mary was really frightened but a power took hold of her and drew her to the edge of that pit. She looked down. "Help me out of this hole." Mary couldn't move, and that thing climbed out of that grave and climbed onto Mary's back and put one hand around her neck and with the other, pointed a finger for her to walk away from those graves. Mary was in kind of a daze and she walked for awhile. That weight was getting so heavy on her back. Finally she stopped; she could go no further.
>
> "Walk on, Mary Culhane." Mary Culhane walked on.

[Audio end.]

Professor Harvey: She's using pitch and rate to distinguish characters—she's got this soft pitch for Mary, and then she varies it up to this really guttural pitch for the dead man. It plays up the tensive qualities between these two characters.

Let's experiment with pitch and rate with one of your characters—go to one of your stories (you can pick the same story you've been working with, or you can choose another one). And pick two characters who you can find tensive qualities between—characters not so similar in manner or in role, but characters where you find some clear distinction.

Think about that first character. This may be someone you actually know, or it might be a fictional character. What sort of pitch does this character speak with? High, or low? Think of a specific time in your story when that character either speaks to another character using dramatic mode, or when the character narrates from his or her own perspective. Try speaking as that character, and try to intentionally drop or raise your pitch to match that character.

Now think about rate. What rate does this person speak with? Rate has to do with rhythm. All of us have a particular life rhythm. We talked about that in our characterization lecture; we have a rhythm that we move about and experience the world with. It affects how we walk, and how we move, and how we interact with the world. It affects the rate at which we speak, too. So, what is this person's rate of speech—is it fast, or slow, or somewhere in between? Try to add a conscious consideration of rate to that character. Now try speaking those same lines with the pitch and rate of that character. Try speaking narration that way.

Either of these are fine to distinguish your characters for your audience. It doesn't take a lot to give some variety to your vocal intonation and to give a clear sense of character difference. You might try the same thing with your other character. Think about how that character is different, and choose a different pitch and a different rate for that character. You'll see the contrast that just these small conscious choices can yield.

Now in the example that we heard by Connie Regan-Blake, the story of Mary Culhane, you'll notice that she also uses her voice to contribute to the emotional arc of the story. She's using pacing and pause (which are both factors of rate). She's using those to shape a sense of growing tension in the story, and it pulls us in.

You'll want to factor these elements into your storytelling—no matter how big or small your story is—you'll want to do this because pacing and pause are easy ways to add dynamism to a story, whether you're telling at your office or you're telling at the dinner table. Pace is the relative speed of your story. There are times when you'll want an easy pace; usually these happen in the introduction when you're first getting to know the characters. There are other times when you want to speed up the pace, usually as you get towards the climax—but really anytime that you want to match the pace of the action of the story.

There's a great children's story about "going on a bear hunt." You've probably heard it—it's an interactive story where you use your hands to open the gate [squeaking], and you slap it shut. And then you slop through the mud [slopping], and then you cross the river [splashing] until you get to the bear cave. Then you turn around as you see that bear, and you run through the river [splashing] and slop through that mud [slopping], going through the mud, and you run through the gate [squeaking] and whew! Safe at last. It's all about pacing—there's nothing in that story, really, that's a nothing kind of story; it's an adventure but there's not that much to it. You go and you come back. But your pacing makes that story an adventure for little kids.

It's the same with adult stories—if I want to tell you about my friend who ran a half-marathon. "OK, so she ran in a race," that's not really going to draw you in, but if I tell you about how she ran, and she ran, and she ran until she didn't think she could go any further and then she got it—she got her medal!

That's a little five-second story, but it holds a little more interest because it's transforming the fact (she was in a race) into an artful story. It takes that audience through a paced journey. Pacing is about building suspense and interest. You'll notice that in that little, short five-second story, I used pause as well. Connie Regan-Blake, she uses pause in her story after the dead man speaks to Mary. And the effect for the audience is that it makes you wonder what's going to happen next.

Many times we're afraid of using pause in conversation because we're afraid we're going to lose the audience's attention, or we're nervous and we just want to get it all out before we forget anything. It's a symptom of our nervous, sound bite society that we feel we have to fill every moment with sound and with distraction.

But don't be afraid to experiment with pause in your stories. It gives the audience a needed moment to catch up and really let the meaning of a story or a piece of action sink in and resonate. That's not "dead time" in your story; you don't have to fill every moment of your story with sound. The pause, it serves a function in stories. When the story is so full that your audience needs a chance to process it all, or when the humor is so much that you want to give your audience a chance to enjoy that moment of laughter. Pauses punctuate stories, so a pause can be a period (marking a serious moment), or an exclamation point (marking a funny moment). Don't be afraid of silence—it can be a very useful thing.

Connie does something in many of her "scary stories" that I want you to pay attention to: She intentionally lowers the volume of her voice at times, so you have to listen carefully to her, and she does this at the moment when she wants to add the most suspense to the story.

She's speaking in a lower volume. She's still projecting from the diaphragm. It's not this breathy whisper—you can still sense that power coming from her voice—but she turns the volume down a notch, and it makes her audience pull in closer, you can imagine leaning in to hear that story more closely. It's one of the seeming contradictions of storytelling. When you want to get your audience pulled into a suspenseful moment and really listen, sometimes you don't want to make your voice louder, so that they can hear you, you want to make it softer so they lean in to hear you even more.

Lastly, I want to mention using your voice with sound effects. In the bear hunt story, sound effects are a major component of that story—so the mud [slopping] and the gate [creaking] and you slapping your hands as you walk along, you can add that too—all these effects are great with kids' stories.

They can be also useful and fun when you're telling stories to adults, so don't count them out. Adults are just little kids, really, and they want to hear a story told well, and they want to really dive into the story. One of the best ways to easily insert sound effects is to add the effect to the particular word of narration that describes that action.

If it's a door creaking open, you could say, "The door creaked open: [creak]." Or you could make the word itself into the sound: "The door [creaked] open," use that onomatopoeia. You haven't lost any time in making that sound effect; you haven't made a big thing of it—it's just adding to what's called the "sensorium" of the story, that full array of senses that a story can evoke, so we hear the door and we can see it better in our minds.

Today we've warmed up your voice. We've worked with using rate and pitch in character distinctions, and we've talked about how pace, pause, and sound effects can contribute to the overall emotional arc of the story and can contribute in drawing your audience in. Vocal intonation is just one of the ways that you can evoke the sensorium of your story for your audience—and we'll end here, because in the next lecture, we're really going to integrate all of these story elements (voice, characterization, narrator, visualization, emotional arc, the audience). We're going to put them all together into a whole experience for your audience.

We're integrating next time; we're adding to this basic vocabulary of storytelling. We're going "storytelling 2.0" next time, playing with the musicality of language, with full possibilities of characterization, and with seeing each of your stories—large and small, for a friend or for a boardroom full of people—each story as a really fun opportunity to engage with others.

Preparing to Perform
Lecture 19

Thus far, we've talked about different elements of a story as separate "things" to experiment with as you tell a story to a neighbor or a colleague. As you're telling a story, you change the pace of how a character talks to add characterization, or change the way you hold yourself to suggest a different character, or use visualization to walk your way from one plot element to the next. But these aren't separate "things" that you do in a story. In this lecture, we'll work on putting these elements together and seeing how they relate to one another.

The Story Outline

- Begin by choosing an entirely new story, one you haven't worked on before in these lectures, and one that is relatively short. Tell, out loud, a 15-second version of this story. You'll use this story to prepare a story outline.

- Think about the background of the story—your research. What is the genre of the story (folktale, personal story, myth)? What is the primary source text for the story?
  - For cultural stories, such as folktales and tall tales, it's useful to try to get at least two or three versions of the story from different authors or oral sources, both for variety's sake and to ensure that you're not plagiarizing someone else's version of a story.

  - You might also investigate what was going on in history at the time of the events in your story and identify the cultural origin of the story. Keep copies of any variants of the story you find, to help your memory if you come back to the story at a later time and to prove that you crafted your version from a variety of sources.

- Next, in your storytelling journal, write down the main problem in the story, focusing on the action of the plot. In one sentence, state the major problem or task that orders the plot.

- List the locations of the story and the historical period. If the story jumps around in time, include that fact, too.

- List the characters in the story and underline the primary character, the one who is the focus of the emotional arc.

- In one sentence, write the outcome of the story's problem or conflict, again, focusing on the plot.

- Finally, state the meaning of the story in one sentence.

- This outline gives you the basic "pieces" of your story. The next step is to order those pieces.

Ordering Your Story
- Using the same story, think about your introduction. What is the first thing you want to say, the opening phrase to introduce the characters? It might be a simple sentence that piques the interest of the audience: "Mama never liked Tuesdays."
  - In considering your introduction, you also need to think about what you must say in order to get the action going. What is the bare minimum that your listeners need to know to understand what's about to happen?

  - Briefly introduce the characters, the setting, and the time period before bringing listeners to the inciting incident that gets the action moving.

- Next, quickly sketch out the plot—the major events—in a numbered sequence, ordered as you plan to tell them.

- Locate and write down the climax of the story. If the emotional arc of your story reaches a climax at a different point from the plotline of events, be sure to note that in your outline, as well.

- Write down the conclusion of the story. Here, you may think of specific wording, as you did with the introduction. Even if you forget the precise wording later, having a good idea of the closing phrase will improve your telling.

- Finally, write down your target audience for this story (your family, friends at work, or business colleagues if you plan to tell the story as part of a presentation). This is the audience that you will imagine for the rest of this exercise.

Performing Your Story

- Stand up, roll your shoulders back, and stretch your arms up above your head, feeling the stretch all the way down your body. Then, drop your arms and head, bend your knees, and fold forward at the waist. From this folded position, relax your neck. Finally, roll yourself upright from the base of your spine.

- Go to the beginning of your story, and visualize the first place all around you. Think in terms of the five senses. What colors do you see in this place? What does it smell like? What background sounds do you hear? As the narrator, see in your mind's eye where the primary character is, even though he or she might not be in this scene. Your knowledge of that character will inform the tone you take in the opening moments.

- Imagine your target audience in front of you and move back and forth as the narrator, from looking at the audience to looking at the scene. Begin by looking at the audience and, if you remember the opening phrase you wrote down, speak it out loud.

- Next, move the audience into the action. Given that the story has just taken off, you should change your pace, even if it's only a subtle change.

- As you bring the audience into the next scene, think about the forces that are propelling and pulling the characters. Let that sense of propulsion push you forward and influence your pacing. Physically move to a new place (step to one side) as you're propelled into the next scene.

- Focus on one character and choose his or her body center. The next time that character speaks, move into that body posture and use a focal point to bring the character alive. Choose another character and give him or her a different rate of speech from the narrator and others in the story.

- Next, move to the plot climax of your story. Use a "little narrator" and give your audience a different perspective; show the tensiveness between perspectives in your narration.

- Somewhere in the scene, add a pause to punctuate some moment in the story. The way you look at the audience when you pause, with either a smile or a more serious expression, carries the force of the pause forward; it's a way of projecting the pause, similar to projecting your voice.

- If you haven't reached it yet, move ahead to the emotional climax of the story. Remember the real reason that you're telling this story. Let that sense of urgency and purpose affect your intonation and how you look at the audience.

- Finally, bring your audience to the resolution. If you can remember the final phrase you wrote down, say it, but if you can't, just say what comes to mind at this point in your telling.

Exaggerating Your Performance
- Try out the body centers of at least two characters on your list. Take on the different centers, walk around in your space, and speak as those characters.

- Take on the body center of your narrator, which will probably be your own body center. Walk in the space, come to a standing point, and stop. Look at your imaginary audience and tell a version of your story using exaggerated gestures, characterizations, and volume.

- Give yourself permission to look ridiculous as you do this exercise, which will help you see the extent of where your energy and characterizations can go. Exaggerate everything in the scene; the big things should be huge and the little things should be tiny, and your voice should reflect those exaggerations.

- Move to the middle of your story and let the climax build, making your voice more dramatic than it would ever really be in telling this story. As you reach the climactic moment, amplify the characterizations.

- Finally, as you reach the resolution of the story, maintain your high energy but relax your pacing.

- When you're through with this exercise, think about any discoveries you made in this exaggerated telling. For example, you may have used your voice in a funny way for a certain character. Try to locate one aspect of the run-through that you'd like to retain in a telling with a real audience.

- Note, too, that the energy you have in an exaggerated run-through is at the same level that you need to maintain when you tell the story. This energy isn't about goofy gestures or voices but about focus and investment in a story.

Your listeners take their cues from you; when you're more interested and invested in what you're saying, they will be more interested, too.

374

Scripting

- Take out your journal again and consider the meanings your story holds. What is significant about the story? Reflect on the meaning from both a cultural and a personal perspective.
  - Contextualize the story in its community, which might be your family or peer group. What cultural purposes does the story serve? What values does it reinforce or instill? Why does the story survive in this culture?

  - From a personal perspective, why were you drawn to this story? What value does this story have for you?

- At this point in the rehearsal process—after you feel comfortable with your story and your characters—script out the story. Scripting helps you work through key phrases and flesh out scenes, but even while you do it, you should be prepared to let go of this wording. Memorizing a script is a surefire way to kill your story performance!

- After you've written the story out, tell it again away from your script; then revise what you've written. Keep the story fluid. Don't allow the act of writing the story down to mummify it. The script is a tool, not a final goal.

- It's a good idea to try out different versions of a story for different audiences before you write it down. Visualize the scenes, try out different voices and postures for the characters, and tell the story informally to friends before you script it.

- After you internalize the story in your body and mind, then use scripting as a way of going even deeper into the images. As you script, try to stay "in scene," visualizing the setting and action in front of you.

- Once you've got a script, make another storyboard in the margins that you can use to refresh your mind about the story before you perform it.

- Scripting, when done at the right time, can be helpful as a memory aid, can help you see connections between scenes, and enables you to plan out your pacing and rhythm, but remember that your wording should be adapted to suit the audience. It's the images that you visualize—not the specific words you write—that remain the same from one telling to the next.

Suggested Reading

O'Callahan, "The Herring Shed."

Questions to Consider

1. Did you discover anything new about your story or storytelling— the possibilities of characterization, for example—while doing the exaggerated run-through?

2. The story outline is designed to be a quick way of organizing your research and thoughts about the flow of your story, as well as a good reference for refreshing your memory about a story later. You won't do an outline for every story you tell, but there may be stories that you want to record in some way on paper—either with an outline or with a script. What is one story that you really want to get down on paper—or in an audio recording—for your family? Can you do that outline, script, or recording this week?

Preparing to Perform
Lecture 19—Transcript

Professor Harvey: Thus far, we've talked about these different elements of your story as separate "things" to try out and experiment with as you're talking with your neighbor or you're telling a story to your colleague. As you're telling a story, you change the pace of how your character talks to add to characterization, or you change the way you hold yourself to suggest a different character, or you visualize to walk your way through the story from one plot element to the next.

But these aren't separate things that you do in a story. They're all working together. Your voice, it impacts the emotional arc, which informs how long your narrator spends talking about a particular part of the story, which then impacts what you visualize for that portion of the story. In this lecture, we're going to work on putting all of these elements in relation to one another. We're going to be playing a lot today, so go ahead right now and give yourself permission to play over the next half hour.

I want you to choose an entirely new story to work on today—a story you might have told people before, but that you haven't worked on before in these lectures. See if you can choose a relatively short story—don't choose the epic saga of your life—maybe something funny that happened to you this week, or a pivotal moment in your life that doesn't take forever to recount, or a children's story, a short story like that if you like.

The first step is to tell, out loud, a very short, 15-second version of that story—talk it through. This is part of that cycle of story development (remember: talking-writing-imaging-playing-rehearsing).

Tell your imaginary audience what happens; take us to the action, get in and get out—what happens in this story? Try a 15-second version. Once you've told your 15-second version, I'd like to tell you about a writing exercise that's very useful. It's short; it's called a "story outline," and it's a form, really, that helps you organize your thoughts on a story.

Of course you're not going to do this with every story that you tell, but by doing these writing exercises on some stories that you really care about, it will help you in the moment, telling those quippy short stories to your neighbor next door—it'll help you in that because this form is all about getting to the meat and the meaning of your story.

First, I want you to think about the background of your story—your research. What is the genre of your story? Is it a folktale, or personal story, a myth? What is the primary source text for your story? If it's a personal story, you can write the family member who you heard the story from, or you can right about that own experience yourself and say yourself as the source of that story.

Also think about any variant source texts that you might have found that can contribute to your telling of this story. So for a personal story, you'd write down the other people who might have witnessed that event or have known the people who you talk about, and if you haven't already, you might think about asking these folks later about their perspectives on the events. It will add to some of the details of your story, details that you couldn't have come up with on your own, from your own perspective.

For cultural stories such as folktales and tall tales, it's really useful to try to get at least two or three versions of the story from different authors or from different oral sources if you can find them. You do this both for variety's sake in hearing different perspectives, but also because of the issue of story rights.

When you're telling this story to your neighbor, they're probably not going to sue you for plagiarizing someone else's version of the story but still, if the document isn't older than 75 years, it's a good idea to check out different versions of the story.

You can also investigate what was going on in history at the time of that event. Some of the most interesting insights come from just a little bit of historical research. You'll want to identify the cultural origin of the story, the country or the culture where that story comes from—that informs the details that you include in the story. If you found different versions of the story, each of them might be from a different culture, so note that as well.

It's good practice, if you're really researching a story for presentation, to keep a hard or e-copy of the variants of that story—again, this is both to help your memory later if you put that story down for awhile and then you're are asked to tell it again, but also it's for this issue of rights (you can prove you crafted your version from a variety of sources and not just one source). You're not just using the word-for-word account from one source.

The next story outline questions dive us into the story itself. In your journal, write down what the main problem is in the story—focus on the plot and the action of the plot. What is the major problem or task that orders the plot of the story? I want you to state that problem in one sentence, no more.

Next, the settings. List the locations of the story—where do you go in this story? Write down the historical period of the events in your story, and if your story jumps around in time, you'll want to include that too.

Next, make a short list of the characters in your story—go ahead and underline that primary character (the one around whom we center the emotional arc of the story. That's the one to really focus on in this lecture today).

Then the resolution. Focusing again on the plot, the action of the story, what is the outcome of the story's problem, or conflict? State this in a simple sentence.

Finally, the meaning. This again has to do with the emotional arc—what is the meaning of this story to you? Try to state that in a simple sentence.

So this gives you the basic bits for your story. Let's get those bits into an order, still working on paper, and then we'll start to play with them on your feet in performance.

For the first time in this lecture series, we're going to work on your specific wording for some things. Don't worry; I'm not saying you have to memorize these words. Please don't just mechanically memorize them, but it's good to think them through. Think about your introduction

Think about that introduction—what is the first thing you want to say, your opening phrase to introduce the characters? It might be something to pique the audience's interest; for instance, "Mama never liked Tuesdays." What do you mean? Why didn't she like Tuesdays?

Think of what might hook your audience's interest from the very start. For the introduction as a whole, you'll want to think about what you have to say to get the action going. What do people need to know (the bare minimum) to understand what's about to happen? Briefly introduce the characters, the setting, the time period, whatever we need (but no more) to get the story going—to get us to that inciting incident that gets the action moving.

After you've gotten us ready to understand the start of the story, quickly sketch out the plot sequence. This is the major events in a numbered sequence ordered as you plan to tell them.

OK, now the climax of your story. The emotional arc of your story hits a climax; if it does at a different point of the plotline of the events, be sure to note that difference in your sketch, like we did with the "Jarius" story in a previous lecture. The plotline action peaked when girl was being brought back to life, but the emotional climax for the narrator happened when Jesus brought that little girl a little piece of bread to eat. The emotional climax wasn't about doing a big miracle; the point was that he loved her like a father loves his daughter. But your plot may peak as the same time as the emotional peak of the story—most stories do this. Locate and write down that climax.

Finally, your conclusion for the story. How does the story end? Again, here's another chance to think of a specific wording—even if you forget that wording later when you're telling it, you'll have thought it through now, and it will make that telling all the better for it. Try to write down your closing phrase. For funny stories, this can be crucial. You want to get your wording right, so that the "funny" lands with the folks.

Finally, write down who your target audience is for that story (your family, or your friends at work, or if it's a story you plan to tell as part of a presentation, then your colleagues at work or colleagues in your group). Try to think of who specifically you'll be telling this story to, because we'll be working with imagining this audience for the rest of our time today.

Later, this is where you would insert your storyboard—you can do that later on if you like. Right now I'm anxious to get up on my feet and start moving into telling the story. So we're going to do a stretch; this is another Kristin Linklater stretch. I want you stand with your legs and feet spread about hip width apart, bend your knees slightly. I'd like for you to just give yourself some shoulder rolls. Then, I want you start stretching your shoulders, starting with your elbows.

Stretch your arms, starting with your elbows, and start lifting your arms up. Your arms in the front are hanging loose, your forearms and your hands, they're all dangling loose. Then stretch from your wrists up to the ceiling, and you'll feel a good stretch all the way down in [your arms], but your hands are still flopping loose, very loose, your fingers are very loose but you're feeling that good stretch all the way down in here. Now stretch with your fingers, as if there are strings attached to the tips of your fingers and it's as if your fingers are going to pop-pop-pop up off into the ceiling.

You're feeling that good stretch all the way down your arms, and then as if you're pulling a light out of a socket, let's release these one at a time. We'll release the hands first: One, two, three, release the hands. And one, two, from the elbows, three. One, two, three, and let your head drop, and just fold your head over and let it dangle loose. Nod your head "yes," shake your head "no." Let yourself just dangle here. You'll feel a good stretch all in your spine, from the base of your spine. What I'd like for you do is to start stacking your vertebrae up one at a time, saving your head and your neck for last because our tendency when we're coming up, is just to do this. [Professor Harvey stands up abruptly.] If you do that, you re-strain all of these muscles right here that you just spent some time relaxing by bending over. Save those muscles for last; start stacking your vertebrae one at a time from the base of your spine, stacking them up, and saving your shoulders, and your neck, for last.

When you get to the top, if you've done this a couple of times, I encourage you to do this stretch, elbows, wrists, fingers, and then down and up. If you do this a few times, you'll get yourself centered enough to where you can feel your head floating there on top of your spine. It's a lovely, centered feeling. It's a perfect way to start your day, the same as warming up your voice.

Just give yourself a few good tongue stretches right now. Massage your cheeks, maybe hum a little bit, [humming]. It's a great way to face the day, whatever storytelling or speaking you're about to do.

I'm going to do some side-coaching while you tell a short version of your story. When I side-coach this with my students, there are moments when I ask them to "freeze" so that I can give them some suggestions. I really want my students to freeze, so they're in the middle of seeing the wolf as it comes charging out of the woods and there was Little Red Riding Hood and she was terrified and then all of a sudden, "Freeze!" I want them to just stay there looking at that wolf, and just listen to what I'm saying and pick up where they've left off, just freeze in that position. I don't want them to come out of that visualization, just stay with it. It's kind of comical, but this serves the good purpose of not wasting time and energy in coming in and out of focus.

I want you go to the beginning of your story, and visualize that first place in your story. Just stay with your story. See it all around you, and remember what we began talking about in the last lecture about the "sensorium" of story experience. Think in terms of five senses. What are two colors that you see in this place? What does it smell like here? What background sounds do you hear?

As the narrator, see in your mind's eye where that primary character is—the character who you sympathize with most. That character may not even be in this scene, but your knowledge of that character informs the tone that you take with these opening moments.

I'm going to side-coach you through a telling of this story. I want you to speak aloud telling this story, and imagine your target audience there right in front of you. Move back and forth as that narrator; move from looking at the audience to looking at this scene, and begin by looking at the audience. You might say that opening phrase that you crafted, if you remember it, but try to stay away from reading what you just wrote. If you can remember a facsimile of that phrase, just say it to this imaginary audience.

Freeze where you are in that scene, and really see what's all around you—and let that inform your wording. Think about that full sensorium, add in details about the smells in that room.

Now I'm side-coaching, remember, so you can talk over me; it won't hurt my feelings, just keep going. Now, something happens that gets the action of the story moving—what is it? Move us to that action—go to that place. Freeze where you are in the scene. Keep visualizing all around you, but listen to what I'm saying. I want you to think about your pacing. Things have just taken off. That should change your pace, even if it's only a subtle change. Pacing is what keeps your plot from plodding along. So jump back into that scene with an awareness of the change of pace. Go ahead.

Pause, and bring us into that next scene of the story. Even if you have to fast forward, go on ahead. Think about what is propelling you from the current scene into that next scene, and what's pulling you into that next scene. Let that sense of propulsion push you forward and let that impact your pacing. What I want for you to do next is to literally move to a new physical location for the next scene. It could be from here to a step to the side, or it could be a few paces, but physically move to a new place as you're propelled into that next scene, ready? Go ahead and move.

Pause. By now, we've gotten to know some of these characters. Have you identified centers of the body for these characters? Choose a character, and choose a center of body for them, and the next time they speak or move, move in that body posture for them, and really use that dramatic mode and focal points to bring that character alive. With a body center, continue, go.

Think of another character in the story. Change your rate of speech for that character. Give that character a different rate of speech from the narrator or other characters. Please continue, go!

Freeze! Now, when I say "go," I want for you to move to the plot climax of the story—the plot climax, take us to that point (even if it's not the emotional climax, that's OK, we'll get to that). This may be the moment in the hero's journey where your primary character, they face that dragon and what happens to that character. There's a conflict here that's about to resolve. Take us to that narrator and take us to some different narrational perspectives. Show us that tensiveness between the perspectives in narration. Ready, try that, go!

Pause in-scene. Freeze. Remember to change your pace to coordinate with this new scene, and somewhere in the scene, I want you to add in a pause to punctuate some moment in the story. What kind of punctuation is it? That will affect how you look out to the audience. You'll either be smiling, or with a more serious look. That look (what you do with your body) carries the force of the pause forward. It's a way of projecting the pause, similar to projecting your voice. OK, try that, go!

If you haven't gotten there yet, move ahead to reach the emotional climax of the story now, and remember that real reason why you're telling this story. Let that sense of urgency and purpose really affect the intonation of how you're looking out at this audience. Really believe what you're saying here. Go!

Bring us to the resolution. It may be funny, it may be quick, or it may take a little bit longer. Take us to that final phrase—if you can remember some version of what you wrote down, say that. If you can't remember what you wrote don't worry about it. Move straight to what you feel led to say when you get into that resolution. Go ahead.

Now come out of that story. Thanks! That is one version of your story. Let's keep going, working on visualization, and transitions, and characterization—and you're going to really have to give yourself permission here because we're going to do an exaggerated run-through of your story.

Go back to your character list. I asked you in the previous version to think of a center of the body for that character. Go ahead and stand in that center of the body. Walk around in the space as that center. Now from that character list, go to another character, and think of that character's center of the body. Take on that character's center and walk around the space as that character and talk as that character—you can say anything, you tell me about the day or what's in the room, but keep that body posture of that character. That might also affect the rate or the tone of your speech as well.

Then go back to your narrator and walk as this narrator would (this will probably be your own center of the body).Walk in the space, and come to a standing point, and stop. Look at the imaginary audience. I want for you to tell a version of that story, but overly exaggerate your gestures, and your characterizations, your volume, everything. Here's what this looks like:

> That girl, she was walking through the woods and she knew the way, she knew where she was going but she went around a boulder and she saw a man. Uhhhh! And he was big and hairy and, oh, he had that hair on legs and his arms. Oh, and her heart, it started going, and he looked down at her, and he said, "How you doing?"

It's ridiculous. You'll look foolish doing this—give yourself permission! This does have a purpose, I promise. Start at the beginning of your story—start overly exaggerated! Really convince me you see what you're seeing. Make the scene even bigger. Whatever you're seeing, the big things are huge, and the little things are tiny, and your voice gets big with the big things, and tiny with the tiny things—play with the musicality of language and your intonation.

Now move to the middle of your story and let that climax really build and really build your voice. It's more dramatic than you would ever be in really telling this story. You would never really tell it this way, but really get into it, go!

Now you're at the climax—you're skipping over things but that's OK—get to that climactic moment and move from one character to the other and overly exaggerate those characterizations. You'll look absolutely ridiculous, but that's the point.

Come to some sort of resolution with the story, still high energy but make your pacing come down from where we've been. Thank you. OK, come to the end now. After you do this, you'll want to sit down and think about what you just did with the exaggerated run-through. You probably did a lot of things that you would never do again when you're telling that story to another person. But you may have just made some discoveries in the way you used your voice in a funny way for one character, or how you creaked a door open. An exaggerated run-through is how I got to that part where the girl sees the wolf and her heart races a little bit and I move my hand across my chest and I pat.

When I'm side-coaching my students through an exaggerated run-through, there's always something that they pick up, almost always. And almost always the energy level and the interest level that you have in an exaggerated run-through, often when you exaggerate it, it really is exactly where you need to be when you're telling a story. Energy doesn't have a thing to do with these goofy gestures that you were doing.

Energy has to do with investment in a story, and focus. Again, we tend to be very lazy in everyday speech; we're not as interested or invested in what we're saying as we could be, and the audience, they take their cues from you. When you're more interested in what you're saying, they will be more interested. When you're more focused, your audience is going to be more focused.

While you're sitting, you may want to turn to your journal again. We're going to move to the next part of the story outline. Now that you've done these couple of versions of your story, I want you to return again to the meaning that this story holds.

What's significant about this story? It could be a funny story, a lighthearted story, but it's still got some significance to you or you wouldn't tell it. It's significant because it reveals something humorous about the world around you, which offers your audience a new perspective on things. Go ahead and reflect on that in two ways: personally and culturally (and culture could be your family culture or your peer group). First, culturally: Contextualize the story within its community. What purposes might this story serve? What values does it reinforce or does it instill? Why do you think that this story survives in this culture? Personally, why were you drawn to this story? What value is this story to you?

Only at this point in your rehearsal process—after you feel comfortable with the story, and you feel comfortable living in the skin of those characters— only at this point would I suggest to you, go ahead and write down your story. Writing down your story is a very useful archive to return to when you haven't told a story in several months, and a written copy of stories, they can be a great legacy item for other people

Scripting in this way helps you work through key phrases, and wording, and fleshing out the scenes, but, like any other rehearsal exercise, you have to be prepared to let go of this wording. That's why I ask you to wait until this point to do this. Remember, memorizing a script is a surefire way to kill your performance. So get up, and tell it again away from your script, and go back and change what you've written. Keep it fluid.

For most people, writing the story down into set phrasing, it paralyzes the story. It mummifies it into text. So if you do script, be prepared to let that wording go—understand that the script is a tool, not the final goal of your wording.

I usually wait until I've tried out a story several times in several different versions for different audiences. I tell it to myself alone; I sit and I visualize the scenes around me; I storyboard it; I tell different versions of the story, longer and shorter versions informally to friends when an appropriate time arises for me to tell it. Most of all, before I write down any wording, I sit with the characters for awhile. I try out these different body postures, and I think about the story in terms of how each of those characters sees the scenes around them.

That's how I got to one of the major images of my version of the "Little Red Riding Hood" story. She sees the woods out in front of her, and all around her, and that's such a powerful image to me. I think that image would be pretty powerful for a younger girl, too. There's all this life and fruitfulness; it's in the opening words of that story. There's this symbolism there in that woods of fertility and fecundity and that inspires what's to come in the story.

It's dark there, too. There are these rich dark greens, and the black of the woods. I remembered as I was working through this story, I remember when

I was hiking in Scotland and there was this deep fir grove that we passed by—it was so dense with the trunks of pine trees. It was so moist and lush, but it was almost black about 10 feet into the woods!

After I get to the point in the story, after I get that point of the story into my body, and once I get that point in my head, then I'll use scripting as a way of thinking and going even deeper into these images. When I script, when I write things down, I stay "in scene," and I visualize each scene, so my fingers might be typing, but my focus is on the scenes and seeing those scenes all around me. I'm not watching the computer screen; I'm looking at those scenes around me. That keeps me from standing above or at a distance from the story—it keeps me in the life and the action of the drama that's unfolding around me.

Then, once I've gotten that script, I go to the margins—I print it out—I go to the margins and I storyboard again. For each scene, I draw out images that represent that scene in the margins, so when I go back to refresh my mind about a story before I perform it, I've got this quick reference right there storyboarding the margins; I've got this margin storyboard. If I forget where I was going with that rough drawing, I can read the written archive to remind myself with more detail.

Scripting, when you do it at the right time, can be very helpful as a memory aid. It can even help in seeing connections between scenes. It can help you find times when you could repeat phrases or lines to help build a rhythm. But don't let that script rule your telling.

The night before a performance, I'll re-read the written archive of the story, and then I'll go to the storyboards. Then the day of a performance, I just go to the storyboards to get the images top of mind. When you listen to recordings of stories where I've told them orally, those recording often differ, sometimes vastly, from that written archive. And they should.

It's the images that remain the same—the scene that I'm trying to communicate. The wording should match the audience—their age level, their background, their familiarity with the subject matter. I can adapt my wording to describe what I'm seeing to this group of people, but only if I've put the images as my focus, not the particular wording for those images.

For some folks, even having a script enables a kind of performance anxiety to set in. It's because we live in such a text-centered society (we revere the written word over the spoken word). When we're telling, we subconsciously hold that written story over our heads and try to remember that, instead of paying attention to the scenes that we're seeing and the audience in front of us. You're not an actor; you're a storyteller. Storytellers work from images, not specific wording.

Another thing about nerves: When I'm commenting on paying attention to pacing, this may seem very self-explanatory, but you get into telling a story for the first time, and it sometimes makes your nerves act up and you may speak very quickly at the introduction, when if you really made yourself aware, you could slow yourself down, knowing that you're going to use that sped-up pace later on near the climax.

In the next lecture, we're going to address how every person has a kind of nervous energy when they're talking to another person, whether you're talking with your neighbor or talking in front of a big group of people. And really, you need that energy that comes from nerves—if you don't capitalize on that energy, your story just falls flat. So next time we're going to try out some tips for how to capitalize on and harness that nervous energy that we all have, even in everyday conversation. We're going to talk about how that energy can contribute to an energized and lively story performance.

Putting Performance Anxiety to Good Use
Lecture 20

The number-one fear among Americans today isn't the fear of dying, aging, or losing one's mind; it's the fear of public speaking. Whenever we speak to other people—whether it's a full-scale public performance or an informal encounter with a smaller group—we all experience a degree of nervous energy. This bodily reaction to public engagement is useful for creating a lively storytelling experience for your audience. In this lecture, we'll look at the physiology behind performance anxiety, the correlation between anxiety that debilitates and energy that enlivens, and practical tools for channeling nervous energy into an energized performance.

The Physiology of Anxiety

- The responses of the body to fear are similar whether you're facing a difficult ski run, a boardroom presentation, or a challenging question from a four-year-old.

- When you encounter a situation of potential danger, your hypothalamus is triggered, which in turn, signals the pituitary gland to release hormones into your nervous system. Those hormones then cause the adrenal glands to secrete cortisol, sometimes called the "stress hormone."

- These hormones trigger your respiratory and pulmonary systems so that your breathing becomes heavier and your heart pumps faster. The purpose here is to get more oxygen into your bloodstream and pump the blood throughout your body to enable you to perform better.

- Notice that this physiological response is what gives your body the energy to perform; it boosts you up. Professional athletes know this, as do professional actors and storytellers. Your physical and mental performance is enhanced with a moderate increase in stress.

- But as we know, too much cortisol in the system can result in long-term health problems. For performers, too little stress can result in a debilitated performance level. Somewhere in the middle is where you feel the adrenaline rush enough to be excited but not overwhelmed.

- Fight-or-flight is an automatic (nonthinking) response of the body that increases the breathing and heart rate. Another region of the brain, the bed nucleus of the stria terminalis, can actually control the physical fight-or-flight response that bypasses thought. The fact that the bed nucleus is thought-linked means that you can train your brain to regulate the fear response.

Breathing and Body Warm-Ups

- How do you engage the bed nucleus to get your breathing, sweaty palms, and rapid heart rate under control and keep cortisol at a manageable level? One approach is to use some techniques of cognitive behavioral therapy to train your brain and body to react positively to the stress of public storytelling.

- Begin by standing up, with your legs shoulder width apart and knees bent slightly. Roll your shoulders back and stretch your arms up and to the sides. Take a couple of deep breaths and exhale. Then, take in a big breath, but don't let it all out at once. Try to let your exhalation last as long as your inhalation. This breathing technique is from Ashtanga Yoga.
  - Maintain that measured breathing, but now, make your breath audible in the back part of your throat (Ujjayi breath). This technique is great for when you feel that your breath is starting to get away from you: Take deep, measured breaths and engage Ujjayi breath. You can even pause in front of an audience to take this kind of controlled breath.

  - If you feel a little dizzy from taking all these deep breaths, sit down for a few minutes. That dizzy feeling is the rush of oxygen entering your brain.

- To warm up your body, follow the instructions for a sun salutation from yoga, concentrating on your breathing as you repeat the position twice. If you're not ready to do the full pose, follow the instructions for the modified pose.

- Another good warm-up is jogging in place for a few seconds. This exercise gives your body the sense that you're using cortisol purposefully. You might even take a jog outside in the days leading up to a performance. Again, you're training your body to recognize an increased heart rate as normal.

Projecting Your Voice
- One of the best ways to use nervous energy in storytelling is by projecting your voice. As we said, when you get nervous, the action of the lungs speeds up, and you have a tendency to try to force air out of the top of your lungs, but there's no power or authority in that kind of breath. You need to learn to use that increased breath to force sound up and out from the diaphragm.

- To use the full power of air entering your lungs, practice saying the consonants in the alphabet, pairing them one at a time with each of the vowel sounds: ba-ba-ba, be-be-be, and so on. As you speak, feel yourself forcing the sound out of your mouth with the power coming from your diaphragm. Try to throw those sounds across the room.

- Along with the vocal warm-ups from a previous lecture, this is a great and ridiculous way to start your day—you can even do it in your car on the way to work. This exercise enlivens your speech and prepares you to project your voice outward.

Readying Yourself to Tell
- Visualization is the best way to remember your story and the best way to center yourself and get ready for telling your story.

- Repeat the visualization exercise from our earlier lecture. Close your eyes and visualize your story scene by scene. Walk through the story in your mind. Don't worry about remembering words; focus on getting into the story.

- Keep in mind that you as the storyteller exist in a place somewhere between your audience and the world of the story that you're telling. That story is your own safe place; no one in the audience knows how the story is supposed to go, and there's no script that you're tied to. Even if you skip a scene accidentally, you can always reinsert it later.

- Once you've run through the story in your mind, it's useful to walk through the story physically in the space where you're going to perform. If you're giving a business presentation, walk through the presentation in the meeting room before the meeting takes place.

- Another useful technique is to assign a specific location to the scenes in the story or to break up where you will stand in terms of

Test takers are encouraged to study in the place where they will take an exam because there is a subconscious association between knowledge learned and recalled in the same place.

the beginning, middle, and end of your story. You might start your story by standing on the left, then move to the center for the middle, and end on the right. You can do this with a lot of movement or very little—just a step. These separations can help you remember the parts of your story and give purpose to your movements.

- Instead of losing your energy through "shuffling feet," plant yourself and make your movements purposeful. This technique allows your energy to come out in your gestures or facial expressions. But keep in mind that less is more in storytelling. Gestures can be distracting if they are just expending nervous energy; you may be able to channel them to facial expressions instead.

Your Personal Style
- Everyone is a storyteller, and every storyteller has a different style. You have strengths as a teller that others don't have—ways of connecting with an audience and even access to specific audiences. Others have different gifts.

- Don't feel that someone else knows the "right" way to tell a story. There is no ideal form for the way you will tell; there is a unique way that you will engage with your audience and adapt to that audience as you craft your story in the moment.

- All of these warm-ups and rehearsal ideas are aimed at preparing you to be ready to have fun and be spontaneous in the moment. It's by rehearsing and playing with stories in a safe space that you will prepare yourself to be free in the moment to relax, harness the energy your body is feeding you, and dive into your story.

Suggested Reading

Linklater, *Freeing the Natural Voice.*

1. Good stress is called *eu*-stress, as in the words "*eu*phoria" ("good feeling") or "*eu*phonic" ("good sound"). Eu-stress is essential in giving a good performance, storytelling or otherwise. Can you think of a time when your nervous energy helped you in a situation? How?

2. Before any big performance, I try to get into the space at least 30 minutes ahead of time and walk through my story—literally walk around in the space and place the scenes in that performance area. How can "blocking" techniques help you remember your stories?

Putting Performance Anxiety to Good Use
Lecture 20—Transcript

Professor Harvey: Did you know that the number one fear among Americans today, it's not a fear of dying; it's not a fear of aging; it's not even a fear of losing your mind—the number one fear over death is of public speaking. That's according to Phillip Zimbardo, he's a psychologist and professor emeritus at Stanford University (it's from his book *Shyness*). The truth is, whenever we speak to each other—whether it's a big public performance (in front of a group of people) or a relatively small engagement (talking just with your friend even), we all get a degree of nervous energy when we're called to speak publicly.

This reaction (and it is a bodily reaction, not just an amorphous feeling; it's something that happens in your body. Your heart rate picks up, your breathing rate increases)—this bodily response to public engagement (whether you're talking with your best friend or your boss or your cohorts at work), that nervous energy is actually useful—it's essential in creating a lively storytelling experience for your audience.

Experienced storytellers know some useful tools for how to channel that nervous energy into an energized performance. Some of the most seasoned public speakers—people who don't think they get nervous anymore—some of these folks miss out on a really engaging conversation with their audience because they don't know how to summon this energy.

Whether you consciously deal with performance anxiety as a barrier to communicating with others, or you want to become a more energized and engaging storyteller, this lecture is designed to teach you the physiology behind performance anxiety, the correlation between anxiety that debilitates and energy that enlivens, and lots of practical tools to help get rid of negative nerves and to channel good energy into positive engagement with others.

Let me give you three scenarios. You're at the top of a ski lift, and you just got off the chair that hoists you up there, and you've got your skis on, your poles in hand, you're facing a downhill slope, towards a slope full of moguls (those are those bumps that you have to navigate through as you swish back and forth). You're facing this steep downward pitch. Your heart starts pumping and you get geared up, and you're a little intimidated; you grip those poles a little bit tighter because your palms are starting to sweat inside your gloves.

Second scenario: You're about to go into a boardroom to give a presentation. You've got your notes, you've got your graphs, you've got your charts, and it doesn't matter how prepared you know that you are. You start breathing faster, and you greet people as you're walking through the door and you can't feel your feet anymore, they're a little numb, and you're trying to remember the first thing you're supposed to say and then they all are there, all looking at you—and your breath gets short.

Third scenario: Your four-year-old comes up to you and asks, "What's sex?" You stare off into space, and your heart, it starts pounding—"What am I going to say?"

These are three different experiences, but our body interprets these stimuli in a similar way—you exhibit many of the same physiological responses. That's what anxiety and fear are. They're responses that the body gives; they're primal. All of a sudden you're facing the bear in the woods, and what do you do? In your body, here's what's going on.

You see this bear (which in the forest of modern culture we've turned into the ski slope, or the boardroom presentation, or your child's question)—you see this situation of potential danger, and it triggers your hypothalamus, which is seated back here in the deeper region of the brain. It bypasses conscious thought in the frontal cortex and it shoots right to the hypothalamus, and that signals the pituitary gland hanging on the bottom of your brain to release all of these hormones (about 30 of them). It releases all of these into your nervous system, so the pituitary zaps that signal to the glands, and the adrenal glands, they secrete cortisol. (It's sometimes called the "stress hormone.")

Cortisol and all of these other hormones, they go shooting through your bloodstream, and they trigger your respiratory system. [Breathing.] Then the hormones, they get your pulmonary system going, so boom ba-boom ba-boom And the lungs are going and the heart's going and it's serving the function of getting more oxygen into your blood, and pumping that oxygen-rich blood through your body, your body can perform better, and you either stand up and fight that bear (or you ski down the mountain, or you give the presentation, or you talk with your daughter about sex), or you get the heck out of there. ("Let me back off this ski lift! To heck with your job! Honey, ask your father about that!") That's fight or flight. Remember, it bypasses conscious thought, bypassing conscious control.

But what I want you to notice about this physiological response is that this release of hormones is what gives your body the energy to perform; it boosts you up. Professional athletes know this, professional actors know this, and professional storytellers know this. So your physical and mental performance actually increases with a moderate increase in stress level.

Too much cortisol in the system, though, that's what's responsible for a lot of long-term health problems. It's why we can clinically connect long-term stress with an increase in hypertension, heart attacks, and also a lowered immune system. Cortisol literally eats away at cells, so too much of it can be a damaging thing in your body, and in the short term it overloads your system; it debilitates you. You can't really speak freely, because you're having a hard time slowing your heart down, and you can't control your breathing. That's when panic sets in.

But we also have to look at this other end of this curve, this other end with too little stress, and an equally debilitated performance level. When you have very little stress—and I mean in the psychological, physiological sense, not in terms of pop culture, where stress has all these negative connotations—but when you experience no stress, there's no cortisol triggered, no increased oxygen to your blood, no increased blood flow, and things are just kind of flowing along. When you're talking with people, this can be very chill and, mellow place to be, but it's not going to yield a dynamic story, and it might just put your audience to sleep.

But you get in this middle area—when you're just jazzed up enough to feel that adrenaline rush, when you're looking down that ski slope and it's terrifying and it's thrilling at the same time—which has something to do with attitude. You feel like you can do this, and you take the plunge, and that adrenaline keeps on going, and it's fun! You don't have to be a wacko like

Evel Knievel to enjoy the rush of experiences like this. You're giving a good presentation, and you can feel that flow of conversation and ideas in your presentation, and it's fun!

So when you get nervous speaking with others, it's because your body has activated this hypothalamus-pituitary-adrenal axis (that's the cortisol system that I was talking about)—fight or flight has been activated. But there's another system going on here too. That's another part of our brains that regulates breathing and heart rate. Our bodies are very smart. This system has a long fancy name, the "bed nucleus of the stria terminalis." The bed nucleus is located right here on the prefrontal cortex, the thinking center of the brain, and it's this system that's associated and connected with thought.

While you've got this non-thinking fear response going on (the fight-or-flight system revs up your body, your heart rate goes up, the respiration goes up, the cortisol starts flooding through your system), there's this other thinking system that can also speed up the heart with adrenaline (it's the bed nucleus).

Research by Dennis Choi at the Simmons Foundation in New York and Michael Davis at the Yerkes Institute at Emory University, among others, these folks says that the thought-linked bed nucleus can actually control the physical fight-or-flight system that bypasses thought. Because the bed nucleus is connected with thought, you can train your brain to regulate your fear response, which is fantastic for us storytellers, because it means that we can train the thought-related bed nucleus to keep from retriggering that physical fear response when we anticipate public performance.

How do we do this—how do we engage the thought system (the bed nucleus) to get this breathing, and sweaty palms, and heart rate all going in the direction we want them to go, and to keep your cortisol at a manageable level? The exercises we'll do today are warm up and rehearsal techniques, but you might also call them cognitive behavioral therapy techniques, because we're training your brain and your body to react positively to the stress of public storytelling—not negatively. We're doing a form of cognitive behavioral therapy aimed at helping you, as a storyteller, to be centered, and enlivened, and ready.

First, let's work on that breathing, on your body. I'd like for you to stand up, your legs about shoulder-width apart, knees bent slightly (remember, you don't want to pass out, don't ever lock your knees when you're storytelling). Stand up, knees slightly bent, roll your shoulders back. Reach your arms up to the ceiling, and stretch over to your right (now I'm mirroring you), but reach over and try to touch this wall, and then reach over to your left and try and touch that wall. Now stretch up and around and back up and arms down.

We're going to employ some breathing techniques from a kind of yoga that's called "Ashtanga yoga"—and don't be turned off if you think, "Oh, yoga's not for me." Just give yourself permission to try these out; we're not doing a lot, and if they're useful, you can keep them. If they're not useful, you can toss them later. But give yourself a couple of good, deep breaths standing here, knees slightly bent (micro-bending the knees), and feel that breath fill your lungs and then exhale. Try not to hold your breath when you get your lungs full. Try not to hold it, but fill your lungs, deep breath, and then back out again. Now I want you to breathe in again, big breath, but don't let it all out in one big gust, but try to let your exhalation last as long as your inhalation did. So I'll count: Inhale one, two, three, four, five—exhale one, two, three, four, five. Again: Inhale one, two, three, four, five—exhale one, two, three, four, five.

Now keep that measured breathing, but I want for you to make this breath audible. What you do is you're keeping an awareness of the breath at the back part of your throat. It's a kind of conscious constriction of the back of your throat, and it sounds like this. [Professor Harvey breathes.]

It's great, you sound like Darth Vader off of *Star Wars*. It's called "Ujjayi breath," and it's a great way to control your breathing in yoga, and it's great for when you feel that breath start to get away from you, take deep breaths, measured breaths, and engage Ujjayi breath, let's try it some more—take a few deep Ujjayi breaths.

This is a great exercise to do before you speak, or if you're in the middle of a story and you find your breath getting away from you. Just use the pause, look out to the audience (yes, I want you to think about what I just said), and inside you know that you're using that time to take those controlled breaths and center yourself again.

You might be feeling a little dizzy right now. If you're feeling a little dizzy, sit down for a second, and know that you need to breathe deeper in your daily routine in order to get enough oxygen into your system! That dizzy feeling is that rush of oxygen entering your brain—your brain is telling you, "Yes, finally! Brain food!" So remember to breathe.

All of this deep breathing will help you remember to take breaths so that you don't have to take a breath in the middle of every sentence. As you're breathing, let's warm up more of your body because all of these systems are connected. We're going to do a sun salutation in yoga. Stand, still with that deep breath, feet together with your ankles slightly touching. Root yourself into your heels. If you're able to do this barefoot, spread your toes wide, so you've got a wide base to plant yourself into the ground there.

Tighten your legs; you'll almost feel an inward rotation of your inner thighs, knees straight ahead. Tighten those core muscles, bringing an awareness into your pelvic area, and try to align your spine from that base of your spine where the vertebrae connect with your pelvic bone, straight up to your shoulders and where the vertebrae connect with your skull bone.

Roll your shoulders back, arms to your side, palms turned inwards, relax your hands, and turn your gaze straight ahead and take a few deep breaths here, maybe practicing that audible Ujjayi breath.

Take a deep breath in, floating your arms up over your head, palms touching together over your head, looking up at those palms, and then breathing out let the arms float down to your sides and fold forward to touch your toes, or as close to your toes as you're able. If you're able, place your palms on the ground about shoulder-width apart. Your head folds all the way down as you fold forward; let it hang there.

Now look slightly forward and take a deep breath in, and on your exhalation put your weight on your hands, and either step your feet backwards one at a time into a pushup position. Or, if you're able, just shoot your feet back, landing on your toes.

The full pose has you bend at the elbows and float about two inches off the ground, in a low plank position. It's important to keep your elbows at the sides. Don't swing your elbows out like a regular push-up position. You want to feel the triceps muscles working a lot on this, so keep your elbows in. If you're not ready for the full pose, just stay with your arms extended.

On your next breath in, extend your arms and bend your spine back, looking up, and give yourself a big stretch in your spine. You'll take your feet and either move them one at a time over so you're resting on the tops of your feet in the back, or you can roll over the toes and rest on the tops of your feet like that—however you're more comfortable getting into this position.

Here, you should try to keep your weight pressed into the thumb and index finger part of your palms. Try not to roll the pressure out to the pinkie fingers or the outside of your hands, but keep that pressure more on the thumbs. Really press all those fingers into the ground, spread fingers wide.

On your next inhalation, lift up from your hips, push yourself into downward-dog position, rolling your shoulders back so that the inner elbow is facing outwards. You don't want your elbows pushing out to the sides, but roll those shoulders back and roll the inner part of your arm to face outwards. Look at your navel—yes, you're navel gazing!—look at your navel, and give yourself five deep, good breaths.

After that fifth breath, look forward, inhale and jump forward, feet between your hands if you're able. Exhale; fold your head down to your knees. Inhale, floating your hands and arms up over your head with your arms, palms touching, looking up at your palms, and exhale, arms down to your sides.

Let's try that sequence again: Inhale arms up, exhale fold over, palms on the floor, inhale look up. Exhale, step or shoot your feet back into plank position. Inhale look up, pressing your arms straight. Exhale to downward dog for five breaths. On the exhalation of the fifth breath look forward, inhale jump forward. Exhale, fold. Inhale arms up over your head standing up, and exhale, relax.

That's better. I often jog in place for a few seconds, too. Controlled jogging—not racing or running—but controlled jogging gives your body that sense that you're using that cortisol purposefully. My practices are jogging and yoga (in my 20s it used to be dancing). That helps your daily storytelling—talking with your neighbors, with your daughter when she asks you about sex—"Oh, OK. My heart's speeding up at that question, but it's OK. It's got a purpose, I can use this. 'OK honey, let's talk.'"

If I know I've got a presentation or performance coming up and I'm not already in that routine, I'll try to go on at least one or two jogs on the few days leading up to that performance, because it trains my body to recognize that increased heart rate as a normal thing: "Oh, this is just what my body does when I exert myself, oh, OK."

When my heart starts to race in anticipation of a performance, those moments leading up to when I tell a story, and even in the moment that I begin speaking, I hear my heart (you can hear it pounding), I hear it and I think, "Oh, OK, normal—this is just what a body does when it's doing something." I train my brain to interpret increased heart rate as appropriate.

One of the best ways to use this energy in your storytelling is by projecting your voice. Remember what we talked about, how the power of your voice comes from down here, from the diaphragm, forcing the air out of our lungs. When we get nervous, the lungs speed up, and we have a tendency to try to force air out of the top of our lungs up here—which sounds like this: And there's no power or authority in that kind of breath. You're fighting against yourself (which is what you're doing—you're waging the battle with your breath and trying to press that breath down into a manageable rate from up here in the top of your lungs). Instead of trying to press that breath down, use that increased breath to force the sound up and out from the bottom, from down here in your diaphragm.

Here are a few ways to do this. Remember our warm-up exercise with "me-YO!" and you force that "yo" sound up and out to the back of the room—

there's a great warm-up that will help you articulate (to get rid of your lazy mouth) and also push that air up and out, and practice saying your story with the full power of that air entering your lungs.

What we do is to separate the vowels out from the consonants in the alphabet. We're going to go through the consonants, pairing each consonant one at a time with all of the vowels. So for the first one, "B," it sounds like this: ba-ba-ba, be-be-be, bi-bo-bu. Now we move to "C," say it with me: ca-ca-ca, ce-ce-ce, ci-co-cu. And with each of these, really feel yourself forcing that sound out of your mouth with the power coming from down here in your diaphragm—it's a muscular thing, a physical thing—from down here below your lungs, in your diaphragm. Throw these sounds across the room; try it with with "D": da-da-da, de-de-de, di-do-du. Let's keep going with the rest of the alphabet. Take breaths when you need them but say the rest along with me: fa-fa-fa, fe-fe-fe, fi-fo-fu, ga-ga-ga, gi-gi-gi, gi, go, gu. And you continue through the alphabet—when you come to Z, end it on a high note—za-za-za, zi-zi-zi, zi-zo-ZOOO!

Now, again, along with these vocal warm ups in our other lecture, this is a great and ridiculous way to start your day. You can do this in your car on the way to work, and you can teach your carpool how to do it. They'll love it! You'll be ready to start your day of speaking with others, and you'll also be prepared to project your voice out. It really helps enliven your speech.

Next, let's talk about being ready. We started out this how-to section talking about visualization, and I did that purposefully for a reason—it's the best way to remember your story, and it's the best way to center yourself to get ready for telling your story.

That exercise we did at the very beginning about closing your eyes and visualizing your story scene by scene, really seeing everything and everyone who's there, and walking through it in your mind, that's a great way to feel ready to tell—you're not worried about remembering words; you're focused on getting into that story, the images.

That story is your safe place, because it's not all about you when you're telling a story. It's about bringing your audience into this other place to be with these people and to see what you see there. You as the storyteller really exist somewhere between your audience and the world of the story when you're telling. That story is a retreat; it's a safe place, and it's your own. Nobody in the audience probably knows how that story is supposed to go, and there's no "script" that you're tied to. If you skip a scene accidentally, you can always reinsert it later—here's how you do that:

> Jack was going along; he was minding his business when all of a sudden he heard this sound: "Fe, fi, fo, fum—I smell the blood of an Englishman!" He stopped and he looked up and there was a giant. (Now I realize that I've completely skipped over the part where he sells the cow for the beans, and the beanstalk, so I go on.) The reason why Jack saw this giant was because days earlier, he had gone out to sell the family's only cow, because they were so poor. But then in the marketplace, he met an old woman selling magic beans.

So you go on, and then you pick back up. It's your story—and you can rearrange it any way you want, and you can fix it in the moment, it's OK!

Once you've run through the story in your head, it's useful to walk through the story physically in the space where you're going to perform. Test takers are often encouraged to study in the place where they will be taking the test or taking their exam, because of that subconscious association between knowledge learned in a place and knowledge recalled in that place. You may have experienced this before when you return to your hometown, and you start remembering all of these things from childhood—and that place, maybe not even a particular thing there, but just being in those surroundings, it triggers memory.

If you're giving a boardroom presentation, it's not a bad idea to walk through the presentation, and any story you're going to include in that presentation, in the boardroom itself prior to your meeting. Even if you're able to be there only a few minutes before the presentation starts, get up to the front (or wherever it is you're going to be speaking), and walk through in your head the different scenes of your story (think of it in terms of that storyboard—first I did this, then this happened, then this, and I end here).

Another useful technique is to assign a specific location to those scenes, or to break up where you stand in terms of beginning, middle, and end of your story—so I start my story by standing here to the left, and when I move to the middle of the story, I move to the middle of the room, and at the end I move to the right.

Or you start in the middle (which is a nice centered place to begin). In the middle of the story, you move over to your left, and then when the story comes to an end, the climax, you move over to your right. For your final concluding words you come back to the center again. You can do this with a lot of movement, or you can do it very minimally (you can do that, step over to your left, and the center, and the right. You can move a lot). But those separations—what actors would call "blocking"—they can help you remember parts of your story, and it can give you purposeful movements.

Because one of our tendencies when we get nervous is to have what I call "shuffling feet." You've seen this—somebody's telling a story, and they're moving all over the place. They're swaying, and they're bobbing and they're weaving and it's not really adding to the story, it's just kind of distracting, and this poor person has so much cortisol that he's just dying to release somehow and it's all getting lost through his feet!

Instead of losing that energy through your feet, plant yourself, and make your movements purposeful. It will help to funnel that energy that you were losing out of your feet and it will help that energy come up and out of your gestures, or your facial expressions. Remember the economy of story performance: Less can be way more.

If you have a lot of gestures for a character, could you channel those gestures completely into your face? Do you need that extra movement? Sometimes it can really add to a story, but beware of gestures that just expend nervous energy. There are better uses for that energy, in purposeful choices.

The last things we have time for today have to do with your own personal style as a teller. Everyone is a storyteller, and every person has a different style. You have your own strengths as a teller that other people don't—

you have your own way of connecting with others, and you have access to specific audiences that other people don't.

Others have different gifts—don't feel like someone else has the "right" way to tell your story. As much as I enjoy Plato, this is one place where he doesn't apply—there is no "ideal form" for the way that you will tell your story. There's the unique way that you will engage with your audience and listen to them to craft your story in the moment.

All of these exercises and warm ups and rehearsal ideas are aimed at helping you prepare to be ready to have fun and be spontaneous in the moment. It's by rehearsing here for a little while, and playing with some stories in this safe space of our time together, that you'll be able to prepare yourself to be free in the moment, to relax, and to harness that energy your body is feeding you, and to dive into your story.

In our final lectures, I want to prepare you for the different kinds of audiences that you might face. There are some specific features of children's audiences, and specific psychological needs at each age range within that child spectrum that you need to be aware of (because telling to a three-year-olds requires something different out of your story than telling for a seven-year-old, or heaven help you, telling to a middle schooler).

These audiences require different things than a boardroom setting might—certainly this audience affects both the kinds of stories that you tell (telling the story of your company, for example), but it also affects how you tell. Most of the time, you're not up at a platform or at the head of a table telling, you're in your living room. You're talking to your friends, or you're at the fence talking to your neighbor.

Next time, we'll discuss the specific needs for each of these kinds of story situations. We'll continue in the coming lectures to give you crucial information on how to hook different kinds of audiences from the very beginning, and what *not* to do when you conclude your story, and some good tips for how to keep your audience's attention throughout your stories.

Adapting to Different Audiences
Lecture 21

M ost of the time, we're telling stories in the course of our everyday lives, and all of the storytelling tips we've learned up to this point can be applied to office parties, presentations, and other common situations. But it's important to note that even these storytelling scenarios are different; there's a difference between telling a story to a friend and telling to a roomful of people. Different storytelling scenarios require you to adapt your story content and your persona as a teller in specific ways. In this lecture, we'll look at the typical parameters of different storytelling scenarios, how stories emerge in different settings, and what specific audiences typically need from a story.

Living-Room Storytelling
- Most of the time, we tell stories in a living-room type of setting, sitting down in close proximity to our audience. Stories usually emerge in these settings in the course of conversation.

- Something in the conversation may remind you of a story, and from your seated position, you start to visualize the first scene that comes to mind. Having that first image in front of you not only establishes the characters for the audience but also helps you settle into this "spontaneous" story and start to see how it will unfold.

- Even in conversation, you can transform what you want to say from an anecdote to a story by making character distinctions, taking on varied perspectives, adding cultural connections, and building a "plot."

- In a conversational setting, your story satisfies at least one primary need for your audience: It provides some common ground to stand on. Your story gives both you and your audience a metaphorical place to stand and a literal way to interact. This interaction occurs as dialogue—stories shared back and forth—and this exchange requires a few things from you as a storyteller.

o Be aware of economy in living-room scenarios. In a living room, you aren't performing; you're "giving ground" for the conversation to stand on. Your purpose is to give more ground to stand on and invite others to add their stories to the mix.

o Be prepared to share your storytelling with your audience. If someone jumps in, you have the choice to ignore, yield, or incorporate. Probably the best choice is to incorporate because that action allows you to draw in other examples as part of the larger story and to share the telling without sacrificing your own trajectory.

Organizational Storytelling

• There are generally three kinds of storytelling opportunities at work: (1) a story told as part of a presentation, (2) the story of your company told to employees or outside audiences, and (3) stories told to build community and camaraderie among employees.

• When you're giving a presentation at work, don't just think about including a story, but look at the whole presentation as one long story. Various scenes are part of the overall arc of the presentation, which has a trajectory and some kind of resolution or ending.

o If you're offering a solution to a problem or findings that your group has made, tell it as a story: Who is the villain? Who do you want to unify your audience against? Personify your idea as the hero. Also, think carefully about the role of your listeners; can you give them a specific role within the story?

o If your presentation is framed as the story of an unlikely hero (your company), then your audience of co-workers can be cast in the role of helpers to that hero. Think of the hero as the company, the villain as falling sales, and the helpers as the co-workers to whom you're giving the presentation.

○ There's a different kind of dynamic in this storytelling scenario; it's more formal, so there is an expectation of a specific kind of performance. You want to be approachable but confident; speaking in a solid, well-projected voice helps establish that persona.

○ Stories also emerge more purposefully in this setting than in an informal conversation. If a story occurs to you in the midst of a presentation, keep it economical and welcome your audience to participate.

○ Stories can illustrate your point, and they're often most useful when they come before an outright statement or outline of your points; use stories as foreground over outlined concepts. This sequence gives your listeners a chance to see for themselves the real-life application and the truth of your propositions.

○ As you're telling a presentation story, you can still have fun with it and commit to it! You don't lose any authority or confidence when you share a story with characters your audience wants to remember; that investment in your story often transfers over to more investment in the other elements of your presentation.

• Similar ideas apply when you are telling a workplace story to convey the history, mission, and vision of your business to employees or outside audiences.

○ Again, personify the company as the hero and the opposing forces it faces as the dragons in the hero's journey.

○ One way to think about your company story is the idea that your company has a beginning and a middle but no end. Your hope is that your business or organization keeps going. Thus, you're bringing your employees into the story during the rising action—they are part of the story of building that business. This approach unifies you and your employees in the same role of working to strengthen the company.

New employee orientations represent a golden opportunity to tell a compelling story about your company.

- In an organizational setting, you also have the chance to ignore, yield to, or incorporate the contributions of your listeners. Keep in mind that it's critical to listen to your employees' stories in the workplace. In fact, professional consultants sometimes use storytelling as a tool to help companies improve internal communications.

  o When you have a chance to hear stories from employees, listen for the implicit values and repeated themes that are communicated.

  o Creating space in the workday for senior employees to tell their stories allows them to mentor younger employees and shares their trajectory with the company, keeping the story alive.

  o If you give people the freedom to tell their stories, you will be amazed at the insights your employees and colleagues will contribute.

Storytelling for Children

- Obviously, in a classroom or other setting with children, the physical environment is different. If you're a teacher, you're often standing at the front of the room, facing a group of students seated in rows. This positioning is inherently submissive for the students; the teacher looks down on the students, and they look up. The same thing is true for a group of children sitting on the floor with a storyteller sitting in a chair in front of them.

- In a setting where there are more bodies in the room, be aware that bodies swallow sound. For this reason, you will have to project the volume of your voice more in a classroom setting.

- Make sure you don't adopt a flat or false persona when telling stories to children. This shows a lack of engagement with and belief in the story.

- In children's stories, there is room to make your gestures bigger and your characterizations more embodied. Young children up through middle schoolers respond well to storytellers who use their whole bodies.

- For infants and toddlers up to age 3, use stories with a lot of action, sound effects, and props. Keep the plots simple and include only a few characters. Smile often in telling stories to this age group, because young children can be frightened by scary faces or mean characters. A good rule of thumb is to make the story as long as the age of the child.

- With preschool children (ages 3–5), give them roles to play and long words to master and use. Introduce science and basic physics stories (how our bodies work, how we build a house), and encourage them to tell their own simple stories (how a seed grows). Again, keep the plots simple.

- In the early elementary school years (ages 5–7), children can start to handle a more developed plotline with clear answers. Children at this age are starting to compare their own strengths and weaknesses to those of others. Tell stories that emphasize a variety of strengths and diverse abilities. Also at this age, children become more interested in telling their own stories.

- For ages 8–10, you can tell longer stories (such as the tales of Snow White or Paul Bunyan) and spooky stories. Stories with surprise endings are good; at this age, children have a better grasp of reality and can handle their expectations being foiled.

- When children turn 11, they start to see beyond their own problems and imagine possibilities outside of their own experiences; they can reason through abstract problems to arrive at underlying principles. Avoid didactic stories, such as fables; let these children draw their own conclusions about a lesson. Stories with riddles and mysteries are also great for this age group.

- Keep in mind that older children will not necessarily start out on your side. They can't take the risk of liking you until their peers give their assent. As a storyteller, your biggest task is to get these children out of the mode of posturing for one another and into the world of the story. To some extent, you have to match your persona to theirs—you have to be "cool," too.

Suggested Reading

Lehrman, ed., *Telling Stories to Children*.

Questions to Consider

1. Think about the permeability of the borders between the three storytelling scenarios discussed in this lecture. When is a boardroom like a living room? When is a living room like a classroom?

2. What kind of boardroom stories are you most called to make, and how can listening to your audience influence and affect that kind of storytelling?

3. What age range of children do you most come into contact with? What are the specific needs of that age range in terms of stories and storytelling?

Adapting to Different Audiences
Lecture 21—Transcript

Professor Harvey: Most of the time, we're telling stories in the day-to-day, and all of the storytelling tips that you've learned up until this point, they can be applied to low-key office parties as well as when you're asked to give a presentation to a large group and you want to include a story. Or, if you want to gear your whole presentation under the arc of one long story.

But there's a different scenario in each of these three cases. There's a difference between telling a story to your friend, and telling to a roomful of people. There's a difference between telling in the intimate scenario of your living room, and telling a story to a roomful of children.

Children age six need different things in a story than children age 10 or 12. Different storytelling scenarios will require you to adapt your story content and your persona as a teller in specific ways. In this lecture, we'll look at the typical physical parameters for these kinds of storytelling scenarios (physically where you will be in relation to your audience), how stories emerge in these different settings. (A story you think of in the midst of a conversation, as opposed to a story that you plan to tell as a part of a prepared presentation.)

What those specific audiences typically need from a story, and it's not about funny stories or dramatic stories—it's not about genre either—I mean, what does this specific audience *need* out of your story—and then you use genre and humor and drama to satisfy those needs. We'll focus on tips for how you handle yourself as a storyteller in each of these situations.

Most of the time, we're telling stories in a living-room type of setting—and I choose "living room" to typify this kind of scene because it's a relaxed setting. You're sitting on the couch with someone, or you're standing with a drink and talking with a couple of friends.

You can think also of a dinner-table kind of setting—you're with friends or invited guests (which can be a little more formal), but on the whole you're with people you know, and your peers, people you feel comfortable with—and that will physically shape how you are in relation to one another.

As a storyteller, you may be sitting—maybe you're leaning back, and you've got a drink in one hand. Or, if you're standing, you're still at a comfortable distance from that person. Your audience is intimate; they're on the same eye level with you, and you're in close proximity. Socially you've established a relationship with these folks already. In this proximity, you don't have to project your voice as much, the volume of your voice, but you still want to speak from the diaphragm (giving your voice power).

Your story will emerge in these situations usually in the process of conversation—somebody says something, and it reminds you of your Aunt Margaret, who made doilies—and what a strange thing it is nowadays for someone to do, to make doilies. But the care that she took in doing this, and how she gave each of those doilies as holiday gifts every year.

Now I'm completely making this up, but for the sake of an example, let's say that you're reminded of "Aunt Margaret," so you start to tell that story. From a seated position, you start to visualize that scene of what you just thought of. You give plenty of eye contact with that person in front of you, but you start to move into that visualization of the place all around you. You see Aunt Margaret, and you see that room inside her house where she used to crochet.

It's great to start with that first image that comes to you, because that will not only establish the characters for your audience—it will help them bond with that story from the get-go—but it helps you settle spontaneously into this story, and to start to see the story unfold around you for yourself.

Now, it's a story. Something happens to build to a climax. From this memory, what did Aunt Margaret *do* that contributed to your life? Rather than leaving it as an anecdote—"Aunt Margaret crocheted, the end"—think in terms of plot. What did she do? "She would make these doilies." OK, now go there, what did they look like?—"And they were simple little round things, she would put them on the backs of chairs." OK now make a connection out to culture: "Her home, it looked like one of those Victorian tea rooms that you see in period movies, with 'all the ladies drinking together.'"

You've added a tangent out,—"So there was always this profusion of doilies around her home, and every holiday all of us girls, we would get a doily—and one day …." Your story goes on from there, whatever you're building to. From that, you can see that I'm giving character distinctions. Even from a seated position, you can give that: "All of the girls, we would get these doilies, and her home, it looked like this Victorian tea room. You can still see—I'm playfully overdoing it—but you can still see this difference in characterizations even from a seated position. You can see those body centers coming out.

In a conversational setting, your story satisfies at least one primary need for your audience. Your audience needs to stand on some common ground to stand on with you. Your story gives both you and your audience a metaphorical place to stand, and a literal way to interact. This interaction happens as dialogue—stories shared back and forth, in the midst of a robust exchange (at least that's the hope).

Your story emerges in conversation, and you're contributing to an ongoing dialogue, not a monologue on your life. When you're in dialogue with someone else, there will be times when you talk and the other person listens, but conversation doesn't always move in this progressive march onwards. Conversation hops: You say something, and someone else chimes in, and then you come back to add in something, and then someone else makes a point. As much as we want to think of ourselves as logical, metered beings, that's not how this conversational scenario works. This will require a few things out of you as a storyteller.

Stay aware of economy in living room situations. In a living room, you aren't performing; you're "giving ground" for the conversation to stand on. Your purpose is to give more ground to stand on, and invite the other person to add their stories to the mix. Say what you need to, build to a climax, enjoy it while you're getting into it, and then get out. Generally if you've been talking for more than a minute and a half nonstop, you're talking too long.

Be prepared to share your storytelling with your audience. Someone may jump in: "Oh, I had an Aunt who was like that. She just sat there all day and knitted, and learned from her." In that moment you have a choice—you can *ignore*, you can *yield*, or you can *incorporate*. If you *ignore* them, you just railroad through what they were trying to add (and you've seen people do this—they don't stop, they just keep going right over what the other person says, only louder).

So, you can ignore your audience. Or, you can *yield* your story for a time to that person, who then takes over (so you ask them to share their story—and you may come back to yours later, or it ends as the anecdote).

Or, and this is often the best way, you *incorporate* their addition into your own story—so it's not an interruption, it's not a pause button. It's something that can add to the growing story all around you. They become a partner in the storytelling, and you're telling together, so you draw in their comment: "Yeah, so there's this whole generation of women who are doing this, making doilies, well, one day ...."

Then you go into your rising action of your story. What you've done is acknowledge that person. You've drawn in their example as part of this larger story that's unfolding for all of you, and you're sharing the storytelling without sacrificing the trajectory of where you want to take that audience— that funny or that poignant memory of Aunt Margaret. (I'm loving Aunt Margaret by now. I kind of wish she were actually real and I actually knew this woman—she's in my head.)

Remember your purpose (dialogue), and be willing to share the storytelling. You can use all of these elements of characterization, narration, and visualization, even with a drink in your hand.

Now I want to bridge from this scenario to the next one, which is a boardroom or organizational storytelling—and I don't want to bridge by asking you to drink at work!—but I want to ask you to consider three different kinds of storytelling opportunities that might be open to you at work.

One is the story that you might include as a part of a presentation at work (so telling stories as a project leader to a group of colleagues in a boardroom).

The second is, if you are in management or you own your business, how you can tell the story of your company to your employees or to an outside audience.

The third example connects us all the way back to that first scenario in the living room. It has to do with how upper management can use storytelling in interpersonal communications with employees to build community and camaraderie.

First, when you're giving a presentation at work, I want to encourage you not just to think about including a story, but to look at the presentation as a whole as one big story. The pieces of your presentations are these various scenes within the overall arc of your presentation, which has a trajectory, momentum, and a kind of resolution or ending.

If you're offering a solution to a problem in your presentation, or findings that your group has come to, tell it as a story—who's the villain? Who do you want to unify your audience against? Present your idea as the hero—personify it. Put it in that role. Also think carefully about the role of the audience. Can you give the audience a specific role within this story?

If your presentation is framed as the story of an unlikely hero (your company), then your audience of co-workers can be cast in the role of helpers to help that hero—remember in the lecture on the hero's journey, Inanna's helper was the one who rescued her from the underworld. You can cast your co-workers (your audience) in that role of helper, and it gives them a role to play in the ongoing story of saving the company. The hero is the company, the villain is falling sales, and the helper is the co-workers who you're giving this presentation to.

This sounds very simplistic—heroes, villains, helpers—but it's classic, and it's tied to the oral nature of storytelling (it's focused on drama and action, and *agon* or struggle) and it takes your audience on a journey in which they have a purpose; they have a role. When your audience can see themselves in the story, it's a strong call to action. These classic features of stories, they have staying power with audiences.

Because you're usually speaking to more than one person, or down a long row of people in this scenario, you'll need to project the volume of your voice more, from the diaphragm. More so than in perhaps a conversational setting. There's a different kind of dynamic going on here; it's more formal, so there's an expectation of a specific kind of performance in the workplace from you. You exude confidence. You want to be approachable, but confident—and a solid voice projecting from down here in your diaphragm, well it does that trick quite nicely.

Stories here emerge more purposefully. This kind of setting usually isn't as impromptu as an informal conversation. Sometimes a story will occur to you in the midst of a presentation, and the same suggestions as before apply (keep it economical, and welcome your audience to participate).

But often with a presentation, you've spent time thinking about what you're going to say, so you have time to work on developing an arc and to think about the meaning of your story.

Stories can illustrate your point, and they're often most useful when they come before an outright statement or outline of your points, so you foreground stories over outlined concepts. Telling the story first, and then drawing concepts and points from that story, it gives your audience a chance to see for themselves the real-life application of your propositions and the truth of your positions.

As you're telling these stories, you can get into them! You can still have fun with them! You're not losing any of that authority or confidence when you confidently share a story with characters who you want your audience to remember, and you have investment in your story. That investment often transfers over to more investment in other elements of your presentation.

Telling a story not only draws the audience in, but starting with a story can put *you* at ease and make *you* more ready to visualize the other parts of your presentation and deliver them in a more calm and fresh way.

There's also another kind of workplace storytelling, and that has to do with how you capture the history, and the mission, and the vision that your business has, and how you convey that through a story that makes sense to your employees and the outside public. It's the same idea here. Telling your company history as a story is a compelling way of giving your audience someone to sympathize (even empathize with). They can empathize with the hero, which is your company.

Remember our lecture on Campbell's hero's journey. Who is the antagonist in the story—in your version, what dragons did you have to face on your hero's journey? What dragons are you facing now in your company?

You may have seen these kinds of stories written in a company handbook. New-employee orientations are a golden opportunity to share this story, not just in writing, but in person with your employees, giving the story of the company, and personally, why do you work here? What guides you? Your story. Because whatever you share with your employees, it doesn't convey squat if you don't really believe in what you're saying. Like any story—like all the stories we've been talking about—you have to tell the truth; tell a story that you want to believe in.

One way to think about your company story is to consider how your company has a beginning, and a middle, but (you hope) no end. Your hope is that your business or organization keeps going, keeps heading up. So you bring your employees into the story often during the rising action—they're a part of that story, building the business. Here's where we bring that Aristotelian diagram back, because your employees are right here in the company story. Just like any story, there are dips and peaks in this rising action, and your company's mission shoots you forward; it's what propels you from one scene to the next, from project to project.

It puts you and your employees in the same role of working together towards the same climactic point, so it can unify and strengthen the company. At this point I want to remind you of something we talked about earlier, when you're sitting on the couch and telling a story, and someone else shares in that story: "Oh, my aunt used to do needlework, too!"

You have a choice: Do I plow through with my own story (literally talk over that person); do I incorporate what they're saying (listen, incorporate, build); or do I cede the story over to that person (your story pauses and the conversation continues)? Listening is so important in any storytelling, and it's no more critical than here, in the workplace. You have to listen to your employees' stories. Sometimes you'll choose to plow through, but often it's best to either incorporate what your employees are saying, or even to cede the company's story and then just listen, with no agenda, to what your employees have to say.

Madeline Blair is the founder of Pelerei consulting firm. They use storytelling as one of several tools to help companies improve communications, especially internal communications, and she encourages using storytelling to understand employees. Sometimes, it's not about "getting" the story; it's about probing around the story to understand what motivates and drives this person. You go out to lunch, and you share stories and you listen, not only for the face value of the story, but the implicit values being communicated through that story. What does this story do for that person? Are there repeated themes throughout their stories?

You also don't want to lose knowledge that retirees take with them when they go. Creating space within the workday for senior employees on the way out to tell their stories, it serves a couple of functions: They not only share in mentoring those who will replace them, but they can share their own trajectory with the company. They can share that with other, younger employees, and that keeps the company's story alive.

It's their story—you can't control it. If you try to shape someone else's story, it just winds up sounding forced and toeing the company line. Give people the freedom to tell their stories, *their* stories—you'll be amazed how many insights your colleagues will contribute when you trust them to tell their own story, and you'll be amazed at how much you can learn.

There's a risk here, yes? Management has to allow ownership of the company's story by its employees, and some employees may veer off the rails, but they also may offer a new and interesting angle to the company's story. For example, one employee was the first to be allowed flex time in the schedule in order to care for elderly parents, or, another employee was the first to be able to telecommute because it made childcare easier. Or, another was the first minority to be promoted to management level.

Both of these scenarios—the living room and the boardroom—both of these are different kinds of settings from when you're talking to children, either in a schoolroom or if you're telling stories to your kids at home. Because we're not talking about the shift from sitting on a couch with one person to standing in front of a class with 10 people; it's not just that. Sometimes these people are little critters whose attention spans are vastly different and their interests are vastly different from the quasi-inebriated pal that you just left at the party. Or the interested, educated colleague who shares the same vocabulary as you do and who understands all the cultural references that you make.

In a classroom, the parameters are different. If you're a teacher, you're often standing at the front of the room. You walk into the classroom, and the seats are arranged in rows pointing forward towards to the front of the room, and the teacher is up here at the front. Rather than a raised platform (like a proscenium stage), the teacher is standing up in front of this seated group of students.

This kind of scenario, standing with them seated, it serves several purposes: For sightlines, you can see the person who's speaking, but it also implies several things. The students aren't facing each other, or arced, so implicitly they will not be communicating with each other; they're communicating only with the teacher. It's implied from this seating position that the audience is in a submissive position. The teacher speaks; the students do not. The teacher looks down on the students (it's a position of authority), and the students look up to listen. It's the same with the kids sitting down on the floor and the storyteller sitting on a chair in front of them.

In this setting, because you're talking with people, some of whom are farther away from you, you're going to have to project the volume of your voice a little more. Be aware that the more bodies that there are in the room, the more those bodies will swallow sound—they literally absorb the reverberation of your voice, and it makes it harder for that sound to travel to the very back. Even if it's a small room, you'll have to speak louder if there are more people in it. Again, make it come from down here, from your diaphragm.

When you speak from the diaphragm, it doesn't tire or hurt your voice like when you're trying to project from your upper lungs, so you can sustain this kind of power when you have to speak with larger groups of people for much more of your day (if you're speaking from your diaphragm).

I'm describing a classroom, but even when you're telling a story to your own kids, even with this, there's a different persona that comes with kids' stories. You've seen people who put on a kind of false-seeming flat persona where, "We're going to tell a story now. Once upon a time, Cinderella lived among the ashes of her stepmother's household."

That's how some folks talk to kids, and that's what many folks fall back on because it's a distanced way to talk to kids. You're not engaged with the story as much as really believing and feeling: "Once upon a time, Cinderella, she lived among those ashes of her stepmother's household."

With kids' stories, there's room not only to believe the story (kids want you to take them and their stories seriously, to believe that story), but there's also room to make the gestures bigger, the characterizations more embodied: "Once upon a time, there was a girl named Cinderella, oh and she lived among the ashes of her stepmother's household."

These more embodied gestures are especially good for young kids, even up through middle school. These kids almost universally love it, and they get into. When you get to middle schoolers, it's a little different, so let's break down each of these age ranges and talk about what a kid needs from stories at these different stages of life.

This information is from a wonderful little resource book; it's from the National Storytelling Network, the national storytelling organization. It's called *Telling Stories to Children*. It has a lot of quick tips on telling to kids of all ages. I want to summarize some of the ideas by Rebecca Isbell and Judy Sima from that text.

Starting with infants and toddlers (birth to age three)—and yes, you can use storytelling even with kids this young—kids are learning language and how to interact with others; they're mimicking. So stories with a lot of action and sound effects, and props—think back to the characteristics of oral thought. It's action centered.

But still, keep it simple. Only a few characters, simple plots. Lots of smiles in these stories—really young kids can be frightened by scary faces or really mean characters. In a story that I read to my two-year-old, I was reading this story to him, and sometimes he'll start to cry and hold me closer when the elephant in this story gets shut outside of a house. We quickly go through that, we summarize that part, and then he helps to push the elephant back into the door of the house. (That's from a book by Jerry Smath, *But No Elephants,* that's the book.)

A good rule of thumb is to make the story as long as the age of the child, so a one-year-old may be able to handle a story that's one minute long, and a two-year-old, a two-minute story. We get into preschool age (three to five), and they start being able to handle three-to-five minute stories. There are three great suggestions for stories for this age group.

First, their social skills and language skills are developing, so give them roles to play and nice long words for them to master and use.

Second, they're asking "why," so it's a golden opportunity to start introducing science and basic physics stories (how our bodies work, how we build a house). Encourage them to tell you simple stories; ask them, "How does a little bean seed grow?"

Finally, keep it simple, with plots they can manage—the three little pigs, the gingerbread man, the three bears. Be aware that kids before age five love fantasy stories, but they can't yet distinguish between fantasy and reality, so at a certain point that they start to ask you questions: "Did that really happen? Can cows really talk? *Is Santa Claus real?*" (You can make your own decisions on the answers to these questions!)

In the early elementary school years (ages five through seven), kids can start to handle more developed plotlines with clear answers: The witch dies in the end. (Sheldon Cashdan has a book about fairy tales, it's called *The Witch Must Die*, and it's true.) If you let the witch run off at the end, just kind of get

425

away, you get kids who are terrified that the witch will come back to get them in the end. So even with little kids, don't try to soften the ending by having that bad character just disappear. Killing them off sometimes makes a happier ending than letting everyone live in the end. Spooky, silly stories for this age range, those are fine, along with more complex fairy tales; for example, "Red Riding Hood," an age-appropriate version of "Red Riding Hood."

At this age, this is when kids begin to compare themselves to their peers in school, and their self-esteem starts to develop based on how they perceive their own strengths and weaknesses in comparison to others. To illustrate this point: One of the best stories I've heard in a while was by a grandfather whose grandson was having a problem with bedwetting around this age.

He didn't say anything to the grandson about being aware of the grandson's problem; he just said, "You know what, when I was younger, I had a problem with bedwetting."

"*Really*, Pop Pop, you had a problem with that?"

"Yeah, and you know what I did?" This grandfather, he told a story. Kids need to feel validated, that their weaknesses aren't the end of the world, and that their unique strengths are important. Stories that emphasize a variety of strengths, and a diversity of abilities, are great.

By now, they're starting to reason (a dime is more than five pennies—they're in the stage of concrete operations). While their own storytelling is limited by their own vocabulary, they're getting more and more interested in telling their own stories.

As you get into ages eight through 10, Judy Sima suggests longer stories ("Snow White," "Paul Bunyan"), and spooky stories. Stories with surprise endings are good. At ages eight through 10, kids kind of have a better grasp of reality and they can handle their expectations being foiled—they even love that twist!

As kids turn 11, they start to see beyond their own problems, and imagine possibilities outside of their own experiences. They can reason through abstract problems, and get to the underlying principles. This is the start of the middle-school years—ages 11 through 14. This is a tough age. Just remember your own years during this time. Your hormones, they're raging, you're awkward and you're self-conscious, and you're coming into gender in a big way. They think they know everything, so it's a good idea to veer from didactic stories. Veer away from fables that just lay it all out there in the end. You can have a lesson, but let your audience come to their own conclusions.

Stories with riddles and mysteries, they're great for this age. You can let them prove how smart they are by letting them figure it out first. Middle schoolers love to be scared (urban legends and scary folktales are great). They also love to be taken seriously, so challenge them with myths and with historical stories.

With this age, the kids are not going to necessarily start out on your side. They're too self-conscious and they don't want to take the risk of liking you from the beginning until their peers give their assent—"Oh, OK, she's cool. OK, I'll listen to her, I'll go along."

As a storyteller, when you're telling to this group, your biggest task is getting them out of their own posturing for one another and to get them into the world of your story. You have to match your persona to an extent with theirs. If they're above all this ("I'm too cool for a story, I'm too cool for the teacher"), well sometimes it's helpful to start out by being "too cool" for the story, too.

You do this in beginning—when you're talking to your audience, when you're getting them ready to hear the story. It's part of the story that's called the "mindset" because it's what gets your audience into the right frame of mind to be open to listening to your story.

Next time we're going to talk about this crucial part of your story, and how you get your audience into the story before the introduction, before we meet the characters, before the story itself really begins. That's the mindset, how you get into and out of the story. That's our topic in the next lecture.

Invitation to the Audience—Mindset
Lecture 22

Now that you have an amazing story to tell, how can you get and keep your audience's attention? This lecture is about on-ramps and off-ramps, devices that help you lead into your story and make it relevant to your audience and help get you out of the story in the end. We'll continue this very practical discussion in the next lecture by focusing on troubleshooting tips—how to get your listeners back if and when they start to wander and how to keep them engaged. But to get to that point, you have to hook them from the outset.

The Audience On-Ramp

- One of the first things any audience needs is a transitional link or "hook" into your story. This is different than an introduction to the characters; it takes place even before that moment. We call this hook a "mindset"; it's how you lead into your story. Your mindset will be different for each audience, because the mindset is all about getting your audience ready to listen to your story.

- The mindset is your audience's on-ramp; like an on-ramp to a highway, it literally gets you from the road you're on (the conversation you're in) to another road (the story you're about to tell).

- Your mindset makes the intellectual and emotional transition for your listeners from what's come before in their lives to what they're about to experience. The mindset is what your audience needs to know (or to feel) in order to be open to hearing your story.

- Note that there's a difference between an audience hearing a story and really listening to a story. When you hear something, it's going on around you, but you're not necessarily involved or interested in that sound. Listening, in contrast, means that you're paying attention and, to an extent, you're making yourself vulnerable because you trust that what you're listening to is worth your time and attention.

Setting the Tone

- One of the main functions of a mindset is setting the tone for the story to come. This is done primarily through your body and intonation. Your embodied presence sets the emotional tone for the telling. If you're energized, your story will be energized and so will your audience. If you're anxious, your audience will be, too.

- For this reason, your first task is to put yourself into an emotional tone that is appropriate for your story. If your story is humorous, it's important to let that show from the beginning to give your audience permission to laugh at what's to come.

- Your listeners are more vulnerable than you think. They want to react in the appropriate way to your story, both for your sake (so as not to hurt your feelings) and for their own sakes (so as not to embarrass themselves by responding inappropriately).

- Your opening tone gives the listeners cues about their role. If they can laugh, you might smile or throw in a joke. If the coming story is scary, you might lean in toward them and speak a little more softly. If your listeners are going on an adventure, you might speak with an energetic and bold voice. In every case, you want to start off at ease. Remember, if you're anxious, your audience will be anxious, too.

- This tone that you create through your body and voice establishes a trust relationship with your listeners. They trust that they can go with you in this story, that you'll guide them and bring them back safely.

- Establishing trust with the audience can be as simple as speaking the first few words of your story with confidence. But sometimes, you may need more than that to hook your audience's attention. The beginning of the "Sanntraigh" story, for example, requires a link between reality and the fairy world.

- To draw your audience into the story, keep these tips in mind:
  - Make eye contact with everyone. Do a full sweep of the audience and then individually look into each person's eyes. This eye contact establishes your connection with the audience.

  - Practice open posture. Avoid folding your arms over your chest. Keep your feet pointed toward your listeners so that you are facing them. Opening yourself up to your listeners encourages them to open up to you and your story.

  - Ask questions to establish a dialogue and make a content connection. Asking questions acknowledges your listeners and gives them permission to participate.

Mindset in Conversations and Presentations
- When you're in the midst of a conversation, often the content-based work of the mindset is at least partially done for you. You may be able to insert a story into the conversation with minimal introduction. But at other times, you may need a bit more to bridge between the topic of the conversation and the topic or place of your story.
  - To build this bridge, you can use a combination of flash-forward and intonation. In order to get your listeners to jump on the train of your story, you might give them a glimpse of the point of connection at the beginning: "I have a friend, and he came back from Argentina with the most detailed work of art…." The tone and rate of your speech may also cue the audience that you're about to talk about something new.

  - Another bridge-building technique is to use transition wording: "I haven't seen detail like that since my friend showed me this piece of art he picked up in Argentina."

- o Notice that in both of these examples, you make connections and give a glimpse of what's to come, but you don't reveal everything—you don't steal your own punchline.

- When you're giving a presentation to a group—whether it's a group at work or children in a classroom—you don't have the luxury of bouncing off of what's just been said to enter into your story. Thus, your mindset must create a springboard for the audience; in effect, you're creating what the audience might say to lead into a story, and then you're responding to it.

- If you're beginning a presentation, verbally welcome everyone and give them a reason for attending the presentation. Set up the common problem that has resulted in the need for the gathering: "You all know that our sales last quarter dropped."
  - o Then use that problem as a way to set up the "story" of your presentation: "Our average customer has been strapped for

A short "story" about the weather or traffic can align you and your audience against a common foe—the heat or rush hour!

cash. Here's our customer: She's bright, she's well-educated, but she just got a cut in salary."

o   Your job is to funnel your audience's attention from the world outside the doors of your performance area into the world of the story. You have to help your listeners tune out the different experiences that have brought them to this room so that they can tune in to your story.

o   In establishing your mindset, don't ramble on. Make this moment as purposeful as any other element of your story.

*   Many of these presentation tips also apply to telling in a classroom. In the first moments, when you're trying to wrangle children into a story, you can also try these tricks:
    o   Ask, "Who's ready to hear a story?" and have children raise their hands in response. Raise your hand excitedly to show that you're excited to share the story.

    o   Ask them to show how they listen (by putting their hands to their ears), look (by pointing to their eyes), and get ready for a story (by putting their hands in their laps). Use any variation of this exercise you like, but give the children some way to "get their wiggles out" before you begin the story.

    o   Ask questions, but be specific about how you want the children to answer: "How many of you have a best friend? Raise your hand!"

    o   Be prepared to incorporate negative comments. If a child says, "I've heard this story before," you might say, "You may have heard another version of this story before, but do you know the real story?"

Words of Caution
*   Don't apologize for your story, and again, don't steal your own punchline. Don't state what the story will make clear. Don't tell

the audience what the story is about, what perspective the narrator takes, and so on.

- Bring the audience to a safe and satisfying place. Don't tack on a happy ending to your story that doesn't fit. And don't make the whole story a dream—don't trick your listeners after they've trusted you!

- When your story ends, give yourself an "I am terrific" moment: Stand in place, make eye contact with the audience, and allow the story to settle in and resonate. Don't rush immediately away. You want a strong finish; allow the final image to "burn into" the minds of your listeners.

- To signal the "off-ramp" moment of your story, decrease the pitch and pacing of your voice (but not the volume).

- Finally, you may want to give your listeners a way to apply to the story to their own lives. But don't be so didactic that you flatten your story with an obvious meaning. Trust your listeners to get what they need out of your story.

Suggested Reading

Davis, *The Grand Canyon*.

———, www.ddavisstoryteller.com.

Forest, *Tales of Womenfolk*.

———, www.heatherforest.com.

Questions to Consider

1. Donald Davis's story about the Grand Canyon is hilarious and touching in its own right, and his mindset in the first part of the story hooks the audience with something universal: taxes. What is one way you can hook your audience through a shared experience?

2. Channeling your listeners' attention from where they've been into the world of the story can be challenging. In what ways do your listeners "tell" you where they're coming from? In what ways can you listen to them from the beginning?

Invitation to the Audience—Mindset
Lecture 22—Transcript

Professor Harvey: Now that you have this amazing story to tell, how can you in the moment get and keep your audience's attention? This lecture is all about on-ramps and off-ramps—how to lead into your story and make it relevant to your audience, and then how you get out at the end.

We'll continue this very practical discussion next time by focusing on troubleshooting tips—how to get your audience back when their attention starts to wander, and how to keep them engaged. But to get to that point, you have to hook them from the outset.

One of the first things any audience needs is a transitional link or "hook" into your story. This is a different thing from introducing the characters; it's even before that moment. It's called the "mindset"; it's how you lead into your story, and your mindset will be different for each audience, because your mindset is all about getting your audience ready to listen to your story.

For example, in an everyday setting, before you start to tell the story, there's usually the moment when someone sparks that memory for you, and you think of that story, and you want to add that story to the conversation. You need a transition to get your audience interested in what you're about to say, and to convince them that what you're going to tell them is relevant to them and relevant to the conversation.

The mindset is your audience's on-ramp. Like an on-ramp to a highway, it literally gets you from the road you're on (the conversation you're in), onto another road (the story you're about to tell). Your mindset makes that intellectual and emotional transition for your audience from what's come before in their life, to what they're about to experience. The mindset is what your audience needs to know (or needs to feel) in order to get them ready (open and available), to get them ready to hear your story. It's the way into the story.

There's a difference between your audience *hearing* the story that has just popped into your mind, and your audience really *listening* to that story. When you hear something, it's going on around you but you're not necessarily involved, or interested, or committed to that sound. I hear the TV in the next room, or I hear the alarm going off for the third time (and I hit "snooze" again). We hear a lot of things in a day, but we don't often listen to them.

I want you to experiment with this. This is an exercise inspired by the composer John Cage. I want you to sit silently for 30 seconds and just listen to the noises and the sounds going on around you. Hear the buzz of the TV, the cars outside, the fan in your heating unit, someone coughing—just listen. There's so much entering our ears but we tune it out because we decide it's not relevant—we hear it, but we don't register it.

John Cage, of course, he encouraged us to listen to these noises as the music that's all around us. You can check out his symphony called *4'33"* (or four minutes, 33 seconds); it was composed in 1952. A pianist, he literally sat at the piano, silently, while the audience listened to the other noises in the room.

There's a world of sounds, and of stories, that we *hear,* but we don't really *register* or listen to them, because in a world of constant noise and sound, our brains can only process so much at a time. We hear a lot, but we choose what we listen to, and we listen to those things that are relevant to our lives.

The mindset of your story calls your audience to listen. Listening means you're paying attention. You're focusing on that thing, and to an extent, you as a listener are making yourself available and vulnerable, because you trust that this thing is worthy of your attention and your time. The mindset gets your audience ready to listen. It sets the tone. It emotionally transitions, and it hooks the audience's interest. Let's take each of these one at a time, and talk about how you'd do this in a variety of settings.

First, the mindset establishes tone. You do this primarily through your body and intonation. Your embodied presence sets the emotional tone for the telling. If you're energized, your story will be energized, and so will your audience. If you're anxious, your audience is probably going to be anxious too.

Your first task is to put yourself into the emotional tone appropriate for your story. If your story is humorous, it might be good to show that from the very beginning—not for the sake of giving a big cheesy grin, but to give your audience permission to laugh at what's to come.

Your audience is more vulnerable than you think. Remember that audience of middle schoolers that we talked about in the last lecture? They don't want to do the wrong thing in front of their peers, so they're kind of standoffish. There's a little bit of that middle schooler that sticks with us even into adulthood, but it's a little kinder. Your audience wants to react in the appropriate way to your story, both for your sake (they don't want to start laughing at the wrong time; they might hurt your feelings), but also for their own sake as well (it can be embarrassing when you respond inappropriately to a story—you start laughing, "Ha!" and nobody else around you is laughing or doing anything like that).

Your opening tone gives the audience clues for what their role might be—can they laugh? You might smile from the beginning, or throw in a joke. Should they be scared? You lean in a little towards them; you might speak a little more softly—as if this is a scary secret. Should they be ready for an adventure? Give them that energy and that zest with a bold voice. In any case, you want to start off at ease—remember, if you're anxious, your audience will be anxious; they're following your cues. So trust the story, and trust yourself to tell that story to them.

This tone that you establish through your body and your voice, it establishes a trust relationship with your audience. They trust that they can go with you in this story, that you'll guide them there and safely back again. Even when you're telling a story where your narrator is skeptical—so you're telling an urban legend that you don't really believe, or you heard about a fantastic feat that you heard someone else did but you don't quite believe it—you've got a skeptical narrator, but you, as the storyteller, have to be someone that your audience trusts enough to listen to.

When your voice at the beginning is confident (you're *sure* that you're skeptical about this story), then your audience will have confidence in you. At that point, they'll trust you. It's only in that safety net of trust that your audience will really listen to your story. You establish this trust through your tone, which is communicated through your body and your voice.

You can do this so simply, and so quickly. I'll show you an example, this is a more performance-based example, but I want for you to listen to how storyteller Heather Forest guides the audience into a story that she tells through song. The story is "The Lute Player."

The mindset is in the first few words. She says, "This is a tale from Russia, and it begins," and then she introduces the characters and goes on with the intro, but listen to how these first three words—"This is a story"—and her use of pause and intonation, listen to how all of those settle the audience into what's about to come.

[Video start.]

> **Heather Forest:** This tale is from Russia, and it begins as the queen, dressed entirely in black, is seated in her chamber. She is mourning the death of her husband.

[Video end.]

Professor Harvey: And then the story begins. It can be as simple as how you say the first few words of your story. But sometimes you need more than that to hook your audience's attention.

Your mindset establishes tone, and it also hooks the audience's interest—it links the audience's realm of experience with the story at hand. I want for you to see some examples of this. The first is setting up a story that you've heard of before, "Sanntraigh." This is a story that I told at the International Storytelling Center's Teller-in-Residence series. Now, most adults in America don't believe in fairies, nor do they have to in order for this story to entertain. But look at the link that this mindset makes to hook the audience's interest and to make them think about the story from the beginning as something that they could relate to in reality.

[Video start.]

438

Professor Harvey: I grew up in that town in northeastern Tennessee where my great-aunt lived. We moved away, I went off, got a bunch of education, and then worked in Georgia, and then my husband and I inherited a farm from my grandparents. We decided to move back, total life change, moved back. Within one year we had both moved from Atlanta, from that six-lane highway commute of Atlanta to a tiny little one-lane gravel road that led up to this property.

In that same year I had a baby, we both switched jobs, so it was a heck of a year. In that year that we were expecting, we came up to that farm and we were trying to decide where to build our house. We looked out over the property and we saw that there were some hayfields and some pasture for grazing animals, it's a working farm, we work the farm. There were some woods over there for critters or for dinner (I come from east Tennessee. We do eat the deer meat, I'm not kidding). [Growl.]

We're looking out and we're trying to figure out where to put our house. On this ridge over there, there used to be a house. It was an old, almost 100-year-old house that had burned down about four years before we inherited the property. My husband, he looked out and he said, "Maybe that would be a nice place to build the house."

I said, "Oh no."

He said, "Why, are you afraid of the ghosts?" Because that house was supposedly haunted.

I said, "No, it's not the ghosts. I'm afraid of the fairies."

He said, "The fairies?"

I said, "Yes, the fairies," and I pointed over to him, and you could see over where that house used to stand, you could see this patch of green, green grass and this trail of green, green grass that was growing much, much greener than any of the other grass around it. If you go out to fields, I know we're kind of in a more urban area, but if you go out, you will see this. Go look out into a field and you'll see these patches of green grass growing much greener than any of the yellow hay around it. Those are the fairy paths. The patches of, those mounds of—you can laugh, it's OK, you can laugh, you can believe it or not. Flickering lights. You can believe it or not, but those are the fairy knolls, and you do not mess with the fairies, because fairies in Scottish folklore and in Gaelic folklore—Gaelic is the Scottish pronunciation of Gaelic—so in Gaelic folklore—I come from East Tennessee, it kind of sounds like a Yankee trying to say the word "garlic": "Gah-lick."

In Gaelic folklore, you don't mess with the faeries, because the fairies, they're not those happy little winged creatures that you see on the front of greeting cards with the little bells on their toes, no. The fairies are dangerous. The fairies will steal your children and they'll leave a sickly one of its own in its place. The fairies, if you build on their mounds and you build on their homes, they will destroy your house.

I said, "No, we're not building there." It's in that spirit that I wanted to share with you a fairy tale.

[Video end.]

Professor Harvey: I'm linking unfamiliar content (fairy paths and the spirit world). I'm linking that with something mundane and hopefully common— the idea of being in your house, or walking out in nature.

You can find these links to the content of your story in surprisingly easy ways. For example, there's a storyteller, very famous, named Donald Davis. He has a story about going on a visit to the Grand Canyon. The mindset for his story starts somewhere completely different than the topic of the Grand Canyon. He starts out by talking about taxes, and about how his father taught him early on that the taxes that you pay, well those pay for different things that you can use. Donald decided at an early age that all of his taxes were paying for the National Park Service, and that the Grand Canyon was his property! That leads into the story—connecting his personal experiences at the Grand Canyon with something everyone can relate to: taxes.

The mindset is a moment to draw your whole audience in, so consider doing the following things. One: Make eye contact with everyone in the audience. Try to do a full sweep of the audience at first, and then individually look into each person's eyes. As we said before, this direct eye contact, it implicates your audience; it draws them in. Your eye contact establishes your own connection with the audience. So sweep, and then greet individually.

Two: Practice open posture. If you've ever taken a leadership class, you've learned about "negative posture," those gestures that close you off from your audience. It's body language that says, "Stay away. Don't talk to me." Folding your arms over your chest, even folding your hands does this to a certain extent. It closes you off. With folding your arms, it literally curves your spine down, and it forces your energy down instead of up and out to the people with whom you're trying to communicate.

Open posture opens you out to your audience. You do this with your arms and gestures as well as how you stand. Pay attention to where your feet are planted. Are your toes facing your audience, or are you partially turned away from them (a quarter-turn to the right or to the left)?

Try to face your audience, feet pointed towards them. It shows that your focus is on them, and it helps establish that trust relationship because you're opening yourself to them; it encourages them to open up to you and not just to hear your story, but to listen to your story.

Three: Ask questions to establish dialogue. Those questions that make a content connection; for example, from the story about my Aunt Mae, I began that story asking a question:

[Video start.]

> **Professor Harvey:** I wanted to share a story with you all. It's a story that we tell in my family and it's one that I tell to my other family members. It has to do with the card game "Old Maid." Did

any of you ever play this card game? OK, Some nods, yes, OK! And you had that special deck of cards. You've seen them? OK. On my special deck of cards—I'm small, right, I wear heels, or I think I'm small—but when I was even smaller, when I was seven years old, the deck of cards just felt so huge to me. They were these big cards and they had these very colorful-looking people on them except for one very special card. And which card was that? The Old Maid. On my deck of cards—

[Video end.]

Professor Harvey: Asking questions like this gets the audience ready to respond—it tells them you're wanting a response from them. Asking questions at the beginning—and throughout your story, but especially here—it acknowledges your audience and gives them permission to participate. Then take their answers and incorporate them. If they say, "No, I've never played Old Maid," well use that: "Oh, let me tell you about it—it's great! You have this special little deck of cards."

I want to give you some specific tips for how to handle mindset in two different situations: in a conversation, and in a presentation. When you're in the midst of a conversation, often the content-based work of the mindset is at least partially done for you: You're talking about fly fishing, for example, and you have a story about your friend who worked for a time in Argentina. While he was there he met this old man who made these flies, hand-made these flies for fishing. He supplied specialty outfitters all over the world, and here was your friend climbing up this hill to meet this guy in this hut, where he made all these flies. That guy gave your friend one of those flies, and the detail on that fly, it was like a work of art.

When you insert that story in a conversation, you could just lead into the introduction of the characters: "I have this friend, he worked for a time in Argentina, and while he was there he met this old man" and you go on with the story from there. But sometimes you need to make a bit more of a transition, make a bridge between the topic that you're on, and the topic or place that the story takes you to.

Say you're talking with your friends about a painting in their home, and the detail in that painting is really unique. It reminds you in your head of the intricately painted flies that this man made, and you want to transition into that story. There are several ways to do this.

Use a combination of flash-forward and intonation. Remember we talked about how your narrator plays with time in stories, not only expanding and contracting time, but also jumping from the climax to the beginning, if that's what serves the audience best. In this situation, to get your audience to jump on that train of the story, you give them a flash to the point of connection at the beginning. Not so much of a glimpse that it gives that story away, but just enough to make the connection.

Sometimes a change in your intonation, and that flash-forward, sometimes that's all it takes. That's the great thing about embodied storytelling— sometimes you can make a transition just in the way you *say* the opening lines of your story. You nuance your tone and your rate of speech, so it cues the audience to know that we're about to talk about something new.

In this case, you're looking at this painting, and you're talking about the detail, and you say, "You know, I have this friend," and then you flash-forward to the connection point in the story—the climax meeting up on the mountain: "And he came back from Argentina with the most detailed work of art." Then you jump right into the story: "He went to Argentina on business, and he happened to meet this man." Then you go on with that story.

Use additional transition wording. "I haven't seen detail like that since my friend showed me this piece of art he picked up in Argentina." You pick right up there with the introduction: "I have this friend who worked for a time there, in Argentina, and he met a man." It sets up the characters and the place of action, and the story progresses right along.

Now you'll notice something very specific about both of these examples: I'm giving connections, and a glimpse of what's to come, but I don't reveal everything. That's something to be very careful of in your mindset and your introduction—don't steal your own punch line.

Sometimes, you can just kill your story by saying too much at the beginning. This isn't a list of facts, it's a *story*; your audience *wants* to go on that journey with you, so don't steal your own punch line by revealing too much at the beginning. That's part of this art. It's just a taste. It's something to link and draw the audience in. Just a smidge of a taste. That's why the on-ramp image, it works so well—it's a thin-but-crucial line that connects you with the highway. Without it, you either can't get on the road, or you plow right into the road and then you're t-boned by a 16-wheeler. Don't t-bone your audience. You need an on-ramp moment. Your audience needs this on-ramp moment. In comparison with the highway (the story), it's a small thing—but you've got to have it to get in.

When you're giving a presentation to a group, whether it's a group at work, or a bunch of kids in a classroom, or to a video audience or audio audience who you can't even see, often you don't have the luxury of bouncing off what's been just said to enter into your story. Your mindset has to create the springboard for the audience. In effect, rather than responding to a conversational topic, you're creating what the audience might say to lead into that story, and then you're saying your story in response to it. So, if you're starting off a presentation:

One: Verbally welcome everyone. If they're key delegates, acknowledge them as appropriate. If the delegates are foreign, it's often nice to greet them in their own language—but just make sure all your pronunciations and your bows correct.

Give them a reason to be there. Now is the time to set up that common problem that has put you there at the front of the room: "You all know our sales last quarter dropped," or, "We've all been feeling the effects of the economy," and then you use that as a way to set up the story of your presentation. "Our average customer has been strapped hard for ready cash. Here's our customer: She's bright, she's educated, but she just got a cut in her salary. She wants to buy our widgets, but she's not sure that she should spend all the money," and your story goes on.

Your job is to funnel your audience's attention from the world outside the doors of the performance area, into the world of the story. The audience has probably come from a lot of different places—some of them have been in the car; others will have been walking outside. There are lots of physical and tonal shifts that this mindset accomplishes. Your goal is to take all of those different experiences, and to help your audience channel them out, so that they can tune in to your story.

Sometimes it helps to acknowledge that they've come from outside: "It's hot out there today, I'm grateful for the air conditioning in here, aren't you?" Or you say something about the traffic: "I got stuck in traffic. Did anybody else get stuck in traffic like I did on the way over here? Why do they always pick morning rush hour to do construction on the highway?"

Those little phrases, that tells a short story. You're aligning you and your audience against a common foe: rush-hour traffic! Acknowledging the struggles outside can help people let go of them for a time, so they can think about something else (your story).

Don't ramble on. You can make your mindset too long. Often when you're nervous about telling, you can ramble at this point. Make the mindset as purposeful as any other element of your story. In a presentation, you'll want to think about your upcoming audience and what you're going to say here. (I rehearse these parts of my story; many professional storytellers do. They're adapted to each audience in the moment, but as a part of our performance, they're prepared parts of the story.)

Many of these presentation tips also apply to telling in the classroom. Telling to a group of kids can be challenging enough, but especially in these first few moments when you're trying to wrangle them in. There are some fun tricks you can use to get them settled.

Ask them if they're ready to listen to the story. "Who's ready to listen to a story?" Ask them to raise their hands—and you do it excitedly, with interest because you want them to be excited and have interest. Then you ask them to "listen," and you ask them to hold their hands to their ears, and "look!" and point to their eyes, and then put their shushing fingers over their mouths. You say, "We're ready for a story," and you model for them how to put their hands in their laps. "Who's ready to hear a story? Then listen, and look, we're ready for a story."

You can use any variation of this that you like, but giving them a chance to get the wiggles out by raising their hands and waving them around, it's a great way to start, and then ending with their hands in their laps gets them focused away from pulling their neighbor's hair, or picking at their noses— they're ready to listen.

Second suggestion: Ask questions, but be specific to your audience's age, and be specific about how you want your audience to answer. For one story I tell, it's about a man and woman and they solve this riddle together, and they get married in the end. To make that story relevant to elementary school kids, I often ask: "Do any of you have a best friend? Raise your hand if you have a best friend. This story has a couple of best friends in it, and they solve their problems together." That sets up their relationship and their courtship as a friendship, which is much easier for that age range to relate to than marital love.

Third suggestion: If you're telling a familiar story, like "Cinderella," sometimes kids love to hear a story they already know, but also be prepared for some bratty kid to say, "Oh, I've heard that before!" and be ready to draw them in. "OK yeah, you may have heard that other version of the story—but did you know the *real* story of Cinderella? Oh, the *real* story's a lot better."

You can even turn that into a wiggle exercise: "He says he's heard that story before; he's saying, 'Psshhh, I know that one!' Can you say that with me? 'Psshhh, I know that one!'" You get the whole audience saying it. "But did you know, there's another version of Cinderella—one you haven't heard, and one that that kid doesn't know! And it goes like this." You go into your story.

So those are some specific suggestions for different settings. Before we move on from the mindset and the introduction, some words of caution. Don't apologize for your story. "Well, I want to tell you something, but it's really not a good story, and I really can't tell it well, and it doesn't end well." Don't worry about—just get on with your story. Let your audience do all of this evaluation, just tell your story!

Again, don't steal your own punch line. Don't state what the story will make clear. You don't have to tell us what the story is about; you don't have to tell us what perspective your narrator takes, or who all the characters are—we'll meet them in your introduction or along the way. Don't lay it out all before us. We want the journey.

Once you're finished with your journey, we come to the conclusion of your story. The conclusion brings an emotionally engaged audience into a satisfying and safe place.

We talked in our lecture on emotional arc about the resolution of your story. I want to emphasize again that you benefit no one in throwing a slap-happy ending on your story. Adults aren't happy; kids aren't happy with it. For heaven's sake, don't make it all a dream—don't jerk the audience around after they've trusted you! What you must do is leave the audience in a safe place. As you're delivering your conclusion, however your story ends, there are some story-performance techniques to consider here.

Have the "I Am Terrific" moment. What this means is, at the end of your story, give yourself a moment to stand there, and making eye contact with the audience, you let the story settle in with them and let it resonate.

Don't rush away immediately from your audience after your story. That's a weak move. It's like walking backwards; it's weak. You want to finish strong, to stand there in place—it's called "burning in" the final image. So you're standing still so you can set that final moment in the audience's mind. If you're in character, you might stay in character for just a moment. Let that image burn in.

I can't tell you how much you need to consciously remember this, because there are so many people who, when they end their story, for whatever audience they're performing for, they end their story, "I'm done and that's the end," [Professor Harvey dashes off]. They run off right after the presentation. They just run right to sit down.

No! Give your audience a chance to process, and to reflect, and to digest. Have the "I Am Terrific" moment.

With your pacing, there's a natural way to put a "button" on the end of your story. Now I'm using a musical theatre term here, and it's when in musical theatre, "A song is just about, to, end." From the way that I said those last three words, and the pacing I'm using, you can tell we're reaching a conclusion: "Da da da da bum ... bum ... bum."

The pitch and the inflection goes down slightly (but not the volume—you can still hear the end word), and the pacing slows down. You can do the same thing with your story. Go back to your story outline. The final words that you say, try to slow those words down. It's the off-ramp moment in your story. Give your audience a way to exit and to come out of the end of the story.

Similar to funneling into the story content-wise, you might want to give your audience a way to apply the story to their own lives, but be careful about this. You don't want to be so didactic in your ending that this lovely story that you've crafted just gets flattened by a slap-you-upside-the-head meaning. Trust your audience to get what they need out of a story, and don't ramble.

So, without any rambling, I'll end our lecture here with just that. Because we'll pick up next time with some troubleshooting tips on how to keep your audience engaged, from audience participation, to lighting and how you arrange the set around you. These tips, they're not just for telling kids' stories, but some of these ideas might make you squeal with glee, or fright. We'll see you then.

Keeping Your Audience's Attention
Lecture 23

Once you've hooked your listeners and gotten them into the story, how do you keep them there? This lecture focuses on the adaptive qualities of storytelling—the need to adjust in the moment to keep your audience engaged. We'll cover all sorts of special occasion advice, as well as general rules to live by as a storyteller. We'll see many examples of professional storytellers' work, and we'll bring these professional techniques into the everyday world, by discussing how you can use props, sound, and audience participation in your stories.

Audience Participation

- One of the easiest and best ways to keep your listeners engaged is to invite them to participate in some way with telling a story. You can ask them to repeat certain phrases or perform certain gestures with you, or you can have audience members tell part of the story or act out certain roles. Participation works with any age level to draw listeners in and keep them engaged.

- In the excerpt by storyteller Donna Washington, notice how the participatory elements keep both children and adults interested. Note, too, that the repeated phrase keeps the pace of the story building.

- Repetition gives a structure for listeners to follow and prevents them from getting lost in a story. When you keep these moments of participation playful, even adults gain a sense of accomplishment. Using repeated phrases and gestures also helps to cement the story into the audience's memory.

- If you're telling a story and you notice that you're starting to lose your listeners, bring them back to the story with an invitation to perform a gesture or say a phrase along with you. This technique gives the storyteller a playful kind of authority as the director of the group.

- This type of participation also gives listeners a sense that they matter. They contribute to the story, but their contributions are structured and manageable for the teller.

- Often, participation works well when you're doing a presentational-style story—in a classroom or boardroom—rather than in conversation with friends.

- One kind of repetition that's useful in living-room scenarios, and any other time you want to add interest through humor, is the "inside joke." The reason inside jokes work so well to keep your listeners interested is that they unite the listeners in a sense of ownership. The story becomes theirs; they share a secret joke, along with the narrator or primary character.
  - Establish something at the beginning of a story, such as a particular character trait, and then return to it at key points in the story.

  - In "The Old Maid," I established a firm characteristic about Aunt Mae (she watched *Days of Our Lives*) and then returned to this endearing habit at the end of the story.

  - You can use this technique to build a character into a friend or to turn a character into a villain.

  - When you're using inside jokes, remember that storytelling is about unifying beyond the moment of the telling. Don't use a joke that might alienate audience members.

Disaster Strikes!
- It's true that forces beyond your control may sometimes interrupt your story. The power may go out, or a jackhammer may start up outside.

- In some cases, such as when a cell phone rings, you can ignore the interruption. Or you can acknowledge it quickly and go back to the story.

- You might also incorporate the interruption into the story. If you're telling "Jack and the Beanstalk" and you hear a jackhammer outside, you might say, "And then Jack heard the hammering of a thousand tiny dwarves in the neighboring village, but he kept walking."

- You can also adapt your story to an interruption. If the power goes out during a presentation, you can wrap it up quickly, using summary to speed up the "events" and get to your resolution.

Using Props and Costumes

- Sometimes, you might want to use a visual aid when you're telling a story. This can be something as simple as a photo or even an abstract representation: "We went to a temple in Mexico, and it was huge; it was like two of these buildings stacked on top of each other."

- When you're telling to children, finger puppets and hand puppets are good props. For other audiences, you might choose a cultural artifact, such as a Chinese fan or a scarf from Finland. The key is to integrate the prop with the story so that it's not a distraction. Use props to draw listeners into a story.

© iStockphoto/Thinkstock.

If you use a cultural artifact in storytelling, treat that object with respect and contextualize it correctly so that it isn't viewed as merely a souvenir.

- Like props, costumes can be useful visual aids, but using a full costume can limit you to one character. Try using costume pieces rather than full costumes, such as hats, scarves, or gloves.

- Keep in mind, too, that what you are wearing is a kind of costume—your suit and tie or your party dress—for a specific performance.

- Whatever you wear, make sure it allows you the full range of movement you need or be prepared to adjust your storytelling to suit your clothing.

Lighting, Music, and Other Considerations

- A sample from the storyteller Brenda Wong Aoki shows how music, costume, props, and lighting can be blended into a story to create what Aoki calls a "monodrama."
    - Note her use of a fan as a "transformational object," an object that becomes something else, in this case, the ocean.

    - Note, too, that her costuming sets the tone and cultural context of the story but doesn't limit her characterization because it's not specific to one character.

- Unless you perform on a stage, you probably won't have to deal with positioning lights or creating a mood through lighting, but you can still change lighting effects to your advantage. Turn the lights down to tell a scary story to children, use a flashlight, or even light a fire! In a boardroom, make sure the lights are adequate for your audience to see you and to be seen.

- Again, you may not have musicians to incorporate music and sound into your storytelling, but if you play the guitar or piano, consider adding those elements to underscore specific moments in your story or to bring characters to life. Think of the musical composition *Peter and the Wolf*, in which each instrument is a different character in the story.

- Along with music, you can also use sound effects to communicate action and push the narration forward. A simple way to incorporate sound effects is simply to use your voice: whizz, buzz, brrrrrrrrrr! Once you've established what a sound means, it can become an inside joke for your audience.

- Depending on the venue for your storytelling, you might have the option to sit or stand. Be aware that a seated position can drain away some of your energy. If you're using a chair or stool, sit on the edge of it or use it as a prop, sitting when characters in the story sit. If you can stand easily, it's usually best to do so.

Suggested Reading

Aoki and Izu, *Mermaid Meat.*

Aoki, www.brendawongaoki.com.

Bodkin, *The Odyssey.*

———, www.oddsbodkin.com.

Harley, *Yes to Running!*

———, www.billharley.com.

Washington, *Troubling Trouble.*

———, www.donnawashington.com.

Weitkamp, www.kimweitkamp.com.

Questions to Consider

1. Participation is a fun way to engage your audience. What is one way you could use repetition with participation to draw your audience into one of your stories?

2. We discussed Brenda Wong Aoki's use of a transformational object, her fan. What is one prop you could use in your story that could serve as a transformational object? What three things could this visual aid represent?

Keeping Your Audience's Attention
Lecture 23—Transcript

Professor Harvey: Once you've hooked your audience and you're into the story, how do you keep your audience there? This lecture focuses on the adaptive qualities of storytelling—how to keep your audience engaged as you adjust in the moment to what that audience needs.

In this lecture, we'll cover all sorts of special-occasion advice as well as some general rules to live by as a storyteller. We'll see lots of examples of professional storytellers' work, and we'll bring these professional techniques into the everyday world by discussing how you can use things like props, and sound, and audience participation in your stories.

One of the easiest and best ways to keep your audience engaged is to invite them to participate in some way with the telling of the story. You can do this in lots of ways: using repeated phrases that you invite the audience to say with you; asking the audience to perform a gesture with you; even having the audience tell part of that story for you or act out the roles.

Now all of this may seem like kids' stuff, but trust me—participation works at any age level to draw the audience in and to keep them engaged. You can use participation as a through-line for your story. Here's an example of a repeated phrase that keeps the audience engaged. This is by storyteller Donna Washington, and it's an excerpt of her story "Epaminandus." This is her version of a traditional tale, and her audience was a mixed group, mostly of adults, with some children. Watch how the participatory elements keep both the kids and the adults interested.

[Video start.]

> **Donna Washington:** Now this time, I want to see everybody running around the house, throwing their arms in the air, you guys ready? About a week later, Epaminandus was running wild around the house, here we go! And his mama says what? "Epaminandus, you are driving me crazy. Go to your grandma's house."

Epaminandus says, "OK, Mama." He left that house, he went up that great big hill to his grandma's house, he knocked on the door, here we go. [Pounding.]

His grandma opened the door and said, "Why Epaminandus, it's good to see you, what are you doing here?"

And Epaminandus said, "Mama sent me here because I was driving her crazy, uh-huh." But that's OK because even if you make your mama crazy, who will always love you?

Audience: Grandma.

Donna Washington: They had a wonderful day. They went out to the barn to clean it up. They pitched the hay. They fed the chickens and the pigs and the geese. They brushed down the billy goats. Right before it was time to go home, his grandma said, "I got a special surprise for you today."

He said, "What you got grandma?" She took him out to the back of the barn where there was a great big old pile of straw, and playing around in the straw were puppies. Oh yes.

His grandma picked up a puppy; she said, "Now Epaminandus, your momma says you can have a puppy."

"Thank you grandma," he took that puppy. He went outside. He put that puppy on the ground; the puppy started running all around his feet. He said, "Now wait a minute, how did my mama say to bring something home if it was running?" Epaminandus picked up the puppy. He took it to the nearest stream, he threw him in the water, threw him in the water, he threw him in the water until the puppy was going [panting].

He carried it on home. His mama took one look at it, she said, "Oh my," she picked up that puppy, she dried it off, she laid it in front of the fireplace, and just in case anybody was worried, the puppy was just fine. His mama put her hand on her hips and she said, "Epaminandus, you ain't got the sense you was born with. That is no way to treat a living thing. When you have a living thing, you take a piece of string, or a piece of rope, tie it real gentle around the living thing, and then real careful, lead it home. Now you remember that!"

What's Epaminandus say? "OK Mama."

[Video end.]

Professor Harvey: That's Donna Washington, and she doesn't sacrifice her characterizations or her pacing or her narration with that—if anything, this repeated phrase keeps the pace of the story building. You can find some repeated element with your story (with Donna Washington, it's this repeated phrase about Epaminandus). You look for some kind of repetition and then you build a gesture or a phrase around that repetition—something quick and easy for the audience to learn and to catch onto—keep it simple.

You can add this to sermons, to boardroom presentations (yes, you can! It may seem silly to insert it there, but it works!), to telling a story to just one child or to a few children. A few things to think about when you're using repetition, and why this works: Repetition gives a structure for the audience to follow—it's like a safety net; it gives them a place to go so they don't feel lost in your story. When you keep these moments of participation playful, adults have that sense of accomplishment.

Repetition can add a kind of playful humor through predictability—you know what's coming. When you use repeated phrases and gestures, it really drives the story into the audience's memory—it makes the story memorable. They might share that story then with a friend later.

Usually these kinds of repetitions take some forethought to build into your story. But you don't have to limit yourself to repetitions when you're doing participation. In the moment of telling a story, if you can tell that you're starting to lose your audience (and you need to keep that constant watch, look for signs that the kids are fidgeting, or that the adults are checking messages), and when you start to see that—and I say "when," this will happen—when you start to see that, rein them back in with an invitation to do a gesture or say a phrase along with you. Here's an example from a story you heard earlier.

[Video start.]

> **Professor Harvey:** Well George Buchannan, he was a fisherman, and he lived in a wee crofting house and every morning he would take down his herring net—his fishing net—now I'm going to ask you to participate with me. Pretend like you're taking down your own herring net from the walls, so reach your hands up and just kind of take that herring net—very good!—reach it down, he would take that herring net, he would take it out on his skiff and he would cast it out on the ocean. Everybody cast your net out, cast your net out, don't hit your neighbor but cast your net out. And he would bring in all of the fish, and he would bring those fish back.
>
> He did that every morning as with this morning, he woke up, took his herring net. Take that herring net down, he'd take it out on his skiff, he'd cast that net out and bring in all of the fish. On this particular day—

[Video end.]

Professor Harvey: So if I notice some folks are getting wiggly, I have them funnel that energy back into the story by physically gesturing in a useful way for the story. Participation serves a few functions in these settings. It gives the storyteller a playful kind of authority as the director of the group (they're literally doing what you ask them to do).

It also gives the audience a way to feel that they matter, that they're contributing, while still keeping their participation structured and manageable for the storyteller. It's also a way for an enthusiastic audience to give the storyteller encouragement to continue, approbation—something more to offer than just polite applause at the end.

Often participation works well when you're doing more presentational styles of storytelling—in a classroom, or a boardroom. When you're sitting on the couch, you probably wouldn't ask your audience to fully embody gestures along with you. The reason for this is that rather than being in that position of authority as the storyteller, you're at eye level with someone, and you're focused on shared authority of the situation. That kind of playful authority that participation implies, it usually doesn't fit here.

But you can use repetition without the call to participation, and it can serve those same functions as repetition with participation: It gives a structure to follow, it can add playful humor, and it makes your story memorable.

There's another kind of repetition that's very useful in living room scenarios, and in any other time you want to add interest through humor—it's the "inside joke." And the reason why inside jokes, they work so well to keep your audience interested, is that it unites the audience in a sense of ownership—it's their story, their secret joke along with the narrator or the main character. It bonds the audience with the story and it keeps them glued there.

The TV sitcom series *Seinfeld* was great for this, and it's formulaic for most sitcoms—here's how it works. You establish something at the very beginning of the story, something your narrator or the main character has a clear attitude about, and then you return to that something at key points in the story.

Let's take an example. We'll use the story about my aunt Mae, the "Old Maid," from the very first lecture: In that story, I established a firm characteristic about a particular person or place (Aunt Mae watched *Days of our Lives*, and she liked to talk with the women on her calling circle). And when you establish this firm characteristic about the character, your narrator has an attitude about that character (so when I'm describing these things, I'm smiling, I approve of her, "I loved Aunt Mae"—it gives the audience permission to enjoy these characteristics about her). Then, later in the story, I return to that characteristic—watch this part from the end of that story, and the audience's reaction.

> **Professor Harvey:** We walked in the door, and *Days of our Lives* was on, and she was on the phone with one of the women in her calling circle, and she was finishing up that conversation so we visited with her for about an hour.

Professor Harvey: The audience nods at this part, and it's funny because your audience knows these things about Aunt Mae; we all know this about her, and it's endearing! In your stories, you can use this technique in two ways: With this story, I use repetition to build Aunt Mae into an endearing buddy (the audience sympathizes with her).

Or, you can use this same technique to turn that character into a villain (the audience just dreads seeing that characteristic because they know, "Oh, there comes such-and-such"). Remember that, if you're telling a story from personal experience, you don't want to alienate anyone. Storytelling is about unifying beyond the parameters of the moment of the telling, and you don't want to turn a fun story into hurtful gossip.

Use inside jokes playfully, and not painfully, with your characters. Look for ways to establish something at the beginning (either a characteristic of another character, or you could even establish a small event as this established "thing" at the beginning). Make that established "thing" something the narrator has an attitude about, and use repetition (pointing back to that "thing") to build humor and camaraderie with your audience.

Repetition and participation are great—you can use them when things are flowing along fine in the story, and you can use them when disaster strikes— when forces beyond your control cause an interruption to your story.

Nature intervenes, and the power goes out. A jackhammer starts whirring away in the room under construction next door to you. It's a large audience of kids, and somebody's child farts very loudly. A cell phone goes off in the middle of your presentation. (Heaven forbid if you're at a board meeting, and the board member does the loud farting!) Storytelling is all about choices, and you have four main choices here:

You can ignore it. Sometimes, this is the way to go. The kid farted, everybody giggles, but you keep plugging right along, and eventually they settle back into the story.

Or you can acknowledge it. If the audience really is getting distracted by the interruption—the kids are saying, "Eeewww!" and they're waving their hands and looking at that poor kid, you can very kindly say, "Yeah, I know that's stinky isn't it—we all do that sometimes, OK, let's get back to the story." You defuse the situation by quickly acknowledging it and going on.

Or you can incorporate it. This can be a very fun way to turn a potential distraction into an impromptu addition to your story. You're telling "Jack and the Beanstalk," and a jackhammer goes off next door. You say, "And then, Jack heard the hammering of a thousand tiny dwarves in the neighboring village, but he kept on walking," and you go on with your story.

Or, you can adapt your story to it. Really, all of these are adaptations, but some interruptions call for a total overhaul of your story—and luckily, your narrator has control over time in your story, so if the power goes out, you can completely pause your story and pick it up again when the disaster is averted. Or you can wrap it up quickly, moving to summary for the rest of the story— and even with summary, when you speed up the events, you can still build to a conclusion with your pacing and delivery, and end with a button on your resolution and your ending phrase. So ignore, acknowledge, incorporate, adapt—those are the "I's" and the "A's" of keeping your audience tuned in when distractions strike.

Sometimes, there are technical aspects that you either need to work with, or that you want to consider adding to your story. We're going to talk about a smorgasbord of options that are available to you to use, why you should and shouldn't consider using them, and how to use them. Specifically, we're going to talk about props, costumes, lighting, and sound.

Props: You might want to use a visual aid when you're telling a story. That can be as simple as gesturing back to a picture on your mantle that sparked a story for you. You might talk about your grandmother's hair, and how she always kept it styled just so, and you use that photo of her as a prop.

One of the most memorable uses of a prop in everyday storytelling that I've ever experienced was when I was working at a small café in South Carolina. I was in my early 20s, and it was just me and another server, the girl who ran the cash register, and two cooks, and the man who washed dishes. The little old woman who owned the place, she would bring in fresh cakes every morning that she'd baked at home and those were our special desserts. The girl who ran the cash register and me, well, we were both saving ourselves for marriage.

One of the chefs, she was just very adamant that we just needed to go ahead and just *do it*—and this girl and I, we had purposely chosen not to *do it*. We were all chopping up vegetables for a salad that we were serving later that day, and this chef, she was chopping and she was telling stories about her failed romances, and she said, "You girls, you just need to go out and you just need find a good boy and you just need to do it, and now you don't want this," and she grabbed a big English cucumber and she holds up the cucumber. "You don't want this, no, you want *this*," and she whacks it in half and holds it up. "This is what you're looking for." We howled laughing. You can find props right where you're at, anywhere, even in everyday conversations.

The purpose of a prop is a visual aid—something that visually guides the audience into a better internal visualization of the story. You can do this with small objects, things you hold in your hand, and you can do this with larger surroundings, so you approximate the size of a place in your story by what's around you: "We went to Chichen Itza, to the temple there in Mexico, and it was huge—it was like two of these buildings stacked on top of each other." And it gives you and your audience a way to visualize that place.

When you're telling for kids, you might use other props—finger puppets work great with younger kids. You can use a bigger puppet. Storyteller Willy Claflin has a little moose puppet he often uses when he's telling to kids, and he fully incorporates it into his stories.

You might choose to use a cultural artifact to use in the story—a Chinese fan, or a headscarf (a *soroka*) from Finland. The key here is to integrate the prop with the story, so it's not a distraction just hanging out there, and it's not a souvenir ("Look at that pretty fan"). You incorporate it so that it adds to the story (drawing interest *into* your story, not away from it, to this object *outside* of the story).

This is especially importantly with cultural stories. You treat that object with respect, and you contextualize it correctly, so that the object doesn't become a souvenir that distances your audience from the culture, like you've acquired that culture somehow through the object: "Look at these precious people, look how precious they are—they make little hats." No, that distances your audience from the people and from the story.

Use the prop to draw them into the story. "They made these hats from dyes, and nettles, and plants—and the man who lived on a hill just outside of the surrounding village, he would wear a hat like this when he walked to the store every day," and then your audience uses the visual in front of them (the hat) to see that man walking to the store. Props are best *not* when they're a token that stands outside the story, but when they're a way in, and when they're incorporated with the story.

Like props, costumes can be very useful visual aids, but because they're on your body, using full costume can limit you to one character, when your story, it takes us to multiple characters. You can choose costumes that you can take on and off, like a jacket, but this can be time consuming and it can interrupt the pacing of the story as you switch from character to character.

Think of costume *pieces*, rather than full costumes. Remember that use of "synecdoche" (that part that represents the whole)—so you could use a pair of gloves to represent your grandmother's formal dress. Or you could use a hat or a scarf to represent other characters—things you can easily manipulate and take on and off.

Bear in mind that your professional garb is a kind of costume. Your suit and tie, or your party dress, is a kind of costume that you wear for a specific performance (the role of executive, or the role of partygoer).

If you're planning to tell a specific story as a part of a work presentation, make sure that what you're wearing will allow you the full range of movement that you want—so ladies, if you're telling a story with characters who stoop and bend, this might not be time for an open blouse or a pencil skirt. Or, if you want to wear that outfit, be prepared to adjust your storytelling to suit your suit.

Now professional tellers work with a range of these technical elements, and I want to show you an example of this, so you can see the other end of the spectrum. This is storyteller Brenda Wong Aoki, she lives in California, her partner Mark Izu is a musician, and they blend stories with music, along with costumes and props and lighting to create what Aoki calls "monodramas."

Now, hers is a highly stylized performance, but you can bring some elements of this kind of storytelling into your everyday storytelling. A fan that she carries became a bobbing ocean, and then it became the souls of hell as they popped up from beneath the waves, and then it becomes a surface where people drank water as it dripped down the fan.

It's called a "transformational object." You see kids do this all the time. They pick up a stick, and it becomes a wand, and then a sword, and then a wall to hide behind, all in the same minute of play. That's part of why a transformational object is so fun—it's not only a smart and creative use of an object, it gets us back to that time when everything held the possibility of play, even mundane objects like spoons and sticks.

You can use props in the same way, as transformational objects. Aoki's costuming sets a tone and a cultural context of the story, but it doesn't limit her characterizations because it's not so specific to one character or another. Here's Brenda's telling of part of a Japanese folktale, and watch, also in this clip, for how the musicians mirror the storyteller's movements as she tells.

[Video start.]

[Drumming.]

Brenda Wong Aoki: There, surrounded by rings of fire in the city of the dead, Kuan-yin saw hungry ghosts with huge, distended bellies who could neither eat nor drink, because their throats were skinny as needles. [Wailing.] The souls of the damned bobbed like beans in boiling vats of blood.

[Pause, then singing.]

Brenda Wong Aoki: Kuan-yin said a prayer, healing water spraying from her fingertips. The hungry ghost drank. Their throats opened; they drank some more. And soon, they became happy boys and girls, ready to be reborn. The souls of the boiling damned transformed into giant lotus petals, floating on pure pools of fresh spring water. Golden light shot from her head; the [stench] gave way to a sweet breeze. Hell became paradise.

[Drumming.]

[Video end.]

Professor Harvey: Brenda performs on a stage, so there are lighting transitions that set the mood for the story. While you probably won't deal with positioning lights, or adding colored gels to those lights to create a mood for your story when you're telling on the couch to that friend, or when you're telling to your kids, you can still think about how you can change lighting to your advantage.

If you're telling a scary story to your kids, turn the lights down softer, maybe light a fire! That lovely flickering light, it does wonderful things to shadows. It creates movement and drama in the room. It's the same with a flashlight—the person who holds the light is the storyteller, and you pass the light to your kids and you let them tell. If you're throwing a party, and you want to encourage your guests to tell stories, don't have fluorescent lights blaring. Put on incandescent lamps, make it softer—set the mood for a story-filled evening.

If you're giving a story presentation, make sure the lights in the room are adequate for your audience to see you, and for your audience to be seen. Often in staged storytelling performances, unlike traditional theatre presentations, the audience isn't plunged into darkness but they're half-lit—so you're not this invisible voyeur, you can see yourself, and you can see your fellow audience members.

It's implied in the lighting that you'll be seen and you'll be a part of what's going on. In many modern boardrooms, you have control over the lighting of specific areas, so make sure that you have the lighting that you want for each group—for the storyteller, and for the audience.

Another aspect of Brenda's work is the incorporation of music and sound with her storytelling—it's a lovely addition. It becomes part of the narration; it helps narrate the story. Again, most of the time, you probably won't have a set of five-foot drums behind you with boys banging on them in coordination with your story.

But you may have instruments in your house that you play—a guitar, or a piano—and you can add these elements as either an underscore to specific moments in your story (to help guide the emotional arc), or you can use them to bring a character to life (think of "Peter and the Wolf," where each instrument is a different character in that story).

Odds Bodkin is a masterful storyteller who incorporates guitar with his telling. The music underscores his telling, and it's just brilliant—this is a portion of Odds Bodkin telling the old English epic *Beowulf*:

[Video start.]

> **Odds Bodkin:** King Hrothgar of the Danes, built Herot, the finest mead hall along the shores of the Baltic Sea. And in Herot with his beautiful wife, Wealhthow, old Hrothgar celebrated the stories of his forefathers, and the exploits in war of his thanes, and voices rose higher in Herot than anywhere in the world.

But, they rose too high. For across the fens, beyond the misty crags, there lived a demon deep in his cave. Born of an ancient race of [Cain], his huge foot-long wolf-like ears twitched and heard something. Something he had never heard before. [Growling.] Grendel did not like that he had been disturbed by the squeakings of men.

[Video end.]

Professor Harvey: Another master of musical storytelling for all ages is Bill Harley. Bill Harley's stories are really genius because he tells stories to children, but he adds in these little pockets of humor that only adults will get, to keep them engaged. Without something for them, adults can get very cranky about stories for children—it's why *Sesame Street* worked so well (and why the show *Barney* drives many adults up the wall).

The Pixar film company is especially great with this—if you've ever seen a Pixar or Disney-Pixar film, you know there's humor in there for all ages. So even when you're telling to kids, throw in some jokes for adults—it'll go whizzing right over the kids' heads and it keeps the adults right in there with you.

Along with music, sound effects are also great—using your voice to whizz, or buzz, or brrrrrrrrrr along to communicate the action. Instead of saying "the bee buzzed" several times in your story, you say it once to establish it, and then later, "Along came [buzzing], coming through the trees." Sounds can help push the narration forward, and when you've established what a sound means once, it can become that inside joke for your audience.

Depending on where you're at, you might have the option to sit or to stand. Sometimes you'll see storytellers using a stool to perch on. The stool is nice, because it gives you a place to rest if you're telling for a while, and you can use it like a prop—sitting down when character sits down in the story, so, "Jack climbed up a mountain and he was so tired, and he sat down a spell and he looked around."

You should be aware that a seated position can draw away some of your energy, so if you're seated, try to keep on the edge of your seat or stool. That forces your energy out and up more, rather than sitting back in the seat, which can slump you down. If you can physically stand easily, it's usually best to stand.

If you're sitting with friends on the couch, sit on the edge of your seat to give you more energy as you tell that story. That's where you want your audience to be (at the edge of their seats), and as their guide you're responsible for prompting that excitement for them.

Those are a lot of possibilities for you to consider in keeping your audience's attention throughout the story. Next time we'll wrap up the course by considering some final tips for how to engage with and read your audience, and how all of these storytelling how-to's, all of them come back to where we began—with oral thought and oral storytelling as a powerful and pervasive cultural force.

Remember Your Stories—The Power of Orality
Lecture 24

This lecture wraps up the course with some final considerations on how to keep an audience's attention, from the technical aspects of microphones and slides, to the more nuanced ways that we read audiences and understand their needs in the moment. Finally, we'll take all our how-to's back to the nature of orality itself as a cultural force that shapes all of us, all the time, everywhere.

Slides and Microphones

- We talked in the last lecture about using props, and you can consider PowerPoint and other multimedia tools as similar to props. PowerPoint slides work best as a well-integrated prop, not the focus of attention but a visual aid to pull listeners further into the story.

- When you're creating slides, think in terms of using images and key words that illustrate or draw out significant points in the story.

- We often think of slides as a way to prompt memory or guide a presentation. It's fine to use slides in that way, but keep in mind that if PowerPoint guides your story, then PowerPoint becomes the narrator, not you. Let the slides support your story. Speak first, then bring up the slide.

- Choose carefully what to include on a slide. If you want to prompt your memory, put up a single word or image as the first slide. Then, when you're ready to come to your bullet points, bring up a second slide with those points. In this way, you remain in control.

- In giving a presentation, you may also be provided with a microphone. Of course, microphones project your voice through speakers so that people can hear you better. But microphones can also malfunction and become more of a distraction than an aid.

o A microphone gives you another way to manipulate your voice; your growl can sound more menacing or your whisper, more ethereal. But a microphone can also throw you off if you're not used to hearing your voice projected.

o Visually, a handheld microphone distances you from the audience, although if you're comfortable holding a microphone, it can sort of fade away. The goal is for it to become an extension of yourself and the story.

o A microphone attached to a lectern restricts your movements, and the lectern probably blocks most of your body from the audience. With a stand, you have the option of holding the microphone yourself and moving freely in the space or allowing the stand to hold the microphone to free up your hands. Lapel and over-the-ear microphones give you the most range of movement and are the least invasive presence between you and the audience.

o If you plan to use a microphone, try to get into the space ahead of time to do a sound-check and to give yourself a chance to practice briefly. If you have a corded microphone, make sure you don't trip over it.

o Remember that even with a microphone, you still need to project from your diaphragm so that your voice sounds confident.

• In all the elements you use to maintain your audience's attention—an engaging mindset or hook from the beginning, as well as technical additions, such as props or costumes—keep it simple. Use only those props that you can handle with ease and that fully integrate with your story. Use only those costumes that help you bring the story to life without limiting your mobility.

- Be selective in your storytelling. Don't oversimplify your stories, but include only those elements that are necessary. Make your story manageable for an oral audience.

The Nature of Oral Storytelling

- Orality is how we know much of what we know, and it's how we retain what we know. We tend to think that everything that matters is written down, but most of the time, knowledge is spoken. It's carried through an oral story before it's canonized in print.

- This was true of the ancient epics—the *Odyssey*, the Epic of Gilgamesh, the Upanishads—and it's true today. Your family history, the stories you tell about yourself that define who you are and shape your identity, the stories of your faith or the truths you hold that shape your daily decisions—these all exist in oral form in your mind and in your body and voice as you retell those stories to others through your words and actions.

- But oral storytelling is ephemeral—it lives in the breath in one moment, and it's gone in the next. Because they're ephemeral, oral stories work well when they latch onto those qualities of the mind that ground them in place.
  - Repetition, for example, mirrors the redundant quality of oral memory, reinforcing themes and points.

  - Keep your stories economical; don't clutter them with unnecessary props or digressions, but get to the meat.

  - Ground your audience in strong images through visualization and characterizations, using your voice as a tool to shape these places and people into life. Those qualities latch onto the image-based and action-centered nature of oral memory.

- Specifically grounding your stories also helps keep you ethical as a teller. You don't take someone's life or words out of context and you're not poaching someone else's cultural heritage; you're contextualizing the story, making specific choices about character and situations.

- Oral storytelling is co-creative. Every story has an audience, and every story exists in relation to that audience. You adapt your stories to suit different audiences, and you're aware of how an audience contributes to a story.

- When you come to the end of a good story—and a good storytelling experience—both you and your audience are in a different place than where you started. The story changes you.

- Storytelling has the capacity, more than any other art form or persuasive medium, to provoke questions, incite dialogue, and reach both the mind and the heart. The vulnerability the teller and audience show in the face of the story widens to encompass others in a shared experience.

Story Trends

- As we've said, stories serve as metaphors for our own inner struggles, to integrate the often contradictory facets of our personalities and desires. They are also powerful metaphors for the struggles that go on in the wider culture and the world around us.

- Look at the story trends around you; start paying attention to the kinds of stories you see in movies or the kinds of stories your co-workers tell. Notice not only the content of these stories but what they represent—the values they express and the wider themes that emerge.

- Of course, stories are entertaining, but they also serve as "code" for cultural mores. The stories we whisper are whispered for a reason—because they have power. The same is true of the stories you tell your children to prepare them to face the world. Your stories tell them where they came from and give them strength.

Nana

My Nana was a note-taker. I think it came from her being a secretary for so many years. She took notes on everything: She'd write on the backs of old envelopes her list of things to do; she'd stick Post-Its all over the kitchen door with our phone numbers on [them]; she'd put a little note on her bathroom mirror to remind her to brush her teeth with her special paste. We always laughed at her tendency to obsessively make notes, until my grandparents passed away. And on the back of every little thing in their home, Nana had written who was in photographs—some of them went six generations back, names we'd never have known—she'd written where she got pottery, and when all my cousins and I said our first little words to her—she wrote all of it down.

And when we went down in the basement of their home.... In the back of that basement, wrapped up in plastic, was an old chunk of wood. And that piece of wood would have meant nothing to us if Nana hadn't left a little note on it: "Mr. Little (my great-grandfather) grafted this apple tree the year he died. The tree limb broke off a few days ago and Tom (my grandfather) wants to keep this graft. D. Little."

…

While my grandfather was alive, he taught me a lot of things. He taught me how to graft trees. He taught me how to love people. And he taught me how to tell stories.

That piece of grafted wood sits on display in our home, along with the note Nana wrote. I think if Nana were here today, she'd still be writing notes—because she knew that the value in a thing isn't the thing itself; it's the memories that thing holds, how that thing connects you back to people you love. There's love, and history, and family in an old piece of wood.

So I write notes. Remember: store up apples for winter. Remember: mom gave me this vase for my birthday. Remember: remember, remember our stories.

- Every story has a narrator and is told from a point of view. Every story is shaped by the context out of which it comes—an economic context, cultural and social contexts, and personal contexts.

Telling Stories
- The best story performances harness the power of the elements unique to a live performance—your voice, your body, and the reactions of your audience. Even if you start to lose your audience—and this will happen to you—consider that a good thing. Think how much better your writing would be if you could get that kind of immediate response from your readers.

- When you remember and tell your stories, the awesome privilege and power and gift for the storyteller as performer is that everything you need is right in front of you—in your visualizations of the story and in the faces and body language of your audience. It's also inside you, in your face, in your body, and in your life and memory.

Suggested Reading

The National Storytelling Network, www.storyweb.org.

Sobol, *The Storyteller's Journey*.

Wolf, *The Art of Storytelling Show*.

1. How has your family culture shaped a story that you know? What truths do you find from your perspective on that story now, and how would you tell that story to others? In a hushed voice? Proudly? With a different hero or heroine?

2. Culture shapes not only how we tell stories but how we can tell stories and even whether or not some stories ever get told. Sometimes, our cultural context directs attention to certain stories over others. Over the course of these lectures, what is one story that has come to the surface that you might not have considered a "real" story before you began? To whom could you tell that story now?

Remember Your Stories—The Power of Orality
Lecture 24—Transcript

Professor Harvey: In this lecture, we're going to wrap up the course with some final considerations on how to keep your audience's attention, from the technical aspects of microphones and PowerPoint, to the more nuanced ways that we read audiences and understand their needs in the moment. Finally, we'll take all of our how-to's back to the nature of orality as a cultural force that shapes all of us, all the time, everywhere.

This course really just scratches the surface of what's out there in the world of professional storytelling and storytelling studies. There are lots of resources to help you grow your storytelling personally and professionally. The best, best place to go from here is to get connected to with the National Storytelling Network.

The National Network can help you get connected with special interest groups and local storytelling organizations in your area that sponsor storytelling festivals and events. Because no matter where you are in the U.S., there's usually an annual festival in easy driving distance to you, where you can hear lively professional storytellers perform and give workshops.

We talked in the last lecture about using props and really, you can consider the use of things like PowerPoint and other multimedia aspects of presentation, you can use these just as you would any other prop. PowerPoint works best when it's a well-integrated prop—when it's incorporated and serves the story. When it's not the focus but a visual aid to prompt listeners to get further into the story, that's when it works best.

If you've got a script up there on PowerPoint, it's not as useful in getting your audience into the story. What you include on those slides, for that, think in terms of images and key words that illustrate and draw out significant points in the overall story. Integrate it with the arc of your story—the arc of the presentation.

We often think of PowerPoint as a way to prompt memory or guide the presentation, and it's fine to use it in this way. But consider this: if

PowerPoint guides the story, then PowerPoint becomes the narrator, not you. Let the narrator guide, let the story carry, and let PowerPoint support.

So you give a story element, and then you bring up a slide that illustrates that part of the story or presentation. You give a story that draws your audience into the point of why you're there, and then you introduce a slide that highlights key aspects of why your findings will work.

Privilege story over slides and outlines. Often this works when you speak first, tell the story, and then you bring up the slide. If you do bring up the slide first, it can prompt your memory (which is nice), but it becomes the background for your story. Do you want people reading the screen?

Because we tend to privilege the written word over orality—and hear me, we privilege it, we don't enjoy it more, but we intellectually privilege it—when you bring up words on a screen, that's the first thing your audience is going to jump to. You're talking, but they're reading; they're not paying attention to you.

That slide becomes a background, so choose carefully what you put up there. If you want to prompt your memory, put a single word or image as the first slide. That prompts your memory to move to the next part of the story, and then when you're ready to come to bullet points about where that story took you, then you bring up a second slide with those bullet points. You guide; the narrator is in control, not the prop. When you privilege story, that's when presentations really come to life.

Something else you may encounter in more presentational situations is when you use props like PowerPoint, you also often use a microphone. In some situations, you'll be provided a microphone; in other situations, you may have to ask for one.

I want to tell you plainly what a microphone does, so that you can make an educated decision on how to use one. I'll start out with statements of fact, and these aren't value-laden statements. It's just what a mic does. Then we'll move to the pros and cons. Here's what a microphone does: It projects your voice through speakers—so, ideally, when you use a mic, people can hear you better. But, it's a technology, and it has the capacity to fail. People hear your volume better, but if the mic is shorting out or if it's humming with feedback, it can be more of a distraction than a help. The pros: You can often be heard better. The cons: If it shorts out, it can be a distraction.

It gives you another way to manipulate your voice—so you can growl and it sounds more menacing in the microphone. You can whisper and it sounds more ethereal. The pros: It can give you a more creative way to use your voice. The cons: When you hear your voice projected, it's going to sound different than you're used to, and if you're not accustomed to using a mic, it can throw you off and it can be a distraction to you.

Visually, a handheld mic distances you from the audience—it's a literal thing that stands between you and your audience. Again, it's not a value statement, it's just a statement of fact. If you're comfortable with using the mic, well it can fade into the background and become a part of you. But if you're not comfortable with it, it can wind up standing out, and we're looking at you holding the mic, rather than looking at the mic as an extension of yourself. That's the goal with all these technical additions—props, costumes, mics— they become an extension of you, and an extension of the story, so it's not a distraction. The pros: It can fade away and just become another extension of the story. The cons: It can be a distraction.

Depending on the kind of mic, it can shape your movement. Let's talk about some of the different kinds of microphones and how they shape your movement. Starting with the most restrictive, there's the microphone that's attached to a lectern—so, if you have notes, it can help you to position these notes in front of you so you can look at them. But that lectern blocks most of your body, and you might have to lean in a bit for that mic to pick up your voice. Clearly, if you move away from the lectern, you lose the mic.

Then, there's a mic on a stand. If it's corded or cordless, you can take it off the stand and it gives you more range of movement. You can approach the audience, you can move in the space more freely, you have the option of having the stand hold that mic, so it frees up your hands. When you're holding the mic, one hand is stuck here holding it; the other is free to gesture.

When you're giving a toast at a wedding, you might have both hands busy—one holding the mic, the other holding your glass.

Lapel mics and over-the-ear mics give you the most range of movement, and they're the least invasive presence standing between you and your audience. These mics, they work with a receiver, like your remote control—and like the TV remote control, if you move too far away from the TV, well the remote, it won't work. The same with on-the-body mics: If you move too far away from that receiver that's picking up the signal from your mic, the mic won't work.

Lapel mics also have a tendency to short out more than over-the-ear mics, and there's a limited range of where you can move your head to get your voice picked up by that lapel mic. But these offer more range of movement.

The pros: When your movement is restricted, it can keep you from unnecessary movements that might distract from your story—it forces all of your energy and motion up here, in your upper body. The cons: Mics that limit your movement can limit your interaction with the audience, and your creative use of the space, and your characterizations.

If you choose to use a mic, here are some things to consider. Try to get into the space ahead of time to do a sound check, just to check the levels and make sure the volume is at a reasonable level for your speaking voice, and also to give you a chance to try out the mic in your hand. Hold it away from you, hold it close to you, get used to having it in your hand.

If you haven't had a chance to work ahead of time with the mic, then you'll need to adjust it when you get up to speak. If you're using a stand mic, you'll have to move that mic stand up and down so that you're not craning your head up or down. You can use your mindset moment to get used to handling the mic. You might even mention it in the mindset—you can acknowledge that you're not used to it, make a joke out of it! That can diffuse the distraction for you and the audience.

If you have a corded mic, be aware of that cord (you don't want to trip over it), but use your other hand to move that cord out of your way. You don't have to look down all the time to see where that cord is; you can feel it with your hand. If it's there in your hand, then you can guide it out of your way until you move where you need to be. You can even have that cord in your hand as you gesture.

Even with a microphone, you need to project from your diaphragm—that diaphragmatic voice projects confidence. It's not just about volume; the mic can fix volume, but it can't fix confidence. That comes from powerful, controlled diaphragmatic breath support.

All of these elements and all of these that you can use to keep your audience's attention—an engaging mindset or hook from the beginning; using repetition and participation; responding to interruptions (ignore, incorporate, acknowledge, and adapt—the I's and the A's); and all these technical additions of props, and costumes, and lighting, sound, microphones, PowerPoint, oh my!—in all of these possibilities, I cannot urge you strongly enough to keep it simple.

Use only those props that you can maneuver with ease, and that you can integrate fully with your story—do I need this prop, or does it clutter? Use only those costumes that enable you to bring the full story to life—does this costume limit my mobility or my possibilities? Use only that music that serves the story in some integrated way—if it's not in service to the story, it's clutter.

Ask yourself critically: Do I need all these characters in my story? Which ones are necessary, and which ones could be dropped, or combined into composite characters? (Remember the story about the miner, Donzel? The narrator of that story was a composite of over 20 different miners who I interviewed.) Does the story need to be this long? How short could I make this story to really focus in on that main purpose and point?

I urge you to be selective in your storytelling, not in an attempt to oversimplify your stories—heaven knows, we don't need any more surface-level stories in our world; our world is craving depth, even depth in humor, real belly laughs! We need that depth. But make your story manageable for an oral audience.

These thoughts about simplicity, they take us back to our first lessons on the nature of *oral* storytelling in everyday life. Orality is how we know much of what we know, and it's how we retain what we know. We think everything that matters is written down, but most of the time knowledge is spoken; it's carried through an oral story, before it's canonized into print and fixed into script.

This was true of the ancient epics—the *Odyssey*, the *Epic of Gilgamesh*, the *Upanishads*, they were all told and sung long before they were written down, and it's true today. Your family history, the stories you tell about yourself that define who you are and shape your identity, the stories of your faith, your beliefs, the truths that you hold dear and that shape your daily decisions—these all exist up here, in your head, in oral thought, and here, in your body and your voice as you retell those stories to others through your words and your actions. We move in story; your actions and choices tell a story to others about what matters to you, your values, your priorities—these all come out in the stories that you tell and they get put into stories as people interpret your everyday choices and take them up into the story that they create in their heads about you.

We remember our world through oral thought, through stories—and while human beings are remarkably clever, the human brain can only keep track of so much at a time, especially in an oral scenario, where you're an audience member listening to someone else tell a story. Here we return again to that nature of oral storytelling, from our first lecture.

Oral storytelling is ephemeral. It lives on the breath in one moment, and it's gone the next; you don't have that book to flip back a few pages and remind yourself of what came before—no, it's gone. Just like those people in your life who are gone, who exist now only in the stories that you tell. Because they're ephemeral, oral stories work best when they latch onto those qualities of the mind that ground them in place. When you use repetition, it mirrors the redundant quality of oral memory, reinforcing themes and points.

Oral storytelling isn't wasteful. Don't clutter your story with unnecessary props and do-dads; get to the meat, and bring us to that belly of the beast, where your hero has to face that dragon. Ground your audience in strong images through visualization and characterizations, using your voice as a tool to shape these people and these places into life, because those qualities latch on to the image-based nature of oral memory, and the action-centered qualities of oral memory.

Keep us grounded in those visualizations as you guide us through the emotional arc of your story. Keep your audience grounded, so that they know where you are. Think of your storyboards. First we go here, we're in this place with these people, and then we go here, and it's in this place that I come to a new realization. Maybe you come to that emotional peak of your story. But that emotion is grounded in some concrete location; it's here at this point in the plot, in that storyboard scene. That's where I know what I know; it's localized in the sense that we know when and where you were when you came to that emotional climax.

Keep your story grounded in action, in specificity, and in location—all those qualities of oral memory that tell you what in your story is going to really stick. We want sticky stories, ones that work well with oral memory and stick there in the mind of your audience.

When you ground your stories in specificity, this helps keep you ethical as a teller because you're not taking someone's life and their words out of context, and you're not poaching someone else's cultural heritage. You're contextualizing the story, making specific choices about character and situations. Grounding stories in well-researched specifics, it helps you keep your story ethically grounded.

Your stories are embodied. Your body is involved in telling the story; you're aware of how your body is a part of what gets communicated (it can be part of your characterizations, using body centers and posture, and gestures that flow out of these body centers). And your body is in relation to other bodies in the space. You're standing with a friend, and you're not just listening with your eyes, and your ears, you're listening with your whole sensory apparatus, listening to their stories, listening for the connections they're making to your own stories, and ways to segue way into what you have to share (through your mindset and introduction of your story). But moreover, you're being a good listener, and you're being a good audience member for their stories.

Your body and their bodies, they make up this shared space of the storytelling experience that's co-creative, because you're never telling stories in a vacuum. Every story has an audience (even if it's just you telling the story to yourself!), every story has an audience, and every story exists in relation to that audience. You adapt your story to suit that audience (adjusting the perspective if you need to, adjusting how long you take with descriptions, or if you summarize whole passages of a story in order to get to that point that this audience needs to hear in this situation and in this telling).

You're aware of how your audience is contributing to the story: "And this happened, oh, and this"—and then the pace of your story builds, and the story piles up. "And this, and this," there's that additive quality of oral memory. Then your friend thinks of something and adds the story—"Oh and that same thing happened to me, too!" In this vibrant storytelling context—on the couch, at a party—you may incorporate, adapt, and acknowledge what they're adding to this ongoing story.

All of it is happening in this triangle of interaction, and that comes back to relationships, which is the most powerful part of any storytelling experience. When you come to the end of the story (which, if you're viewing storytelling as a dialogue, means that the end of your story is just the beginning of the next story), you're in a different place than you were when you started out.

It's like that Aristotelian chart for stories, where the conclusion leaves you on a higher plane than when you began in the introduction; and like the hero's journey, where that hero returns but is changed somehow, able to hop back and forth between two worlds that were once inaccessible to him. When you come to the end of a really good story, and a good storytelling experience, you're in a different place than where you started. The story scoops you up and it takes you, and your audience, and the subject somewhere, and it leaves you changed.

Just like you and me. If you've followed me this far, at the end of all our stories for this course, you and I are in a different place than we were when we started out this course. The stories have moved us into a different place—not just learning about storytelling, but you've learned more hopefully about yourself, and about me.

In that triangle of interaction, storytelling has the capacity more than any other art form or persuasive medium, to provoke questions, to incite dialogue, and to reach both the mind and the heart because of the vulnerability that the teller and the audience show in the face of the story that's widening to encompass all of us in this shared experience that changes the hero. Because stories work symbolically, they change us as well.

Because stories serve as metaphors. They are metaphors for our own inner struggles to integrate these contradictory facets of our personalities and our desires ("I want to do this, but I really *should* do this"). They are metaphors for our struggles against our personal dragons and our inner fears and anxieties; and they're powerful metaphors for the struggles that go on in the wider culture, and the world outside of us.

Look at the story trends around you. Start paying attention to the kinds of stories that you're starting to see in popular films and in movie theatres; start paying attention to those stories that your office mates may be telling. These trends reveal the wider anxieties and desires of the culture (whether it's wider American culture in the movies, or the cultural climate of your own office).

Start paying attention to stories that surround you every day—the stories you hear from radio pundits, or from your family members, or in your house of worship. Not only the content of these stories, but what they represent—the values they express, the wider themes that emerge, that convey how these stories function for their tellers.

Because stories are entertaining, yes, but they also serve as code for cultural mores. The stories that we whisper, they're whispered for a reason. Stories do something for us, and the telling of those stories does something, how we tell. Whispering does something—that story that you tell only your best friend in a hushed voice, because unleashed into the outer world, that story has power.

Stories that you tell to your kids at home, to prepare them to face the world—to tell them about your family, where they come from—these stories have power for us. They give us strength. Strength to find continuity with the past and buoyancy in the present. Sometimes they give us the background to narrate our own life story against. The same with myths and sacred stories: If you have a faith story, that story has power; it shapes material decisions for you.

Orality is where we live—story and storytelling are all around us. Don't ever lose sight of that *telling* aspect of story—they're inextricably linked. Every story—*every* story—has a narrator. Every story is told from a point of view. Every story is shaped by the context out of which it comes. The economic context, and how that weighs on the story and on the storyteller. The cultural context, and how that presses in on the story, shaping it under the force and weight of social pressure, and drawing out stories selectively because the questions that provoke those stories are deemed important and valid. Culture shapes the stories we tell, and those stories, in turn, shape the changing identity of that culture.

The best story performances harness the power of the performance elements unique to live performance. You've got your body there in that space with these other bodies. You've got eye contact with them; you can see when your audience is following along with your line of thought. You'll see them nodding. You'll hear them laughing. You'll see them jump with fright, or see them lean in a little closer when you reach that compelling part of your story.

Also, and this will happen to you too: You can see when you might start to lose your audience, when you haven't provided enough detail for them to follow your thinking—and this is a good thing! Think of how much better your *writing* would be if you could get that kind of immediate response from your readers.

I'd like to end with a story:

> My Nana was a note taker. I think it came from her being a secretary for so many years—she took notes on everything—she'd write on the backs of old envelopes. She'd write her list of things to do; she'd stick post-its all over the kitchen door with our phone numbers on it, and she'd put a little note on her bathroom mirror to remind her to brush her teeth with that special little paste. We

always laughed at her tendency to obsessively make notes, until my grandparents passed away. On the back of every little thing in their home, Nana had written who was in photographs—some of them went six generations back, names we never would have known. She'd written where she got pottery, and when all my cousins and I had said our first little words to her—she wrote it all down.

When we went down in the basement of their home, and that musty smell of the basement, it filled your nose as we walked down those uneven, poured concrete steps. You walked into that basement. It still had her cans of her homemade pickles on one side and these stacks of boxes on the other. One of those boxes had a note on it, "These items are the miscellaneous collections of Doris Little. Signed, D. Little. June, 1978." Notes on everything. In the back of that basement, wrapped up in plastic, was an old chunk of wood. That piece of wood would have meant nothing to us, if Nana hadn't left a little note on it: "Mr. Little," (my great-grandfather), "Mr. Little grafted this apple tree the year that he died. The limb broke off a few days ago and Tom," (my grandfather), "wants to keep this graft. D. Little."

When my grandfather was alive, he told me a story about his father's art of grafting. He said:

Well, I guess we's a kind of a storytelling people, and a lot of the stories I tell is true happenings, you know, it happened. But of a night, we had two porches on that old house, one of them was one that faced the front and there was another that we called the Back Porch out by that old apple tree. That porch, it wasn't very big, but it was, seemed like the place that we'd gather of a night, especially if company was there under that tree. You know like, Uncle Joe, or Uncle Ed, or Uncle Clyde, or Uncle Will, or any of those people that was there, seems like we'd sit on the back porch by that tree.

The men, they would usually chew tobacco and they'd sit on the edge of the porch and they'd spit off the porch, you know. There was that apple tree there, great big growing. My daddy, he grafted it years before that. That means, grafting is "changing." What kind of apples is important. Half had one kind of apple on it and half had the other, original apple. My daddy, he'd go wherever it was and he would graft trees. Now everybody wasn't real good at it. That had to be an art, I'd say.

But this one, it had such good apples on it. They was early, early striped apples. They was red striped. Oh, they was so good, they'd get ripe, long about now, they'd begin to, in June. Anyway, that old apple tree was right out from the porch, about, probably, eight feet out from that porch. The way the thing had grown up, the water had kind of washed, there wasn't any grass under that old apple tree. There's a root that run out toward the house, and it was about eight inches from the root down to the ground. And that is where I would sit on that root. It made just a perfect seat, and my back, it would just fit back into that old apple tree right there. That's there's where I'd sit and listen to the stories.

Oh, and they'd tell em, oh you know, they'd tell em year after year, the same stories. Then they'd be adding on another year's worth, you know, and they'd tell about going a certain night, and doing this and that, you know, getting one up a tree, you know and what happened. You know, and I'd just sit there, that tree up my back, grafted. I was just as content as a boy could possibly be, I reckon.

While my grandfather was alive, he taught me a lot of things. He taught me how to graft trees. He taught me how to love people. And he taught me how to tell stories.

That piece of grafted wood, it sits on display at our home, along with the note that Nana wrote. I think if Nana were here today, she'd still be writing notes, because she knew that the value in a thing isn't the thing itself. It's the memories that that thing holds, and how that thing connects you back to those people who you love. There's love, and history, and family in an old piece of wood.

So, I write notes. Remember: Store up apples for winter. Remember: Mom gave me this vase for my birthday. Remember: Remember, remember our stories.

When you remember and tell your stories, the awesome privilege and power and gift for the storyteller-as-performer is that everything you need is right out there in front of you, in your visualizations of the story that's around you, and in the faces and body language of your audience. It's *inside* you, in your face, in your body, and in your life and your memory.

I hope this course has encouraged you to recognize the pervasive quality of storytelling that's all around us, and the power of stories to influence decisions and to shape identity. Storytelling is the most personal thing that we do. It's the most human thing that we do.

Thank you for being willing to be vulnerable and playful as we dove into your stories. I hope that you see that you have a warehouse of stories in you.

Credits

Piano Performance by Sue Keller.

Title music supplied by Getty Images.

Bibliography

Aoki, Brenda Wong, and Mark Izu. *Mermaid Meat: The Secret to Immortality and Other Japanese Ghost Stories*. Audio CD and Book. Directors Jael Weisman and Robin Stanton. Berkeley: Pele Productions, 2007. As beautifully and artfully told as it is packaged (with full-color woodblock prints by Yoshitoshi), this is only one of Aoki and Izu's powerful collaborative storytelling/monodrama works.

Bell, Lee Ann. "The Story of the Storytelling Project: An Arts-Based Race and Social Justice Curriculum." *Storytelling, Self, Society: An Interdisciplinary Journal of Storytelling Studies* 5, no. 2 (2009): 107–118. Storytelling in the classroom and curriculum.

Bettelheim, Bruno. *The Uses of Enchantment: The Meaning and Importance of Fairy Tales*. New York: Vintage, 2010.

Blair, Madelyn. *Essays in Two Voices: Dialogues of Discovery*. Jefferson, MD: Pelerei, Inc., 2011. Blair offers resources and consulting for corporations and organizations.

———. *Riding the Current: How to Deal with the Daily Deluge of Data*. Chagrin Falls, OH: The Taos Institute Publications, 2010. Blair offers resources and consulting for corporations and organizations.

Bodkin, Odds. *The Odyssey: An Epic Telling*. Audio Recording. 1995. OddsBodkin.com Digital Download Service. Downloaded May 11, 2012. A four-hour original retelling of Homer's mythic saga, with accompanying original guitar score. Oppenheim Platinum award-winning recording.

Bogart, Anne. *A Director Prepares*. New York: Routledge, 2001. If you ever need inspiration, encouragement, or audacious wisdom as an artist, it's in this book.

Bogart, Anne, and Tina Landau. *The Viewpoints Book: A Practical Guide to Viewpoints and Composition.* New York: Theatre Communications Group, 2005. These exercises are specific to Bogart's technique of developing ensemble theatre, although the warm-up exercises are useful even for the solo teller. An essential guide if you're preparing to do tandem or group storytelling.

Boje, David M. "Breaking out of Narrative's Prison: Improper Story in Storytelling Organization." *Storytelling, Self, Society: An Interdisciplinary Journal of Storytelling Studies* 2, no. 2 (2006): 28–49. Encouragement to break free from the prison of Aristotelian structures and experiment with plot.

Brecht, Bertolt. *Brecht on Theatre: The Development of an Aesthetic.* 13th ed. Edited and translated by John Willett. New York: Hill and Wang, 1977. Useful theory concerning how direct eye contact (epic mode) implicates your audience in the questions and actions going on in any performance.

Breen, Robert S. *Chamber Theatre.* Ellison Bay, WI: Wm Caxton Ltd., 1986. A foundational text in the world of performance studies. Though specific to the adaptation of literary texts, the methods are easily applied to storytelling. Breen offers a practical introduction to the use of point of view in storytelling and methods of using epic, lyric, and dramatic modes in performing a story.

Burch, Milbre. "What the Queen Saw." *Sop Doll and Other Tales of Mystery and Mayhem.* Audio CD. Kind Crone Productions, 2002. Award-winning collection of stories, including this excellent retelling of "Snow White" from the queen's perspective.

Campbell, Joseph C. *The Hero with a Thousand Faces.* Novato, CA: New World Library, 2008.

Campbell, Joseph, Bill Moyers, and George Lucas. *The Power of Myth.* DVD. Producers Alvin H. Perimutter and Joan Konner. Silver Spring, MD: Athena Studio, 2010. Seminal PBS series of interviews with Campbell by Bill Moyers. This DVD set also includes conversations between Campbell and filmmaker George Lucas.

Cashdan, Sheldon. *The Witch Must Die: The Hidden Meaning of Fairy Tales.* New York: Perseus, 1999.

Choi, Dennis C., Amy R. Furay, Nathan K. Evanson, Michelle M. Ostrander, Yvonne M. Ulrich-Lai, and James P. Herman. "Bed Nucleus of the Stria Terminalis Subregions Differentially Regulate Hypothalamic-Pituitary-Adrenal Axis Activity: Implications for the Integration of Limbic Inputs." *The Journal of Neuroscience* 27, no. 8 (2007): 2025–2034. Neuroscientific research suggesting that a region of the brain that accesses thought (the BNST) can regulate the fight-or-flight stress response (HPA stress responses); in these lectures, the link is made to controlling performance anxiety.

Collins, Rives, and Pamela J. Cooper. *The Power of Story: Teaching through Storytelling.* Boston: Allyn and Bacon, 1997. Good chapters on visual memory and a great overall storytelling preparation guide, including interviews with professional tellers.

Conquergood, Dwight. "Rethinking Ethnography: Towards a Critical Cultural Politics." In *The Sage Handbook of Performance Studies*, edited by D. Soyini Madison and Judith Hamera, pp. 351–365. Thousand Oaks, CA: Sage, 2005. An ethical model for co-creating performances based in dialogue with audiences, not diatribe or monologue.

Davis, Donald. *The Grand Canyon.* Audio CD. Atlanta: August House, 2006. Davis is truly a master storyteller. In this collection, he hooks the audience from the start with a short "mindset" that connects paying taxes (a universal experience) with his sense of personal property ownership of the national parks system. *Storytelling World* award-winning recording.

Davis, Michael. "Neural Circuitry of Anxiety and Stress Disorders." In *Neuropsychopharmacology: The Fifth Generation of Progress*, edited by Kenneth L. Davis et al., pp. 931–951. Philadelphia: Lippincott Williams & Wilkins, 2002. Davis maps out the brain's anxiety pathways.

De Las Casas, Dianne. *The Story Biz Handbook: How to Manage Your Storytelling Career from the Desk to the Stage.* Westport, CT: Libraries Unlimited, 2008. Good advice for storytellers who want to begin putting themselves out there professionally.

Dworkin, Motoko. *Tales of Now and Zen.* Audio CD. Available from www.motoko.folktales.net. A follow-up to her Parents' Choice Silver Honor Award–winning first CD, this collection features stories from folklore, myth, and original stories, with accompanying music.

Ellis, Elizabeth. "Storytelling and the Development of Ethical Behavior with Elizabeth Ellis." Interviewer Eric Wolf. *The Art of Storytelling Show.* 24 August 2012. www.artofstorytellingshow.com. A wonderful interview with Ellis on the deep value of storytelling and the values storytelling can impart.

Ellis, Elizabeth, and Loren Neimi. *Inviting the Wolf In: Thinking About Difficult Stories.* Atlanta: August House, 2006. Further outlines the storytelling triangle in the specific context of difficult stories, incorporating issues of trust and permission.

Forest, Heather. *Tales of Womenfolk.* Audio CD. Available from storyarts.org/store. Forest's style of storytelling blends music, story, and song into nuanced tellings of traditional and personal tales. She is a prolific storyteller and writer—this is only one of her many resources. Among numerous other honors, she has won the NSN Circle of Excellence and Parents' Choice awards.

Gentile, John S. "Prologue: Defining Myth. An Introduction to the Special Issue on Storytelling and Myth." *Storytelling, Self, Society: An Interdisciplinary Journal of Storytelling Studies* 7, no. 2 (2011): 85–90. Considers the multiple definitions of myth and introduces a full issue of the journal on the topic.

———. "Stories of the Otherworld: An Interview with Eddie Lenihan." *Storytelling, Self, Society: An Interdisciplinary Journal of Storytelling Studies* 5, no. 3 (2009): 152–175. Lenihan is an Irish storyteller, folklorist, and passionate defender of the fairy faith.

Harley, Bill. *Yes to Running! Bill Harley Live Double CD*. Audio CD. Seekonk, MA: Round River Records, 2008. Bill is fantastic at keeping his audience's attention and using guitar, zany voices, not-afraid-to-be-silly characterizations, and sharp wit, while still remaining an approachable persona. This recording earned the following honors: Grammy Award, NAPPA Gold Award, Parents' Choice Silver Award, Creative Child Preferred Choice Award, and Just Plain Folks Award.

Kling, Kevin. *Alive*. Audio CD. Kevin Kling / East Side Digital, 2006. Available from www.cdbaby.com. Kling is a riotous and heartwarming teller—an NSN Circle of Excellence Award winner and one of my favorites. I have a preference for live recordings, and this is a great one.

———. *The Dog Says How*. Wadena, MN: Borealis Books, 2007. The title story is a powerful, humorous, and poignant recount of Kling's motorcycle accident and its aftermath.

Langellier, Kristin M., and Eric E. Peterson. *Storytelling in Daily Life: Performing Narrative*. Philadelphia: Temple University Press, 2004. An approachable introductory analysis of how we use storytelling in everyday contexts; helpful for thinking about all the stories we have and tell.

Lehrman, Betty, ed. *Telling Stories to Children*. Jonesborough, TN: National Storytelling Press, 2005. A wonderful source for quick advice on telling to children of all ages. The lectures especially make use of Judy Sima's and Rebecca Isbell's contributions.

Lepp, Bil. *Seeing Is Believing*. Audio CD. South Charleston, WV: Bil Lepp Storytelling, 2009. Live recording of funny, "family-friendly" tales for young and old alike.

Linklater, Kristin. *Freeing the Natural Voice: Imagery and Art in the Practice of Voice and Language*. New York: Drama Publishers, 2006. Wonderful exercises for vocal-physical warm-ups and understanding how the voice works.

Lipman, Doug. *Improving Your Storytelling: Beyond the Basics for All Who Tell Stories in Work or Play.* Atlanta: August House, 2005. An excellent, comprehensive look at the process of story development—its artistry, joys, and challenges.

Long, Beverly Whitaker, and Mary Frances Hopkins. *Performing Literature: An Introduction.* Dubuque, IA: Kendall Hunt, 1997. Sadly, this book is out of print, but it is worth finding; it provides succinct advice on how to perform in lyric, dramatic, and epic modes. Highly applicable information when adapted for a storytelling context.

Lundberg, Sara (director/producer). *Cords (Hear Us and Have Mercy).* Online film. 2008. http://www.youtube.com/watch?v=5rJ8nCTgZ2Q. Accessed May 12, 2012. Sara Lundberg's two-minute film of the vocal folds at work is a fascinating, funny, and somewhat disturbing look at the inner workings of the trachea as it shapes sound.

MacDonald, Margaret Read. *The Storyteller's Start-Up Book: Finding, Learning, Performing, and Using Folktales.* Atlanta: August House, 2006. Good, quick chapters to get you started telling, including 12 tellable tales.

Meisner, Sanford, and Dennis Longwell. *Sanford Meisner on Acting.* New York: Vintage, 1987. A foundational approach to discovering characters from the "inside out." You can apply many of his characterization techniques for the characters in your stories.

Meyerhoff, Barbara. *Number Our Days.* New York: Dutton, 1978. A moving, best-selling account by an academic and oral historian, documenting the oral histories of members of an elderly Jewish community, their struggles to seek integration for their lives through telling stories, and Meyerhoff's storytelling-based oral history program with them in their community center.

The National Storytelling Network. www.storynet.org. If you want to get plugged into the world of storytelling, start here—the national organization dedicated to connecting and supporting storytellers and the art of storytelling. Information on membership is on the site.

Neimi, Loren. *The New Book of Plots.* Little Rock, AK: Parkhurst Publishers, Inc., 2012. Good ideas and outlines for a variety of plot structures, clearly and succinctly laid out.

Norfolk, Bobby. *Bobby Norfolk: Stories.* Audio CD. Pittsburgh: WOS Studios, 2007. A live recording of seven stories performed at the Children's Museum of Pittsburgh, with delightful characterizations, expression, and movement.

Norum, Karen E. "Stories to Transform, Not Shatter: Mr. Peabody's Advice for Organizations." *Storytelling, Self, Society: An Interdisciplinary Journal of Storytelling Studies* 2, no. 2 (2005): 106–120. Encourages us to consider how perspective, here framed as types of stories (blame, despair, futility, hope, joy, triumph), affects organizations.

O'Callahan, Jay, and John Langstaff. "The Herring Shed." *Stories and Sea Songs.* Audio CD. Marshfield, MA: Artano Productions, 2004. A moving story based on oral history accounts of a small Newfoundland town's transformation during World War II; wonderful to share with children.

Okpewho, Isidore. "Rethinking Epic." *Storytelling, Self, Society: An Interdisciplinary Journal of Storytelling Studies* 5, no. 3 (2009): 218–242. A survey of oral epic study, including the work of Milman Pary, Albert Lord, and John Miles Foley and contributions from African studies, with a focus on the social and cultural contexts out of which epics spring.

Ong, Walter J. *Orality and Literacy: The Technologizing of the Word.* New York: Routledge, 2002. A foundational text on the uses of orality throughout history and how oral memory works.

Pantheon Fairytale and Folklore Library. New York: Pantheon. A series of books highlighting folktale and folklore traditions and tales from around the world, by a variety of authors.

Park, Alice. "The Two Faces of Anxiety." *Time.* December 5, 2011. A concise and approachable overview of anxiety's workings in the body, with quotes from actors and comedians who deal with performance anxiety.

Regan-Blake, Connie. *Chilling Ghost Stories: Haunting Tales for Adults and Teens*. Audio CD and digital download. Available from www.storywindow. com. These are some of the first stories I ever heard from the professional storytelling world, and they remain some of my favorites. "Mr. Fox" and "Mary Culhane" are classics. A *Storytelling World* Honor recording.

Regan-Blake, Connie, and Barbara Freeman (The Folktellers). *Storytelling: Tales for Children and Techniques for Teachers*. DVD. Asheville, NC: The Folktellers, 2007. This duo of cousins helped found the modern storytelling revival; their advice is timeless, and their storytelling is magical. This DVD provides both sample storytelling and a good overview of the process of story development.

Rocha, Antonio. *Under African Skies with Antonio Rocha, Including Mime Tips for the Storyteller*. DVD. Twilight Productions, 2008. Parents' Choice Award–winning recording, providing insights on movement and the use of the body from a masterful and highly entertaining storyteller.

Ryan, Patrick. "The Storyteller in Context: Storyteller Identity and Storytelling Experience." *Storytelling, Self, Society: An Interdisciplinary Journal of Storytelling Studies* 4, no. 2 (2008): 64–87. This is an excellent article on the necessity for storytellers to focus on the story and the audience, rather than their own bravado. You'll notice that Ryan uses the term "genuine storytelling," which is a loaded phrase.

Rydell, Katy, ed. *A Beginner's Guide to Storytelling*. Jonesborough, TN: National Storytelling Press, 2003. A great startup guide for beginning storytellers, with short articles from professional tellers, educators, and professors.

Sacre, Antonio. *A Mango in the Hand*. Illustrated by Sebastia Serra. New York: Abrams Books for Young Readers, 2011. This story and *La Noche Buena* illustrate Sacre's gift as a bilingual teller.

————. *La Noche Buena: A Christmas Story.* Illustrated by Angela Dominguez. New York: Abrams Books for Young Readers, 2010. In this story, Nina travels from New England to Miami and learns about Cuban holiday traditions from her grandmother.

Segal, David. *Joseph Campbell: An Introduction.* New York: Garland, 1987. Offers useful criticism of Campbell's tendency to conflate myths cross-culturally.

Sherman, Josepha. *Mythology for Storytellers: Themes and Tales from around the World.* Armonk, NY: M. E. Sharpe Reference, 2003.

Sobol, Joseph. *The Storyteller's Journey: An American Revival.* Chicago: University of Illinois, 1999. Historical overview of the modern storytelling movement.

Stern, David Alan. *Acting with an Accent.* Audio CD and booklet. Lyndonville, VT: Dialect Accent Specialists, Inc., 2007 (1979). Stern offers audio courses specific to a variety of cultural dialects for American and English-speaking performers. If you want to use an accent for your characters, this source will help you understand how specific dialects work in the mouth and give you practice with them.

Stone, Elizabeth. *Black Sheep and Kissing Cousins: How Our Family Stories Shape Us.* Piscataway, NJ: Transaction Publishers, 2004. An approachable and thoughtful book about how family stories work—and "work overtime"—to shape identity.

Washington, Donna. *Troubling Trouble.* Audio CD. Available from www.donnawashington.com. Washington's skills as a storyteller engage her audiences and keep them hooked. This recording of traditional folktales earned a 2007 Parents' Choice Gold Award.

Weigle, Marta. "Women's Expressive Forms." In *Teaching Oral Traditions*, edited by John Miles Foley. New York: Modern Language Association, 1998. A feminist critique of Campbell's work.

Windling, Terri. "The Path of Needles or Pins: Little Red Riding Hood." *Journal of Mythic Arts, Endicott Studio.* August 2004. www.endicott-studio.com/rdrm/rrPathNeedles.html. Accessed July 6, 2012. Windling is the founder of Endicott Studio, which houses a compendium of non-scholarly but highly interesting and accessible articles on folktales, folklore, and mythology. This article references Vandier's interesting research on the cultural context of "women's work" and its connections to "Red Riding Hood."

Wolf, Eric. *The Art of Storytelling Show.* www.artofstorytellingshow.com. Wolf has been interviewing professional storytellers and collecting their wisdom for years; this website is a nice window into the world of storytelling.

Wolkstein, Diane, and Samuel Noah Kramer. *Inanna: Queen of Heaven and Earth, Her Stories and Hymns from Sumer.* New York: HarperCollins, 1983. Wolkstein's books on myth and fairy tales from many cultures are wonderful, and this text provides more insight into her telling of the Inanna epic. I would recommend any of her books for a storytelling library. More information is available on her website, dianewolkstein.com.

Zimbardo, Philip G. *Shyness: What It Is, What to Do About It.* Boston: Da Capo Press, 1990.

Zipes, Jack. *Breaking the Magic Spell: Radical Theories of Folk and Fairy Tales.* Lexington, KY: University of Kentucky Press, 2002.

————. *The Brothers Grimm: From Enchanted Forests to the Modern World.* New York: Palgrave, 2002. A wonderful and approachable read, providing a scholarly perspective on European folktale traditions, including delightful chapters on "Cinderella" and fairy tale as myth/myth as fairy tale.

Storyteller Websites:

Aoki, Brenda Wong. www.brendawongaoki.com

Bodkin, Odds. www.oddsbodkin.com

Davis, Donald. www.ddavisstoryteller.com

Dworkin, Motoko. www.motoko.folktales.net

Ellis, Elizabeth. www.elizabethellis.com

Forest, Heather. www.heatherforest.com

Harley, Bill. www.billharley.com

Kling, Kevin: www.kevinkling.com

Lepp, Bil. www.leppstorytelling.com

Regan-Blake, Connie. www.storywindow.com

Rocha, Antonio. www.storyinmotion.com

Sacre, Antonio. www.antoniosacre.com

Washington, Donna. www.donnawashington.com

Weitkamp, Kim. www.kimweitkamp.com

Notes

Notes

Notes